WELCOME

Just over seven million Raspberry Pis have been sold around the world. That makes this credit card-sized PC one of the most successful computers the UK has ever made. It's quite amazing really, that a tiny UK charity, dedicated to making computing and computer science affordable and available to people from all walks of life, should end up with such an incredible success story on their hands.

You can learn more about the Raspberry Pi Foundation's charitable and educational aims at **raspberrypi.org**, but regardless of what you want to do with your Raspberry Pi – be it for fun, for education, or as a proof of concept for a multimillion-dollar invention – The Official Raspberry Pi Project Book has something to inspire, help, and guide you on your journey. Whatever you decide to do with your Pi, I hope you have fun doing it.

Russell Barnes

FIND US ONLINE raspberrypi.org/magpi   **GET IN TOUCH** magpi@raspberrypi.org

EDITORIAL
Managing Editor: **Russell Barnes**
russell@raspberrypi.org +44 (0)7904 766523
Technical Editor: **David Whale**
Sub Editors: **Laura Clay, Phil King, Lorna Lynch**

DESIGN
Critical Media: **criticalmedia.co.uk**
Head of Design: **Dougal Matthews**
Designers: **Lee Allen, Mike Kay**
Illustrator: **Sam Alder**

PUBLISHING
For advertising & licensing:
russell@raspberrypi.org +44 (0)7904 766523
Publisher: **Liz Upton**
CEO: **Eben Upton**

DISTRIBUTION
Seymour Distribution Ltd
2 East Poultry Ave
London
EC1A 9PT | +44 (0)207 429 4000

MAGAZINE SUBSCRIPTIONS
Select Publisher Services Ltd
PO Box 6337
Bournemouth
BH1 9EH | +44 (0)1202 586 848

CONTRIBUTORS
Alex Eames, Sam Aaron, Gareth Halfacree, Lucy Hattersley, Richard Hayler & Son, Phil King, Simon Long, Martin O'Hanlon, Les Pounder, Richard Saville, Richard Smedley, Sean Tracey, Rob Zwetsloot & many more Pi-loving people!

This official product is published by Raspberry Pi (Trading) Ltd., Mount Pleasant House, Cambridge, CB3 0RN. The publisher, editor and contributors accept no responsibility in respect of any omissions or errors relating to goods, products or services referred to or advertised in the magazine. Except where otherwise noted, content in this magazine is licensed under a Creative Commons Attribution-NonCommercial-ShareAlike 3.0 Unported (CC BY-NC-SA 3.0). ISSN: 2051-9982.

Contents

GET STARTED WITH RASPBERRY PI
Learn everything you need to know to become a pro with your Raspberry Pi
PAGE 06

Projects

Tutorials

Reviews

172

178

Cat Catcher 112

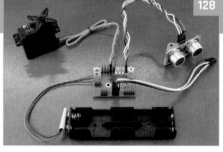
128

130

Raspberry Pi

GET STARTED WITH RASPBERRY PI

Learn everything you need to know to become pro with your Pi

1 **The ingredients you need**

2 **Set up your Raspberry Pi**

3 **A tour of Raspbian**

4 **Installing & updating software**

5 **Use the GPIO pins**

Let me help you get started

Congratulations! You've got yourself a brand new Raspberry Pi and you're ready to start using it for learning code, creating amazing projects, or just simply to power a home theatre. While the Raspberry Pi is generally very easy to use once you know how, it's that initial learning experience that can be a bit tricky for some.

Have no fear, though: we've put together the ultimate guide to getting started with your very own Raspberry Pi, from learning what all the ports and pins on your Raspberry Pi are for, to actually getting it up and running with your own monitor, mouse, and keyboard.

Whatever you want to use your Raspberry Pi for, you need to start here with the basics.

The little Model A+

As well as the 'standard' Raspberry Pi, the Raspberry Pi 2 Model B, there's also a smaller version of the Raspberry Pi that you can use. The Raspberry Pi Model A+ is a cut-down version of the original Raspberry Pi, with a little less power at its disposal and fewer connections on it. It's favoured by people who like to make big physical projects, due to its diminutive size and low power requirements. It also has only one USB port and no Ethernet port, making it slightly less useful to some.

THE INGREDIENTS FOR A RASPBERRY PI 2

USB ports

The Raspberry Pi 2 has four USB ports, allowing you connect it to keyboards, mice, WiFi dongles, and USB sticks containing all your files. Since the ports don't provide much power, if you want to add a USB hub to the Pi you'll need to find one that comes with an external power supply.

Ethernet port

The traditional way to connect to the internet is via a wire called an Ethernet cable. You'll find a few similar ports like this at the rear of your router at home that will let you connect the Raspberry Pi directly into it. This method is easier to set up than WiFi and may provide faster internet, but you're then limited by the length of the cable.

GPIO header

This comprises the general-purpose input/output (GPIO) pins. They're a set of connections that have various functions, but their main one is to allow you to connect to the Raspberry Pi with an electronic circuit. You can then program the Pi to control the circuit and do some amazing things with it.

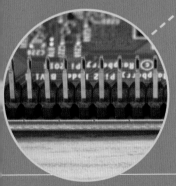

Audio out

This looks like a headphone socket because that's exactly what it is. A 3.5mm jack to be precise, this allows you to connect the Pi to computer speakers, or you could even plug in your favourite headphones and have a Raspberry jam.

MicroSD card slot

A little SD card is used as the Raspberry Pi's hard drive. This is where the operating system will live once you've put it on there. Most computers won't be able to directly connect to a microSD card, but you can get an adaptor that plugs into normal SD card slots.

Power

This is the kind of small charging port you might find in your smartphone. This micro-USB port means you can power the Pi with the right kind of mobile phone charger or directly from your PC – however, it's best to use the official Raspberry Pi power supply to make sure the Pi is getting enough power.

HDMI port

This is an HDMI port, the kind you'll find on the back of most modern TVs and computer monitors. Use a standard HDMI cable to connect your Raspberry Pi to your chosen screen, to see (and hear) whatever it's doing. You'll definitely need to plug it in to set up the Pi.

CONFIGURATION TOOL TABS

The four tabs in Raspberry Pi Configuration allow you to set up various aspects of your Pi...

SYSTEM

Here, you can set whether your Pi boots to the desktop or the command line (CLI), set up autologin, and change password. There is also an overscan setting which is useful for getting rid of the black border around your desktop if there is one.

INTERFACES

Under this tab, you can enable or disable various interfaces on the Raspberry Pi, including the camera and other connectors.

PERFORMANCE

Here, you can set up overclocking and GPU memory allocation to optimise performance for the particular task you want to perform (e.g. HD video playback).

LOCALISATION

This tab enables you to set up the correct language, time zone, and keyboard layout.

Setting up a media centre

We touched on OpenELEC on the previous page, and how it can be used to make a home theatre PC. This is a PC that hooks up to your TV and powers all your media needs. You can find OpenELEC on NOOBS, and installing it is very similar to Raspbian: you select OpenELEC and hit Install!

OpenELEC runs on Kodi – software that lets you connect to your other computers over the network, as well as some online web services such as YouTube. It can play just about anything, but you need to show it where the files are. When adding folder locations to either Video or Music, you can find any shared folders via the SMB option, or you can simply plug in a USB hard drive full of videos and music and play them straight from the menus.

SOFTWARE CONFIGURATION TOOL

Once Raspbian has booted and is showing the desktop, click the Menu button at the top left of the taskbar to open the main menu. From there, select the Preferences option and then Raspberry Pi Configuration from the submenu.

This opens a tool which can be used to configure various options on your Raspberry Pi. Note that you don't need to change most of these options at this point, but one that is important is the 'Expand Filesystem' option.

Since Raspbian doesn't take up much space to begin with, you need to tell it to use your entire SD card if you want to make use of all the free space on it to store files. So, click the Expand Filesystem button under the default System tab of the Raspberry Pi Configuration menu, and then reboot your Pi when prompted – choose Shutdown from the Menu, then select Reboot and hit OK.

Read more about the configuration tool's other options at the top-right of this page.

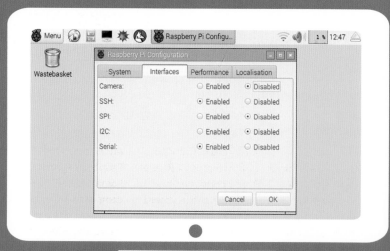

Various options are available under the four tabs, including enabling interfaces

SET UP YOUR RASPBERRY PI

01

Hook it up, install it, use it!

DOWNLOAD NOOBS
The Raspberry Pi comes with many operating systems you can use, which you could manually install yourself if you wish. There's a much easier way to install these OSes, though, and that's via the New Out Of Box Software, or NOOBS. It holds all the latest versions of the Raspberry Pi operating systems and you can grab it from the download page at: **raspberrypi.org/downloads**.

We prefer to use the full version of NOOBS, as it comes with Raspbian already downloaded, making the process slightly faster than with NOOBS Lite. However, all the other operating systems will be downloaded as they install, on both versions of NOOBS.

02
INSTALL SD CARD
While that's downloading, you'll need to get your SD card ready to work on your Raspberry Pi. This will require you to format it, so if there are any files on the card you want to keep, now's the time to take them off. You'll need to install the SD Card Formatter 4.0 tool to prepare the card, which can be downloaded from the SD Association: **bit.ly/1alC3Wp**.

Once you've formatted your SD card, extract the files from the NOOBS zip folder and put them all on the card. That's it: NOOBS is installed to your SD card and ready to use!

03

CONNECT THE CABLES
Take the SD card adaptor out, retrieve the microSD card, and slot it into the Raspberry Pi; this is very important, as the Raspberry Pi won't be able to turn on properly otherwise. To start with, you'll need to plug in an HDMI cable between the Raspberry Pi and your screen, an Ethernet cable for your router (or a USB WiFi dongle), along with a mouse and keyboard. Finally, when everything you need is plugged in, you can attach the power cable to the Raspberry Pi.

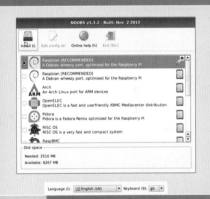

04
INSTALL RASPBIAN
The Raspberry Pi will turn on and display some text on the screen – you can ignore this until it gets to a menu which lists all the available operating systems. It allows you to select multiple OSes at once, but right now we just want to use the one that's called Raspbian. This is the main operating system for the Raspberry Pi, with all the official apps, software, and learning documents. Upon selecting Raspbian, click on Install and it will begin the Raspbian installation process, which may take a little while to complete.

Alternative operating systems

PIDORA
A bit like Raspbian, but based on a different core operating system. This is something people a bit techy can use for a slightly different Raspberry Pi.

ARCH
A very basic operating system that works entirely from a command line, no mouse and keyboard required. You'll really need to know your computers to start with this.

OPENELEC
An OS to turn the Raspberry Pi into a home theatre PC, complete with the Kodi software that plays music and videos as well as web video.

RISC OS
A throwback to your school days, RISC OS is what used to be on old Acorn computers. The Raspberry Pi is in many ways derived from them.

A TOUR OF RASPBIAN

Top right icons

Access the various menus, programs and settings for Raspbian; almost everything you do will start here

These icons let you quickly launch certain programs, such as the browser, the terminal, and the Mathematica programs for hardcore maths and graphing

The various open windows are listed on here; much like in other operating systems, you can click between them when you need to change location

This area offers quick access to tools such as WiFi to ensure your Raspberry Pi is running just fine

Top right icons

WIRELESS INTERNET

This shows the state of your internet connection; solid blue lines means it's connected!

VOLUME

Control the volume of your Raspberry Pi from here. This will work whether you're getting sound from the HDMI port or via headphones.

PROCESSING POWER

The Raspberry Pi, while small, has a lot of processing power. This tells you how much is in use, so if it's running a little slow and this gauge is at 100%, you'll know why.

TIME

Set the time to be anywhere in the world! The Raspberry Pi relies on the internet to tell it what time it is.

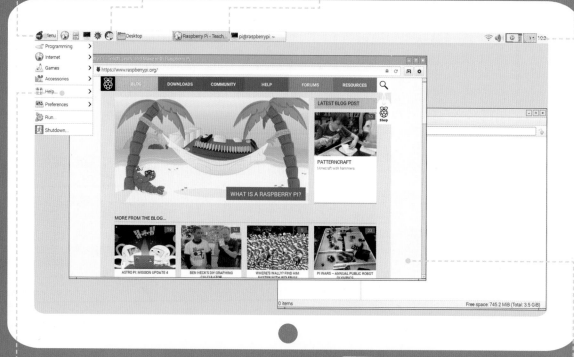

Programs and apps are categorised to make them easier to find – if you can't find the app you're looking for, you might need to go through all of them

Raspbian should feel familiar to most PC users

Windows here work just like any other kind of operating system: you can drag them, change their shape, and close them using your mouse

---

Raspbian looks and works very similarly to the kind of operating systems you're used to, except that the menu is now at top of the screen! Raspbian is based on something called Debian, which is a version of Linux, a highly customisable operating system that can be tweaked enough to run on the Raspberry Pi. It works extremely well, and even on the tiny Raspberry Pi it will almost feel like using a normal computer!

There are a few important icons on the top panel that you should make sure you're aware of.

The Menu is where all the programs and apps live; just like in any other operating system, you can access them from here and they'll open up in a new window. You'll find all the settings in here as well, in case you want to tweak the way Raspbian looks and works.

Next to the menu is a row of quick-start icons to quickly launch

software. The globe picture is the Raspberry Pi browser, your access point to the internet. The cabinet represents the file system of Raspbian, allowing you to browse

" The cabinet represents the file system of Raspbian "

any documents or images you have saved onto your Raspberry Pi. The picture of the screen is the terminal, and it's what you use to run commands via text on the system,

REMOTELY CONNECT TO YOUR RASPBERRY PI

The Raspberry Pi is extremely flexible due to its design, and because of this it will let you connect to it from another computer via a system called SSH (Secure Shell). All you need to connect to it from another PC is the IP address of the Raspberry Pi and a way to access SSH. For the latter you can get PuTTY, a piece of software specifically made to let you easily connect to another system via SSH.

To find out the IP address of the Raspberry Pi, you simply open up a terminal window and type in `ifconfig`. It will list all the details of your network connections, including the IP address; this is listed as 'inetaddress'and may look something like 192.168.0.20. To connect to it, you need to use 'pi@ 192.168.0.20', give the password of 'raspberry', and then you can control your Pi from the command line.

Look through the menu categories to find the software you want to use right now

Settings and preferences allow you to modify the look and feel of Raspbian

Browse files and folders on the Raspberry Pi, and use the same drag, drop, copy, and paste functions of other operating systems

Access the command line and control the Raspberry Pi with text commands. Almost like a hacker... almost

Connect to WiFi

In the right corner of the top panel, you'll find access to WiFi. If you have a compatible WiFi dongle for the Pi, clicking on this will drop down a menu that shows you all the available wireless networks you can connect to.

Click on the wireless network you want to use and you'll be shown a box that lets you put in your password. It will actually display what you're typing in, which should make it easier to type, but make sure your neighbour isn't peering through the window trying to copy it down!

The Raspberry Pi should now be connected to the internet! It will automatically set all its options from your router that will let it talk online. Open the browser and go to your favourite website to make sure it works. The Pi will remember your wireless details and connect whenever it's on.

---

something you might have to do for more advanced projects.

The file system of Raspbian is a little different from something like Windows. Instead of having a C:/ drive with a My Documents folder and programs kept in Program Files, everything is spread out in multiple folders on the root, or top of, the file system. What could be considered My Documents is a folder called Pi in the Home folder on the root. You may see it referred to as the 'home directory', and that's why.

To turn off the Raspberry Pi when you're done for the day, you go to the Menu and press Shutdown. This makes sure everything is safely disconnected and turned off before the entire computer turns itself off. As the Raspberry Pi doesn't have a power switch, you'll have to manually unplug the Pi to fully turn it off standby, and you'll have to unplug it and plug it back in to turn it on again.

Raspbian is quite a simple interface, then, very similar to how you may have used computers in the past. You're now ready to start learning how to code and create your own excellent projects!

INSTALLING AND UPDATING SOFTWARE

Expand and maintain Raspbian for a long-lasting Raspberry Pi experience

INSTALL NEW SOFTWARE

You're not limited to the software that's just on Raspbian when you install it. Raspbian has access to thousands of different programs that you can download and install, just as you would with smartphone apps. Raspbian doesn't have an app store, though, so you need to install them using the terminal.

This does require you to already know what the software is called to install it in the terminal, since you can't browse the software in the same way as on your phone. If you're not sure of the exact name of the software you want, you may have to Google it. Otherwise, if you're looking for a specific kind of app, you can use a command like the following to search for it:

```
$ apt-cache search ftp
```

It will return a list of packages and their details. The package name is how you install the software; in our case, FileZilla comes back as an FTP client. Its package name is 'filezilla'. So, to install it, we use:

```
sudo apt-get install
filezilla
```

This will download the package and any other necessary software it needs to run, and install it to Raspbian.

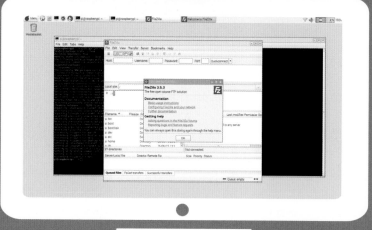

When it's installed, you can immediately start using your new software, no restart required

It may look like gobbledygook, but it's telling Raspbian which software needs to be updated

UPDATE YOUR SOFTWARE AND OS

The software on Raspbian will be periodically updated online, bringing with it bug fixes and security updates. Those don't automatically sync with the Raspberry Pi, though, and you should regularly check to see if there are any updates for your system. This is handled entirely in the terminal again, much like the software installation.

The update process consists of two parts: first you need to update the repositories; this is the list of available software and their versions kept on your system. You do that by first entering the command:

```
sudo apt-get update
```

This will check online to see the state of the software repositories and report back to the Raspberry Pi, saving any changes. It will then determine what software can be and should be updated, but you then need to tell it to perform the update with this command:

```
sudo apt-get upgrade
```

Every now and then, there may be a major update to the Raspbian operating system, bringing with it big changes like a new interface or browser, etc. It's very rare, but when it happens, you can perform the upgrade with:

```
sudo apt dist-upgrade
```

Raspbian asks you to agree to an installation with a simple press of Y

USE THE GPIO

Make your first small project with a bit of code and the GPIO pins

The GPIO port is one of the most powerful tools at the Raspberry Pi's disposal, allowing you to connect directly to an electronic circuit to control it. In such a system, the Pi is referred to as a microcontroller. This is what makes the Raspberry Pi great for big projects, as you can use it to program a machine or circuit, and even have it connect to the internet via the other Raspberry Pi functions so that it can control contraptions with web data.

Each of the GPIO pins can do something different and very specific. At the basic core, though, you can have them provide power consistently to part of a circuit, program a power switch to one of the pins, and even have it sense a change over the pins (thanks to resistance). These three basic functions allow you to do a lot, and can be programmed with Python.

```
import RPi.GPIO as GPIO
import time

GPIO.setmode(GPIO.BOARD)
GPIO.setup(7, GPIO.OUT)

GPIO.output(7,True)
time.sleep(1)
GPIO.output(7,False)
time.sleep(1)
GPIO.output(7,True)
time.sleep(1)
GPIO.output(7,False)

print "Done"

GPIO.cleanup()
```

We're going to wire up an LED bulb to be programmable from the Raspberry Pi, to turn it on and off again a few times. For this, you will need a breadboard prototyping circuit board, an LED, a 50-ohm resistor, and some wires. Refer to our Fritzing diagram on the right, to see how it's wired up; the negative end of the LED goes to a ground pin on the Raspberry Pi (which is where the flow of electricity ends), and a programmable pin goes through the 50-ohm resistor to provide power to the LED when it's turned on.

Open up IDLE, the Python programming software, and create a New file. Save it as **led.py**, and input the code from the code listing. What the code does is first tell Python to use the GPIO module so we can connect to the GPIO pins, by **importing** the module. We then import the time module so we can create a delay between commands. We then tell the code to treat the GPIO pins as the number they are on the board, and to turn the seventh pin into an **output**. We alternate between **True** and **False** so that it turns the pin on and off. Once it's cycled a few times, it will **print** the message 'Done' into IDLE, and finally turn off the GPIO pins.

You can do a lot more with GPIO if you want to, and this is a good way to start before moving on to bigger projects.

You can connect directly to the Raspberry Pi without needing any special slots over the pins

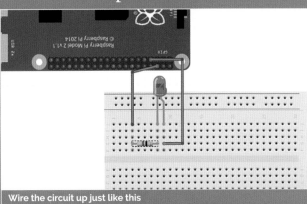

Wire the circuit up just like this

PIN 1	PIN 2
+3V3	+5V
GPIO2 / SDA1	+5V
GPIO3 / SCL1	GND
GPIO4	TXD0 / GPIO14
GND	RDX0 / GPIO15
GPIO17	GPIO18
GPIO27	GND
GPIO22	GPIO23
+3V3	GPIO24
GPIO10 / MOSI	GND
GPIO9 / MISO	GPIO25
GPIO11 / SCLK	CE0# / GPIO8
GND	CE1# / GPIO7
GPIO0 / ID_SD	ID_SC / GPIO1
GPIO5	GND
GPIO6	GPIO12
GPIO13	GND
GPIO19 / MISO	CE2# / GPIO16
GPIO26	MOSI / GPIO20
GND	SCLK / GPIO21
PIN 39	PIN 40

PROJECTS SHOWCASE

There's no better way to be inspired into action than to see what the rest of the Raspberry Pi community is making (and how)…

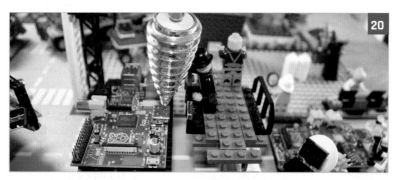

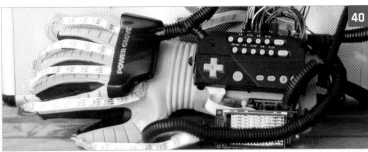

Projects

MAKERS:
THE NEXT GENERATION

The Raspberry Pi is inspiring a new generation to learn how to hack and make amazing projects. We chat to four young makers about their impressive creations and achievements, and why they do them with the Raspberry Pi...

Zach

Name: Zachary Igielman
Age: 15
Location: London
Studying: 12 GCSEs
Twitter: @ZacharyIgielman

After teaching himself to code in Visual Basic at just 11 years old, Zach moved on to Objective-C and released several apps on the iOS App Store. Since discovering the Pi, he's learnt to code in Python and has built his own autonomous robots, enhancing them with a variety of sensors. He also helped 4tronix to develop the Pi2Go. A regular Raspberry Jam attendee, he has run many different workshops. Remarkably, Zach conducted a successful crowdfunding campaign on Indiegogo in early 2015 for his PiPiano musical add-on board (**bit.ly/1wsBmci**), raising nearly twice the original goal.

Tell us about some of the Pi projects you've worked on.

Along with my robots, I've done some cool work with the Camera Module: I programmed my Pi to do time-lapses. I made a tutorial for using an accelerometer with the Pi. I also ran a sensors workshop teaching line and distance sensing with my own materials.

Elsewhere I've been working on a self-balancing robot, which led to giving a talk on PID control theory for robotics at a Raspberry Jam... I have tested all sorts of Pi add-on boards, from LED to analogue, leading me to build my own.

How did the idea for the PiPiano come about?

I wanted to create a piano with my Pi, but adding switches to a real piano would be a wiring nightmare... My solution was to create a simple, piano-style add-on for the Raspberry Pi, which includes buttons in a piano octave formation and a piezo transducer for sound output. After trying it on

a breadboard, and being swamped with bundles of spaghetti wiring, I opted to lay out the idea on a PCB (printed circuit board).

PiPiano teaches programming, soldering and electronics, through reading the buttons, making traffic lights with the LEDs, playing a scale on the buzzer, and finally making a PiPiano. It uses a special chip so all 17 components connect to three [GPIO] pins.

What is it you love about the Raspberry Pi?

It's really cheap; I can afford a few of my own and I'm not always worrying about breaking an expensive computer. It's portable, easy to ferry from event to event. It's got an amazing community, which enables me to meet cool people, learn lots and have amazing opportunities. It has lots of documentation and a great forum for learning anything with it. It is very programmable [and] it can plug into electronics, unlike most computers.

BIG PROJECT: PIPIANO

Plugging directly into the top of a Pi, this musical add-on board features 13 buttons in a piano key formation, a piezo transducer for sound output, and three LEDs. Designed to be educational, it comes with documentation which takes you from the basics of soldering the board and setting up the software, to

programming a fully working piano at the end. PiPiano comes soldered (ready-made) or as a kit, and with either a standard or stacking header. When not used as a piano, it's also a handy controller with an ample supply of buttons. It is also the basis for Pimoroni's Piano HAT. Learn more at **pipiano.com**.

Following an invite from Jimmy Wales, Amy presented a keynote speech at the Campus Party EU 2013

Amy

Name: Amy Mather
Age: 16
Location: Manchester
Studying: 9 GCSEs (already has an A* in Computing)
Twitter: @minigirlgeek

Already into electronics at the age of 12, Amy integrated an Arduino kit into a model volcano for a school homework project, which she was then asked to demonstrate at Manchester's first Mini Maker Faire. After getting hold of a Pi, she learnt Python and created her own version of Conway's Game of Life, even outputting the display to an LED matrix. Most notably, Amy teaches both adults and children to code and works closely with the STEM network to inspire other young people to get involved in computer science. This has led to her giving keynote speeches at many prestigious technology events. At ICT 2013 in Lithuania she received an award as the European Digital Girl of the Year.

How did you get started with programming?
I first got interested in coding when I was about 12, following a Manchester Girl Geeks workshop that I attended that was an introduction to JavaScript using Codecademy. I thought Codecademy was an amazing platform for learning how to code and I continued with their courses (you can find out more at **codecademy.com**).

What's so great about the Raspberry Pi?
It doesn't matter if you accidentally blow bits up on it – you can get another one! Or if the SD card corrupts, it's not the end of the world: you can reformat it. The Pi allows you to make all kinds of remarkable projects and there are so many awesome add-on boards. Also, the community's really welcoming and friendly, so they're open to any of your questions. I think the whole environment is just amazing.

Do you have any new Pi-based projects planned?
My school has just asked me if I have any ideas for ways that we can link the coding club and the STEM club. So I'm thinking about how to help them through the use of Raspberry Pi-based projects. I've helped out with teaching coding workshops and I'm currently leading a series of soft electronics workshops as the volunteering section of my Silver Duke of Edinburgh Award.

And you also make speeches at numerous events?
Yes, I speak at quite a lot of conferences, about how we can get more kids involved in STEM (Science, Technology, Engineering, and Mathematics) and why it's really important that we do so.

What advice would you give to other young coders?
Just get involved, find out where all the local events are, and get involved with the community; you'll definitely learn a lot more from talking with other people who are interested in similar things, rather than just sitting alone at home and doing it by yourself.

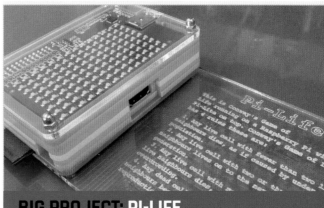

BIG PROJECT: PI-LIFE

Amy first came to the attention of the international Raspberry Pi community after giving an impressive presentation of her Python version of Conway's Game of Life – a zero-player game simulating cellular replication – at the 2013 Manchester Raspberry Jamboree (**raspberrypi.org/amys-game-of-life**). In it, she enthused about her love of coding and detailed how she developed various implementations of Life, including one with the Pi outputting the resulting patterns to an 8×8 LED matrix via a connected Arduino Mega. Since then, she's created a more compact version using a Pi-Lite LED add-on board.

Right Lauren created a portable Pi-powered system to sync the lights in Charles Peachock's juggling clubs to a music track

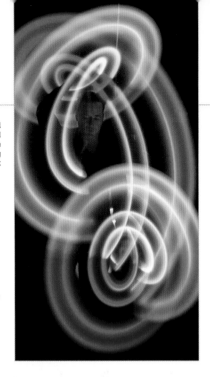

Lauren

Name: Lauren Egts
Age: 16
Location: Stow, Ohio
Studying: High School
(Hathaway Brown)
Twitter: @laurenegts

When she was just nine, Lauren's father taught her how to write some Bash scripts. Using Scratch on the Pi, she later created The Great Guinea Pig Escape game and demonstrated it at a local Maker Faire. A long-time member of Akron Linux User Group, she has presented talks on GlusterFS and teaching kids to code on the Pi. She's an NCWIT Aspirations in Computing Ohio Affiliate award winner for 2014 and 2015, and is also an intern at the NASA Glenn Research Center G-VIS Lab. Recent projects include creating a Pi video wall (at NASA) and designing a portable LED lights system for professional juggler Charles Peachock.

What do you especially like about the Pi?

One thing that I really love is its versatility. I've used it in a variety of projects, and seen it used in even more! The Pi is so small that it can be used practically anywhere, which means it can be used in [so many different] projects.

What was it like being an intern at NASA? How did it happen?

It happened at the Cleveland Mini Maker Faire. I had my booth where I was presenting on Scratch and the Raspberry Pi. I was helping a friend take her booth out to her car, and my dad shows up with some other guy who I later found out was Herb Schilling, now my mentor at NASA. Turns out Herb had gone to my booth while I was away, and my dad had told him all about me. When Herb and I met, he was so impressed with what I had done with the Pi that he invited me to shadow him at NASA. After my shadow day, Herb invited me to come back for a few weeks over the summer! We figured out some dates, and that's how my internship happened!

Are you planning to do any more Pi projects when you return to NASA?

It depends on what projects I am assigned to but I would absolutely like to finish my work on the Pi video wall... Herb is very interested in showcasing the power of low-cost computing devices like the Pi. Finishing my work will require taking care of a few bugs in code, as well as fixing the aforementioned hardware issues. After the video wall project is done, hopefully it will be displayed outside the G-VIS Lab, playing a video that explains what the lab does when people walk by.

BIG PROJECT: PI VIDEO WALL

During her internship at NASA, Lauren – working with fellow intern Nick Patterson – did a proof-of-concept project to create a Pi-powered video wall (**go.nasa.gov/1DYEa2v**). Since they only had access to what was in the NASA G-CVIS Lab at the time, different-sized monitors were used, but the end result was still impressive. The setup involved connecting four Pis to a master computer via a router. The PiWall software package (**piwall.co.uk**) was used to split up the video display into four tiles, one for each monitor. Lauren hopes to improve the setup when she returns to NASA.

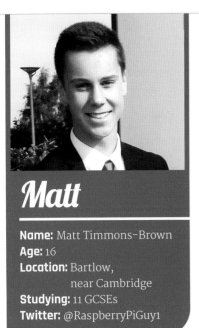

Matt

Name: Matt Timmons-Brown
Age: 16
Location: Bartlow,
near Cambridge
Studying: 11 GCSEs
Twitter: @RaspberryPiGuy1

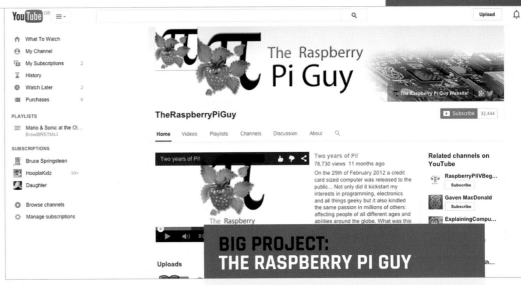

Better known as The Raspberry Pi Guy, Matt runs a YouTube channel dedicated to Raspberry Pi video tutorials. Amazingly, he only started coding and making around three years ago, upon discovering the Pi Foundation's credit card-sized PC. So far he's created projects of varying complexity, including a Pi-controlled model railway, but his real passion is robotics – in particular, making two-wheeled robots and pushing their abilities to the max. His latest project involves building an accessible robotics platform, with a complete set of learning materials, using 4tronix's Pi2Go-Lite. To this end, he has filmed a YouTube series called 'Raspberry Pi Robots'.

How did you first get involved with making?

I am the quintessential Raspberry Pi product: a schoolboy who now has a love of computer science because of the Pi... In the summer of 2012 I managed to get my hands on my first Pi and ever since then I have been in love with programming, making (robots!) and computer science. The Pi opened my eyes to computing and for that I am incredibly grateful!

Why did you decide to set up your own YouTube channel?

I am a very recent convert to the ways of Pi. As a result, I originally found computing a fairly hard subject to get into; there is all of this foreign jargon and sometimes it can be incredibly confusing... In September 2012 I realised that I had built up a considerable amount of knowledge on the subject and I thought it would be a great side project to teach people some of the stuff I'd had so much fun learning. I turned to YouTube as a way of doing this because I found the most easy way to learn something is by watching someone go through something step by step... On 1 September 2012, The Raspberry Pi Guy was born and I have been publishing videos ever since; I am just about to hit the 2 million view barrier on YouTube, something I never imagined!

What's so great about the Pi?

There is no other product out that there has the same ethos: to teach people about computing by introducing them to a [new] experience. After all, how many single-board computers has the average person seen? How many terminals have they programmed in? Scratch that, how many people have actually programmed?! The Pi is a gateway to the world of computers and [has] introduced me to a lifetime interest... It has inspired millions and continues to do so.

BIG PROJECT: THE RASPBERRY PI GUY

Matt's YouTube channel (**youtube.com/user/TheRaspberryPiGuy**) has been running for over two years now and has proven immensely popular, amassing over 42,000 subscribers. "Dedicated to teaching the masses how to make the most of their Raspberry Pi computer", it provides a plethora of step-by-step video tutorials. These range from basic setup to attaching various add-ons and creating numerous projects – including, of course, robotics. The latest addition is the Raspberry Pi Robots series, which Matt hopes "will engage people in computer science through the most exciting medium: world-conquering robots."

Get making!

Our young experts offer a lot of good advice for how to get started with coding and making...

> There are lots of free online resources, such as Codecademy, to help you learn to code. Just Google 'coding courses'.

> Look out for local events and get involved – it's much more fun than trying to do it alone at home!

> Events such as Maker Faires and Raspberry Jams can give you ideas to try, and a place to exhibit your projects and make contacts.

> Join a robotics team if you're interested in making robots and entering them into competitions.

> Even if something seems hard to start with, keep trying: if you set your mind to it you'll achieve it. And you're never too young to start!

> However, remember to always have fun with what you're doing. If you don't like something, don't waste your time with it.

Mad scientists working on the original Model B Rev 1. A surprisingly accurate account

The Raspberry Pi 2 takes centre stage on this elaborate rocket. A brilliant nod to Astro Pi

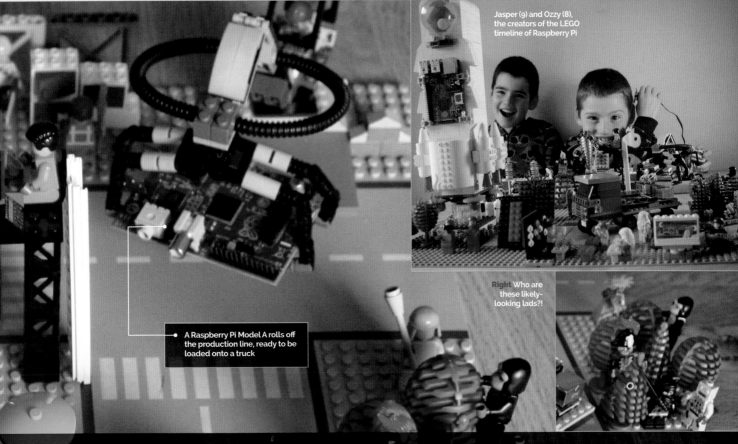

Jasper (9) and Ozzy (8), the creators of the LEGO timeline of Raspberry Pi

A Raspberry Pi Model A rolls off the production line, ready to be loaded onto a truck

Right: Who are these likely-looking lads?!

LEGO-LUTION OF PI

Ozzy, **Jasper** and **Richard Hayler** celebrate their collection of Raspberry Pis the only way they know how

W hen Richard Hayler isn't working for the Foreign Office, he's a Raspberry Pi enthusiast, CoderDojo mentor, and Code Club volunteer. "Pretty much everything else revolves around my sons, who love getting involved with all things Pi," he says.

Besides test-driving his educational material, Richard's sons Ozzy (aged 8) and Jasper (9) are often to be found hacking and making with the Pi. Their latest creation is this rather marvellous Lego scene designed to celebrate the evolution of everyone's favourite credit-card-sized PC.

"I recently liberated my Rev 1 Model B from the BrickPi robot and thought that it would be nice to take some photos of all the different versions I own," explains Richard.

"I didn't get round to it straight away, and it languished on my list of 'things to do'. Then I was lucky enough to get a free Pi 2 on the day of launch by tracking down the Element14 PiCycle (**bit.ly/1DpL9Es**), which reinvigorated my interest in the idea.

"I asked the boys if they had any ideas of how to make the pictures more exciting than just a bunch of Pis on a desk, and they immediately suggested this."

After discussing a few ideas, Richard's youngest, Ozzy, suggested creating a Lego timeline showing the Pis being used in different ways. "This morphed into a scene which follows the Pi from the design phase, through manufacture in a Pi factory, to being loaded onto a lorry. Then we have some children using

it in a school, and finally, a Pi being strapped to a rocket, ready to launch up to the ISS to celebrate Astro Pi."

Each stage of the design boasts a more modern model of the Raspberry Pi, Richard explains, not to mention the addition of a couple of 'Easter eggs', including a rather suspicious-looking group consisting of a pirate, monkey, robot, and ninja.

What's next for the Haylers? "[We're] putting together some hardware based around the Model A+ for kite-mapping photography, that will record the altitude and orientation of the kite, and use it to have some intelligence about when (and when not) to capture an image." You can see more of the Haylers' Pi timeline, and learn more about the family's other projects, at **richardhayler.blogspot.co.uk**.

RASPBERRY PI CLUSTER

David Guill shows us what happens when he's left in a room with 40 Raspberry Pis, two 24-port switches, 5TB of storage, and an ATX power supply

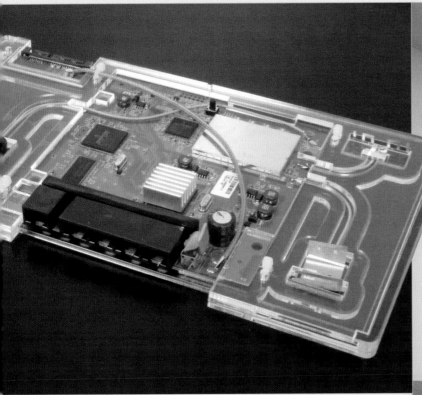

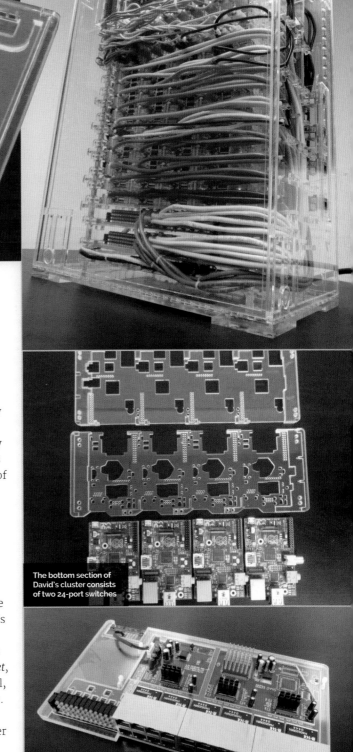

A computer cluster is 'a set of connected computers that work together so that, in many respects, they can be viewed as a single system'. Clusters can be anything from a few cheap computers networked together to supercomputers made up of thousands of individual 'node' systems, designed to undertake complex tasks like modelling weather or trying to beat humans at chess.

Back in early 2014 David Guill, a recent MSc Computer Engineering graduate, showed the world his rather impressive project to create a computer cluster consisting of 40 Raspberry Pis.

He created his cluster entirely single-handedly, right down to the custom laser-cut acrylic case.

A new direction

A year on, we caught up with David to find he's still working hard on his pet project, and it seems it's taking him in new and exciting directions. "While it wasn't one of my original goals, the most important work I've done on it so far has been in porting software to ARM," says David. "I spent some time trying to get Apache Mesos working properly on it." It's a worthy distraction since ARM is fast becoming a real player in the server market, meaning David's work could have real value in the coming years.

"While I've mostly been fixing supporting tools as I discover they aren't ready for ARM, I'll also be writing some of my own tools . My objective is to have a suite of tools with insignificant diminishment of returns for expansion, where the millionth node in a system would contribute nearly as much as the tenth did when it was new."

Virtual worlds

David's ultimate goal, though, is quite different – he wants to move into virtual reality. "My end goal is to develop detailed virtual reality simulations, like you might see in a hybrid of *Minecraft*, *LittleBigPlanet*, and role-playing games in general, with deformable planetary worlds. Of course, this is still hobby work – I have no guarantee that it'll ever get close to completion."

You can learn more about David and his work on the Raspberry Pi Cluster at **likemagicappears.com**.

The bottom section of David's cluster consists of two 24-port switches

Most of the mid-section is made up of ten rows of these bad boys

The plate on an empty section of his dashboard was a perfect place to affix the buttons

ANDY PROCTOR

A man with great entrepreneurial spirit, Andy was a tinkerer as a child and worked as an electrician as a young man. Now he drives his iData Truck.
idatatruck.co.uk

His Raspberry Pi is powered by the cigarette lighter, providing ample power for his purposes

Andy's top tip is to use this 40-pin ribbon from Maplin so that the wires don't come loose

iDATA TRUCK

Quick Facts

- Andy learned to program for this project
- The community has already begun making his code better
- Most of the electronics come from a SunFounder starter kit
- Andy uses an iPhone to connect his Pi to the internet
- There will soon be a live camera stream from his lorry

A Raspberry Pi-powered lorry? It's not as strange as you think, as **Andy Proctor** shows us how he automates deliveries with Pi

Braving the often-congested motorways of Great Britain, we find our hero Andy Proctor – lorry driver and truck hacker extraordinaire – live-tweeting his schedule as he picks up, and delivers, the nation's shipping containers. There's much more to his tweets than meets the eye, though, and it all started with him finishing up his previous business and becoming a lorry driver.

"I was tweeting '#m25' and '#m12', and I noticed it was being retweeted automatically. I contacted the guy who was doing it and he told me it was powered by a Raspberry Pi and a bot. I looked up what a Raspberry Pi was and

decided that I wanted to push a button and send a tweet."

The transition from being a successful business owner to a lorry driver hadn't had the best impact on Andy, and his wife encouraged him to play about with his new Raspberry Pi on their honeymoon. With a background as an electrician, website builder and tinkering with computers and electronics as a kid, some of the Pi came naturally to him.

Humble beginnings

"I started off with Tweepy and Scratch to make some lights flash, and built a little box with a board for the lights, which made me happy! I then did the same in

Python, learning along the way, and within six weeks I had created the box with the four buttons that you see now."

The iData Truck was born and not only did the buttons tweet out his current status, it emailed his office – a task he would have been doing manually anyway. He published a video on YouTube describing his setup, which got picked up by the Raspberry Pi Foundation and even the BBC. Andy isn't finished yet, though.

"I only have four things I can transmit," he laments. "So now what I'm doing is a barcode-scanning version. I've printed off loads of barcodes which I can stick to the back of my time sheet and

> STEP 01
Press the button
When Andy loads or unloads, he presses one of the four preselected buttons on the iData Truck so he can let his company know what he's up to.

> "Not only did the buttons tweet his current status, it emailed his office"

then I'll be able to scan them. If it's just scanning to say 'start of day', 'end of day' or 'on a break', it will tweet that but not email it. If it's 'running 30 minutes later' or 'box on'/'box off', it will still email it to the office. So there will be a split of what data gets sent where."

What's next?
Next on the list for Andy is a camera – Pi-powered, of course – in a blind spot of his lorry that will display on his dashboard and hopefully make it easier to manoeuvre while reducing the risk

of accidents. He also has further plans for the iData Truck beyond his personal use of it.

"I've approached the people that make the software that everybody uses in the industry and they said if one of their customers wanted to use that, then that's fine, they'd support it… one person's been in touch that can make the hardware, a box to put it in, the switches in the panel, and the software, should I want to develop it further."

So next time you pass a container lorry on the M3, give it a wave and you might end up on iData Truck TV.

> STEP 02
Wait for the beep
You need to hold the button down for half a second: "It kept getting really hot, so I had to put a delay in to stop the processor working so hard from all the loops!"

> STEP 03
Email and tweet sent
An email is sent off to Andy's company to let them know of his status, and a tweet is sent to the @iDataTruck Twitter feed for everyone to see what he's up to.

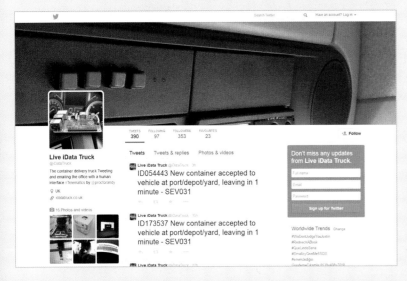

Left The information on the iData Truck stream is always expanding. Andy initially had trouble with duplicate tweets until he started using timestamps

ID121554 Shippng container now loaded by customer and sealed, departing 2 mins - SEV031

MARK PARRISH

A .NET developer with a software consulting firm, who grew up playing Nintendo's ground-breaking consoles.
imgur.com/a/1RUwa

Some parts couldn't be soldered to the SNES due to wiring limitations – the HDMI port connects directly to the rear

It's powered by a standard Raspberry Pi Model B because the microSD adaptor is the best interface

Mark has soldered the SD card directly to the main board, while the USB and Ethernet are soldered directly to the controller ports

SNES PI CASE

What happens when you turn a Super Nintendo into a Raspberry Pi? F-Zero becomes Raspbian, among other things...

You walk into a room and see a SNES. A classic, a legend, one of the greatest videogame consoles to ever be crafted by the hands of man. Beside it is a cartridge of the original *F-Zero*, perhaps not the best in the series but an excellent game nonetheless. You slam it in (gently though, they're both 25 years old), flick the power switch, and look for a controller. Suddenly, a Raspberry Pi logo shows up.

This isn't a Super Nintendo. It's a Raspberry Pi case that used to be a Super Nintendo.

"Like most great ideas, [I got it] from watching others and seeing what they were building," Mark

tells us. "[Also] how they were solving particular problems... then taking those ideas and improving on them in my own creative way."

His own creative way is frankly incredible. Instead of just fitting the Raspberry Pi into an empty case, he soldered parts of it directly to the original motherboard of the broken SNES he was working on. Most of the work on this project was the physical customisation part.

"The software side is easy since there are a numbers of solutions out there that have already been proven to be successful. The majority of the work I've done is with the physical part, and is easily 90-95% of the time invested."

Just about everything he could connect through the SNES has been done in that way, and just about everything uses the original port locations. USB and Ethernet are routed through the two front controller ports, the HDMI is in the old AV out, the power has been converted, and an on/off switch has been fitted into the aerial connector. That's not the best part, though:

"In my design, I've moved the SD card from the Raspberry Pi and connected it inside an actual game cartridge. I've noticed a few more failed boots than normally would be expected. Other than that, it works beautifully!"

Left Mark interfaced directly with a microSD card converter to allow booting from the cartridge

Image: Evan Amos CC BY-SA 3.0

A common sight in '90s households – but this SNES holds a secret

A Nintendo console needs Nintendo controllers, surely? "I have two ideas," Mark tells us. "One is to take an original USB controller that works natively with the Pi and cram that into a controller housing. The result would look like the original controller. The other would be to map the current controller to the USB spec that the Pi expects. I haven't done a lot of research on this approach; however,

> # Figuring out these problems is the fun part of tinkering with gadgets

figuring out these kinds of problems is the fun part of tinkering with gadgets."

While the internet likes to go a little bit mad whenever someone posts a new classic console mod like this, it sounds like this is nothing compared to the joy of actually doing it:

"I'm always amazed at the beginning of a project like this, that you have a workbench full of parts that by themselves do little or nothing. Then at some point while putting the parts together, something new and useful is created and essentially 'comes alive'."

POWERING UP THE SNES PI CASE

>STEP-01
Jack in
Plug your HDMI, power, Ethernet, and USB devices into the various ports – the controller connectors hold the latter two, in case you were wondering.

>STEP-02
Grab a game
Search through the game library for *F-Zero*. Make sure it's the right version of *F-Zero*, the one with an SD card of Raspbian on it. Slot it in the top of the SNES.

>STEP-03
Flick the switch
Unfortunately, the original power button won't help you here. Behind the SNES and next to the power cable is the on/off button – flick it to bring the SNES Pi to life.

SOUND FIGHTER

Cyril Chapellier and Eric Redon have brought a new
dimension to the phrase 'duelling pianos' with
an installation designed to turn two pianos into
controllers for a game of Street Fighter Alpha 3

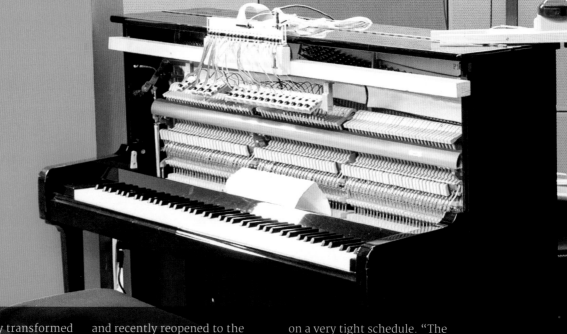

"**W**e seamlessly transformed
two classical upright
pianos into PlayStation 2
controllers using custom
analogue piezo triggers, a Pi B+,
and Arduino Unos, and created a
specific Python 3 firmware to map
a classical playing style onto the
Street Fighter Alpha 3 gameplay,
including combos and the like,"
explain the French duo.

The concept was pitched for
the reopening of the Maison
de la Radio, a historical radio
building in the heart of Paris.
"The building has been the
home of the French public radio
stations for more than 50 years

and recently reopened to the
public as a cultural space, offering
a wide spectrum of entertainment
choices, such as live concerts,
workshops, and live radio shows,"
the pair explain on their blog.

To celebrate the reopening,
Cyril and Eric worked on the
overarching concept of bringing
'an alternative visual identity to
music', which led to the idea of
trying to bring the general public
back in touch with classical music
and classical instruments (like
the piano) in this completely new
and unique way.

While the concept was gladly
accepted, the project itself was

on a very tight schedule. "The
go-ahead was given on 1 October
[2014], the shooting of the teaser
video was to take place on 12
November, and the live event on
the weekend of 14 November."

The video shows classical
pianists Alvise Sinivia and Léo
Jassef, from the Conservatoire
National de Paris, duking it
out as *Street Fighter*'s principal
characters, Ryu and Ken. You can
see it at **youtu.be/7v2B71RUaqQ**.

Learn about the making of
the 'Sound Fighter' installation
in incredible detail on Cyril
Chapellier and Eric Redon's blog,
at **foobarflies.io/pianette**.

Above **The project cleverly interfaces a piano to a PlayStation 2 controller so the game can be 'played'**

Above **The public were invited to test this novel take on 'duelling pianos'**

Above **Alvise Sinivia and Léo Jassef, from the Conservatoire National de Paris, demonstrate the installation**

A portable VCR from the 1980s houses this Raspberry Pi project, complete with original buttons and carrying handle

MARTIN MANDER

A database manager for Norfolk's Children's Centres who has a love of 'upcycling' vintage technology to incorporate modern components.
instructables.com/id/1981-Portable-VCR-Raspberry-PI-Media-Centre

The VHS is a four-port USB hub that connects to the Pi located on the side of the case. The screen is on the other side

Everything is stored inside the case, meaning you just need to power it and control it

RASPBERRY PI VCR

An Eighties video player or portable digital entertainment centre? Spoilers: it's the latter, and it looks truly amazing...

Portable video playback is a modern concept, right? Before magical internet-connected phones in our pockets, there were portable DVD players in cars. Laptops had DVD drives and video software a bit before that as well, so perhaps it's a little older than you might initially consider.

Meet the Sharp VC2300H and have your world turned upside down. This contraption from the ancient past of 1981 was able to play video stored on magnetic tape and housed in a big plastic rectangle – also known as a VHS. If you're not

old enough to know what one of those is, ask your parents (or better yet, Siri). You did have to hook it up to a TV, but being able to lug it around was quite a novelty really, taking inspiration from portable stereos of the age.

This version is slightly different, though, as its creator Martin Mander explains very succinctly:

"I picked [this] up for 'spare or repair' on eBay for £6 – a top-loading VCR that unusually stands upright and has a carrying handle. I stripped out all of the internal circuits and replaced

them with modern tech, with the Pi running the show, a powered USB hub housed in a pop-out VHS tape, an Arduino-powered clock, and a 15" HD TV panel integrated into the back of the unit."

The whole setup runs Raspbmc, the XBMC spin of Raspbian, and also allows you to stream from places like YouTube and the BBC iPlayer via WiFi. There's even a built-in IR sensor for media remotes.

"I'd made several other projects combining retro TVs and LCD panels before, but these were always tied to

Some of the physical buttons are used for fun lights and exposing the USB ports, and you can just about see the Pi through the side

a PC or video source," Martin tells us, when asked why he decided to put a Pi in it. "This time I wanted to make a much more interactive all-in-one device. The Raspberry Pi looked like the ideal solution on form factor alone and when I nosed around at the fan and support sites, I was impressed by the scale and enthusiasm of the community.

the old push buttons with modern microswitches – next time! With the case already painted and the TV panel installed, I settled for just integrating the basic Play/Rewind/Fast-Forward buttons with the Pi,

> ## I stripped out all of the internal circuits and replaced them with modern tech, with the Pi running the show

I'd experimented with APC (Android PC) boards in the past, but a lack of updates and support turned me off taking these any further."

Although all the physical buttons on the original machine still mostly functioned, Martin was unable to get them all working with the Raspberry Pi: "I spent several weeks looking into different ways of connecting up the hardware buttons to the Pi via USB, working my way through a series of stripped down gamepads and keyboards. One evening I wondered if I could maybe use an Arduino to mimic key presses, then the more I researched, it struck me that the Pi itself had GPIO ports and the buttons could possibly be connected directly... Ultimately, I think the 30+ year-old switch circuit was the reason I couldn't get this to work; in retrospect, I should have replaced

which I did using the circuit from a pound shop USB mouse."

While some more work may be required to perfect this fascinating project, overall it works really well, according to Martin. So if you ever find an old portable VCR at a car boot sale, maybe you can make yourself a cheap, portable media player with retro charm.

Below There's a custom paint job and a bit of Pi branding, but really you'd have to take a close look to realise it's different

GET WATCHING!

>STEP-01
Turn it on!
There are several buttons required to turn the full thing on. First the switch for the mains supply, then the switch to activate the lights and clock and other fun things, and finally the switch for the Pi.

>STEP-02
Add peripherals
Need to add some storage or a USB keyboard/mouse? Eject the cassette. That's where the USB ports are for the Pi – don't worry, you don't need to put it back in.

>STEP-03
Select a show
Raspbmc is running on the screen installed on the rear. Using an IR remote, you can select from local media or streamable videos on any supported service.

JOHAN TEN BROEKE

Software developer with a passion for good software, art, music, graphics, and print. Works with creative partner Jeroen van Goor.

fullscreennl.github.io/led-mirror

> The main driver board, designed with Osmond PCB for Mac, includes a 4MHz main clock running at 3.3 volts

> A single PCB column element drives eight LEDs. The PCBs are connected with ribbon cables

> A camera is mounted on the front of the panel

LED MIRROR

It's not every day that you are able to see yourself in a whole new light, but the LED mirror has managed to crack it

We wouldn't say Johan ten Broeke was a vain man, but he does spend an inordinate amount of time in front of a mirror. Catch his ghostly white, silhouetted reflection, though, and you will see exactly why – for this is no ordinary mirror, but a large and rather special panel powered by a Raspberry Pi.

Created as an art installation, the mirror consists of a staggering 2,048 LEDs. When someone stands in front of it, a camera picks up their movement and creates a series of snazzy effects. "Myself and Jeroen van Goor are imaging enthusiasts and we got the idea for the project when we were playing around with a Raspberry Pi Camera Module," Johan says. "We thought it would be an entertaining device."

Eating & sleeping LEDs

The project began on a small scale. "We built a prototype of several small 8×8 LED dot-matrix digits," Johan explains. It soon grew. Before long, the pair were connecting LED-strip PCBs together using ribbon cables, strapping them to an off-the-shelf reinforced floor grate using cable ties, and hand-soldering hundreds upon hundreds of LEDs at a pitch of 38mm apart, in a hugely repetitive process which took them both three days.

The effect is nothing less than stunning, however. "Although the displayed images are very abstract, spectators identify themselves instantaneously due to the feedback of their motions. This triggers people to move and wave in front of the mirror," says Johan.

Best of all, the mirror is adaptable. The horizontal spacing of the LED grid can be varied to compensate for narrow viewing angles, while the slim design of the LED modules allows the lights to be applied on curved surfaces. It gives the mirror wide-ranging potential.

"Some people have suggested the LED mirror belongs in a nightclub-like environment, close to a DJ set or something like that," enthuses Johan. "It certainly draws a lot of attention, so perhaps shopping

> "Some people have suggested the LED mirror belongs in a nightclub-like environment, close to a DJ set or something like that "

windows and interiors would be a good setting. It could be used for game-assisted physical therapy, for people who are recovering from injury and need exercise. Patients could 'hit' moving virtual sensors and the software app could produce progress reports to the therapist."

There's an app for that

Johan and Jeroen have written four main apps to accompany the mirror. The home app has 4×4 pixel sensors which are triggered when the change in pixel value exceeds a threshold; the recording app retains 10 seconds of display

data at 15 frames per second and plays them back in reverse; the difference app displays a silhouette of spectators; and the drawing app only allows the brightest pixels to come through to the screen, allowing users to draw in white on a black canvas (or vice versa), with a flashlight or similar device.

"It's really adaptable and it could be made even bigger than

the current screen size of 122cm by 244cm," Johan says. "The Maxim chips allow for a maximum of 256 cascaded devices on a single SPI bus and we use 16 chips right now. You could use a second SPI device in the Pi, allowing for a second 256-chip chain, making it 32 times as big." To which, on reflection, we can only stand in amazement.

USING THE LED MIRROR

> STEP-01
Plug in and play
The LED mirror is plugged into the mains and once it is switched on, you need to stand in front of it. There is a tiny camera mounted in the centre of the installation.

> STEP-02
Select a mode
The home app gives a generic view of the camera and accesses the other apps. Recording mode lets you create an animation. The difference mode lets you admire the view.

> STEP-03
Create a picture
In the drawing mode, grab a flashlight and create cool pictures on the mirror's 32×64 pixel canvas. After a while, the recording, difference, and drawing apps return to the home app.

Top Left As the user moves in front of the mirror, the LEDs power off to reflect the motion

Top Right A total of 2,048 LEDs were needed for the Raspberry Pi LED mirror project

JACK SMITH

A sales and IT assistant in the manufacturing industry, Jack knows his way around computers, but this was his first Pi project.

RASPBERRY PI ARCADE

Save money at the arcade and shoot down space invaders from the comfort of your own home

A s kids, we all dreamed about having arcade machines at home so we wouldn't have to spend loads of money at the arcade to beat *X-Men* or figure out if Reptile was real in *Mortal Kombat*. While home consoles existed, it wasn't until the mid-Nineties that they came close to the quality of an arcade experience. The arcade was an experience, albeit one now lost to time; however, that hasn't stopped people trying to recreate it with modern tech. Enter the Raspberry Pi Arcade by Jack Smith.

"The idea was heavily inspired by the iCade by ION," Jack tells us, referring to the iPad dock that makes it look like an arcade cabinet. "I really liked the idea, but I don't have an iPad and I wanted something much more open. I had purchased a Raspberry Pi the previous week, which I had already been using to play games, and figured it would be the perfect match."

The Pi Arcade itself uses a Raspberry Pi running Raspbian with EmulationStation over the popular RetroPie, and has a 7" TFT display along with an authentic joystick and four buttons. It also

Quick Facts

> The project took two weeks to complete

> *OutRun 2* is Jack's favourite arcade game

> The original plan was to gut a Game Boy or SNES

> His next project is a light-gun arcade cabinet

> Jack's favourite game to play on the Pi Arcade is *Contra III*

Don't just limit yourself to arcade games, as EmulationStation lets you play from retro consoles

An authentic arcade joystick and four buttons are driven by the Pi's GPIO pins

Built from MDF wood and based around the old Atari 2600 for aesthetics

> " I really wanted that retro look, similar to that of an Atari 2600 or a Moog synthesizer "

connects wirelessly for Jack to maintain it and add games. As for the cabinet itself, Jack made it himself:

"I designed the cabinet from scratch. I used SketchUp for the plan, mainly because it's quick and easy to use and also gave me the exact measurements required to make it out of wood. I'm not the best craftsman, so a friend of mine who makes children's toys from wood was a big help. The cabinet is made from MDF, but

Above A hollowed-out interior houses the Raspberry Pi and the wires for the authentic arcade parts

I really wanted that retro look, similar to that of an Atari 2600 or a Moog synthesizer, so I used black paint and some rolls of Fablon to achieve that.

"It works surprisingly well," continues Jack. "The one issue, as many people have said, is that it only has four buttons. I intended it to have six, but I had miscalculated the size of the buttons and could only fit four. The controls that are on it, however, feel responsive and very similar to the real thing. Most of the emulators work very well; however, it does struggle with PS1 and some MAME games, but hopefully the newer model of the Pi will give it the extra muscle it needs."

While it may not have quite enough buttons on the cabinet, you can plug in an Xbox 360 controller to have a little more control over the games – although it may ruin the experience a little.

"It was a great feeling [finishing the Pi Arcade]. The finished product really did take me back to the old bartop arcade machines I remember playing on holiday when I was a kid."

Above Small but mighty – the Pi Arcade can play games from over a 25-year time span

INSERT COIN TO PLAY

>STEP-01
Power it up
The machine is powered by a portable battery – plug it into the Pi and activate it for the arcade machine to start turning on. It should run fine for a few hours.

> STEP-02
Choose your emulator
After loading EmulationStation, you can choose what to play on as long as you have some appropriate games to load on that particular emulator.

> STEP-03
Just have fun
Play using the controls or by plugging an Xbox 360 controller into it, and just enjoy the retro arcade experience on your sofa with no sweaty men to jostle with.

#OZWALL

For his flagship art installation in Nashville, Joseph Hazelwood brings old and new video technology together with the Raspberry Pi

The #OZWall video installation, the brainchild of Joseph Hazelwood, sits in the 'Escaparate', the focal point of Nashville Tennessee's centre for world-class contemporary art, OZ Arts (**ozartsnashville.org**).

Before becoming a hotbed for creatives, the space was actually a cigar warehouse that held over 100,000 of the owner's private cigar blends.

"From what I'm told, it was originally one of the largest cigar humidors in the world," quips Hazelwood, before getting to the crux of the project.

"A visitor to OZ will walk in the Escaparate and be drawn into an interactive multimedia experience. We like to think of this installation as a canvas for other artists to build upon, and that's the beauty of open source and platforms like the Raspberry Pi."

Hazelwood has effectively retrofitted six vintage TVs with modern LCD panels, though he plans to double this to 12. "Each TV is outfitted with its own Raspberry Pi 2. We used the code from the CCFE Pi Wall project (**ccfe.ac.uk/computing_projects.aspx**) and tailored it to our needs.

"Right now we have it displaying one large image and switching content via video editing, but in the long run we plan to use the Raspberry Pis to switch content and to make the wall more dynamic and interactive. We may also add cameras, motion detectors, and other sensors to the room/building for all manner of interactivity."

You can learn more about the #OZWall video installation and Joseph Hazelwood's fascinating penchant for juxtaposing old and new technologies at **hazelwoodlaboratories.com**.

Below As shown from the rear, each TV in the #OZWall video installation is powered by its own Raspberry Pi 2

Below The programming aspects of the project were taken care of by developer Phillip Lehner

Below Joseph Hazelwood retrofitted and lovingly restored old TVs with modern flat screens

Image: Sam Frawley, www.samfrawley.com

H.A.L. 9000

Willem Koopman opens the pod bay doors on his latest Raspberry Pi project: a fully functioning H.A.L. 9000

I nspired by a BBC Radio 4 documentary celebrating the theatrical rerelease of Stanley Kubrik's 1968 epic *2001: A Space Odyssey* (**bbc.in/1vc3NG8**), Willem Koopman decided to build his own homage to this particular piece of cinematic history – a working model of H.A.L. 9000, the ship's computer.

Much like the original H.A.L. who so famously lost his digital marbles part way through the film, Willem's effort still needs code to be added and polished: "The eventual plan is to have it as a work bot, so that when the website breaks or someone make a loud noise, we can take a picture for prosperity and/or automatically shame the perpetrator." But it already performs some suitably clever – and fitting – parlour tricks.

"At the moment, it runs a very lightly modified version of Jasper (**jasperproject.github.io**), which

Below The business end of the project comprises the Pi, speakers, a Camera Module, and a USB microphone

Sci-fi fans will instantly recognise the design, which is near identical to the one in the film

Below Willem used an old wide-angle lens converter to create H.A.L.'s iconic 'eye'

Below Hiding behind the lens is the Camera Module and two LED lights, one on either side

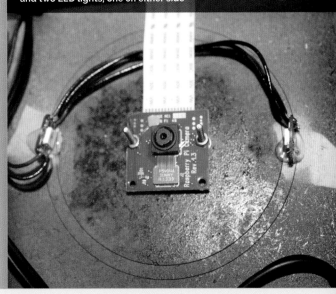

asic Siri-like behaviour. k it to do various things e time, check emails ok – basically, all the s things that Jasper to do. You can also en the pod bay doors." the Raspberry Pi- lements, there was t of work involved in e case to look just right – he eerie fisheye with its d backlighting. esearching how the as made and found e 'eye' was a standard m fisheye. Many years ght a wide-angle lens (the sort used to make l videos before many re born). I dug it out, and owballed from there." g is catered for by two d LEDs. e itself was created -cut MDF. "Cheap laser

cutting is the most marvellous innovation of modern times," enthuses Willem. "Just create an SVG, send it off, and a few days later precisely machined parts arrive in the post. I can design and build straight dovetail joints to within 0.2mm, all without a chisel!"

While the cutting was pain-free, the painting process has been anything but. "I spent about three weeks trying different techniques to get the glossy spray paint to actually stick." Willem says that the moral of the story is to always use a decent undercoat, but stay away from spray primers. "Lightly sand to get rid of the brush strokes. Repeat."

You could potentially set up Jasper to create your own personalised Siri with the Pi, but until then you can learn more about Willem Koopman from his blog: **secretbatcave.co.uk**.

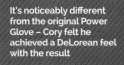

It's noticeably different from the original Power Glove – Cory felt he achieved a DeLorean feel with the result

Some of the original PCB had to be cut away to allow the Arduino to fit inside, but most buttons still work

CORY KENNEDY

A family man and a cyber defence professional, who is also the co-founder of Kansas City's premier information security meetup, SecKC. **imgur.com/a/9JXbT**

Play on your own or with a friend via the screen on your wrist, using a Wii Remote, the control pad, or your fingers

PWNGLOVE

Quick Facts

- It took seven days from conception to presentation
- Cory's son helped with the soldering
- The Power Glove was an official Nintendo licensed product
- It accepts two Wii Remotes as controllers
- It was created as part of a 'show-off' meetup

The infamous NES peripheral, the Power Glove, has been the butt of many jokes and centre of a lot of nostalgia. What happens when you don't need the rose-tinted glasses any more?

L et's face it, once you take off your rose-tinted glasses and forget the quotes and memes surrounding cult 1980s adver-film *The Wizard*, you're left with a barely functional peripheral that is very much a product of its time. The Power Glove was a novelty and, while it captured the minds of many young children, it never quite lived up to its promise at the time. Apparently, it's this exact reason that got Cory Kennedy motivated.

"The PwnGlove was a project rooted in the desire to build

the memory my 12-year-old self was deprived of, thanks to the marketing genius behind Power Glove's capabilities," Cory explains to us. "I saw other people doing all sorts of projects with Power Gloves and I thought it would be a perfect match to pair it with retro NES gameplay."

The PwnGlove was originally created for Cory's information security meetup's 'Hacker Show-off Contest', where he had 15 minutes to wow the crowd with his invention. Although the focus

was information security, Cory wanted to try something else:

"I wanted to do something different, mainly because where I am today professionally is rooted in tinkering – not only with computers at a young age, but also videogames… I wanted to be the kid from the 'now you're playing with power' ad. Which is exactly why I added the NeoPixel array."

As well as being a pretty good fit for the inside of the Power Glove, the Raspberry Pi came in very handy for enabling

> As well as being a pretty good fit for the inside of the Power Glove, the Raspberry Pi came in very handy for enabling Bluetooth and Arduino interaction

Bluetooth, Arduino interaction, and access to the actual games.

"The bodywork was tough, mainly trying to resist the urge to take away from the original look too much," Cory says, regarding actually getting everything into and around the glove. "I say that, but then I take a look at the monstrosity it has become and I have to say… It now reminds me of the *Back to the Future* DeLorean."

He did try to use as much of the original parts as possible, though.

"It leverages all the original components, modified physically a bit to cut [out] the non-essential PCB, to allow for room for new components. There are four original bend sensors (thumb, index, middle, and ring), which connect to an analogue multiplexer living in the palm housing, which sends that data back to the Arduino. This is all piped over Bluetooth back to the Raspberry Pi. The wrist pad buttons are mostly intact (programming buttons

aren't working), and they are set up now to do things like allowing the Konami code and switching the colour and pattern sequence on the NeoPixel array."

Cory is forever making tweaks to his PwnGlove, improving it in minor ways to solve what he sees as problems, but admits that most people don't even notice.

"To be honest, the reactions it gets from people, especially kids, certainly makes those imperfections disappear."

Above The lights on the glove are supposed to pay homage to advertising material for the Power Glove

Above Left An Arduino can be found in the original circuit compartment, plus a screen and Raspberry Pi on the wrist

START PLAYING WITH POWER

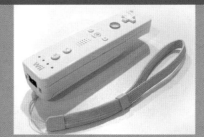

>STEP-01
Konami coding

To get into the PwnGlove, you need to use the password. This is entered using a special sequence of keys: Up, Up, Down, Down, Left, Right, Left, Right, B, A, Start. 30 extra lives await.

>STEP-02
Choose your game

The RetroPie interface comes up, enabling you to select any compatible game from your library. It's best to use the buttons on the pad to select one.

>STEP-03
Team up with a bad dude

Throw a Wii Remote to a friend and you can then rescue the president, save the princess, fight the Red Falcons, or swear at Battletoads together.

TOM SHERLOCK

Our intrepid astronomer is a software developer at Wolfram Research, and has a background in optical and atomic physics, with a long-time interest in photography.
bit.ly/1HSxF4U

> Using the standard Raspberry Pi Camera Module, Tom is able to do some astrophotography

> The Raspberry Pi Model B+ is just the thing to perform the complex calculations for the telescope

> This custom-made mount slots snugly into the viewfinder of the telescope and ensures the Pi camera isn't affected by stray light

MATHEMATICA TELESCOPE

The Raspberry Pi has access to a huge amount of mathematical power and knowledge, thanks to Wolfram's Mathematica – here's how one man uses it for stargazing...

Quick Facts

> The whole thing only took a few hours to make

> You don't need a very expensive telescope for this project

> You can see the camera preview on a remote desktop

> Tom wants to have Wolfram control the motors next

> The whole Pi setup weighs less than a normal CCD camera

Space. The final frontier. This is the adventure of Tom Sherlock. His mission: to explore the stars from his backyard, using a telescope to photograph stunning cosmic vistas. And he's managed to make the process much better and easier for himself by using a Raspberry Pi.

He needs more than a Pi, though – it's good, but it's not good enough to photograph close-ups of the Moon. In this particular instance, the Raspberry Pi is connected to a telescope using a custom-made mount to slot it into the eyepiece, so that the Raspberry Pi Camera Module can take these excellent photos. On its own, it's impressive enough, but Tom has added a few more tricks to make it a truly unique Pi project – namely, he can control it with Wolfram Language and Mathematica.

"Mathematica combines a powerful language, device control, and image processing facilities with a great deal of built-in data," Tom explains to us. "This includes astronomical data, so it was not hard to see the advantage of having one piece of software which could manage all these tasks in a unified, scriptable way."

Tom actually works at Wolfram on Mathematica, so is well versed in the ways of the language and Mathematica itself. He's also an amateur astronomer, which is where the idea came from in the first place:

"Over the past decades and especially in recent years, amateur astronomy has become more and more dependent on computers for various tasks, like planning observations, pointing and driving the telescope, capturing and processing images and data, and finally sharing images and data with other astronomers.

"Typically, you have to run several different packages on several different computers to accomplish these tasks. For example, you might plan observations with one package, control the telescope with another package, capture images with still another package, and then

"It has to be controllable from a computer," Tom elaborates. "Many scopes these days have computerised mounts, and the computer built into the mount will let you select any object in the mount's internal database and slew the scope to that object. Generally, these

Above The Pi camera might not be of the highest fidelity, but it can take stunning shots when used correctly

> On its own, it's impressive enough, but Tom has added a few more tricks to make it a truly unique Pi project

process the images with one or more additional packages, sometimes involving specialised plug-ins."

Tom was able to solve all these complications, thanks solely to the Pi having Wolfram available with Raspbian. Just having a Pi and some coding skills is only one part of the challenge, however, as telescope selection is also important.

mounts will also allow you to connect them to an external computer and then, using the correct protocol, specify an arbitrary set of coordinates. Since Mathematica has the coordinates of hundreds of thousands of different objects, you can easily look things up and have the scope slew to that object."

It all sounds good in theory, but just how does it work in practice?

"Remarkably well, considering how much the Pi is doing. The main problems I found were more details than anything else. It takes a bit of time to look up astronomical coordinates on-the-fly, so I found it was better if I did that ahead of time instead of 'in the field'."

Above Just a Raspberry Pi Model B+ is needed to perform the complex calculations needed for the telescope

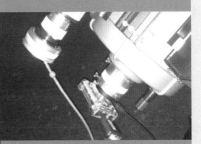

HIUTMUSIC

Creative technology agency Knit built an internet radio
with a difference to entertain Hiut Denim's workforce...

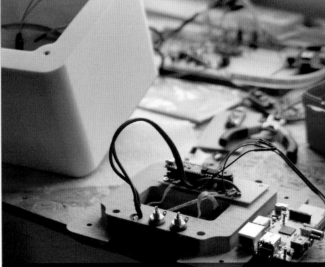

Above **The project also uses an Arduino Nano, partly to help reduce the CPU load on the Raspberry Pi, which uses up to 70% on decrypting Spotify tracks**

Above **A ring of NeoPixels is used to create the geographically controlled light effect**

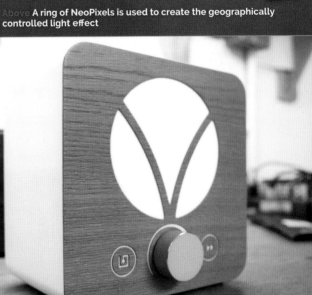

Above **Capacitive touch sensors are used for the 'skip' and 'save' buttons**

T he #HiutMusic jukebox is a rather beautiful Twitter-powered music player that takes pride of place in the Hiut Denim Factory on the west coast of Wales, where 'the music is loud and the coffee is strong'. It was created by Knit, a creative technology agency that approached Hiut Denim with an idea to help customers connect with the boutique jeans company.

"We wanted to facilitate a dialogue between Hiut and their fans through the emotion of music, creating an opportunity for customers to have an impact on the people that make their jeans," explains Jack Chalkley, head creative technologist at Knit.

It's powered by an internet-connected Raspberry Pi, which uses the Spotify and Twitter APIs in a rather novel way. "It plugs into the existing sound system on the factory floor and fans can request a track by posting a tweet that includes #HiutMusic, the artist, and track title," says Jack. The tweet is

detected and the song is queued up and played, but the project doesn't end there.

"Hiut's jean makers can skip, save, and adjust the volume of tracks on the face of the radio," continues Jack. "The 'skip' button and volume knob do exactly what you would expect, but the 'save' button saves the current track to a favourites playlist and a tweet is sent from the **@HiutMusic** Twitter account, sharing the request." What's more, the backlit display on the front of the #HiutMusic jukebox changes colour based on how far away the track request was sent. The further the sender, the warmer the colour displayed. "For example, a request from Wales would turn the display light yellow, whilst a request from New Zealand would illuminate deep red," explains Jack.

You can learn more about the #HiutMusic jukebox at **weareknit.co.uk**.

POCKET PIGRRL

Adafruit's Ruiz brothers are back with a 2015 refresh of their brilliant Nintendo Game Boy project that's half the size and twice the fun of its predecessor...

Last year it was the 25th anniversary of the legendary Nintendo Game Boy handheld console; to celebrate, **Adafruit.com** came up with a great project for Raspberry Pi emulation fans, called the PiGRRL.

Suffice it to say that the project was a resounding success and **Adafruit.com** has returned with this 2015 refresh, named the Pocket PiGRRL. It uses the Raspberry Pi Model A+ and a 2.4″ PiTFT HAT (with a resolution of 320×240 pixels), making for a much smaller and lighter project than its predecessor. According to its makers, it's about half the size overall, measuring 118mm tall and 69mm wide.

To create the controls, instead of using a SNES controller as before, the makers have opted to use cheap and easily sourced tactile switches soldered to a cut-down Perma-Proto PCB, which is wired to a ribbon cable and connected to the Raspberry Pi's GPIO pins. While some readers might be wondering how you can play *Super Mario World* with just two buttons, you'll also find instructions and 3D printing

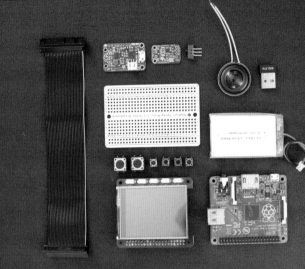

Below There aren't a great deal of parts for the Pocket PiGRRL, making it a great introduction to more advanced Pi projects

Below The files you need to 3D-print the chassis are available for download on the project's webpage. If you don't have a printer, you can order 3D printed parts online

Below Here you can see the audio amp (top left) and the power charging unit (top right). The three wires leading to the side of the chassis control the power switch

files for a four-button version of the Pocket PiGRRL.

To power the project, the Ruiz brothers are using the PowerBoost 1000C, which features a built-in load-sharing battery charger circuit, meaning you can power your Raspberry Pi while it charges the project's ample 2,000mAh Li-Po battery. The Pocket PiGRRL even features an audio amplifier and a tiny 1W mono speaker.

While you're free to set up the software side of the project in any way you like, the Ruiz brothers have opted to use RetroPie

(**bit.ly/1lYZkDg**), a great emulation package for the Raspberry Pi that enables users to play games from all sorts of classic systems.

It's fair to say the project isn't particularly taxing to build, though you will at least come out of it an expert solderer. You're definitely going to need helping hands with a large magnifier – some of those joins need precision work!

You can learn more about the project, and find out how to build your own Pocket PiGRRL, on the Adafruit Learning System via **learn.adafruit.com/pocket-pigrrl**.

SPACED OUT

Dave Akerman's frequent and eye-catching forays to the edge of space have made him the Raspberry Pi's foremost near-spaceman

I t may have proven to be one small step for man, but space travel has certainly been one giant leap for the tiny Raspberry Pi. When the makers of this bare-bones computer came up with the device, no one in their wildest dreams would have thought it would boldly go where few other machines have travelled before: to the stratosphere and back. But thanks to the Pi community's very own 'spaceman' Dave Akerman, that is exactly where it has been,

**Below Dave
Akerman and
Heston Blumenthal
during filming for
the celebrity chef's
UK TV series**

and the results have been nothing less than stunning.

Dave is a high-altitude ballooning enthusiast who has been tethering Raspberry Pis to helium balloons and sending them to the edge of space since 2012. His hobby and choice of computer have been attracting much attention since, leading to a rather hectic life for the software programmer, and helping to show further evidence of the adaptability of the Pi.

In the Pi's lifetime, Dave has appeared on television, become something of a YouTube sensation, and worked with a celebrity chef, making him one of the most well-known users in the ever-growing Pi community. Not that he's complaining about becoming a Pi celeb. "The Raspberry Pi had two big effects [on my high-altitude ballooning]: the addition of live images and all of the media attention," Dave tell us. "I expected the former, but not the latter. It's all been good, though."

High-profile performances

One of his most high-profile recent performances came on the BBC 2 show *Stargazing Live* on 20 March 2015. Dave was invited to rub shoulders with the likes of the European Space Agency astronaut Paolo Nespoli and Paul Franklin, the visual effects supervisor of the Hollywood movie *Interstellar*.

Stationed at Leicester racecourse, Dave was asked to launch a 434MHz (RF link) balloon equipped with 'Pi in the Sky' telemetry boards to capture stills and video from above the clouds of the solar eclipse taking place that day. The Raspberry Pi soared to a maximum altitude of 30km, taking in images, before popping and landing in a field just south of Leighton Buzzard – a huge success which delighted viewers and the BBC. "It was just a shame that there was so little time to explain the flight," says Dave. "The images shown weren't near our best ones either, but these are the limitations of live TV."

Even so, the flight proved to be a thoroughly enjoyable experience for the radio amateur. "There was so much rehearsal that by the time the cameras were live, I was pretty relaxed," says Dave about his long, busy and exhausting day. Unfortunately, he did not get to meet the main presenters, Prof Brian Cox and Dara Ó Briain, since they were based at Jodrell Bank, just a few miles from Manchester Airport – "I'd have been unlikely to get permission from the CAA to launch – and yes, I did ask!" Dave laughs. Nevertheless, he is fired up about the total solar eclipse that will take place on 21 August 2017 in the USA. "The whole thing

a webcam, and that's been replaced by a Pi camera," he tells us.

"Back then, I also handmade the radio boards, but now I use PCBs, which makes things simpler and more reliable. The very first Pi flight used linear regulators with more batteries than was strictly necessary, meaning that the inside of the payload box got very, very warm. Nowadays the tracker board and Pi all use switching regulators, so fewer batteries are needed."

The LoRa module

To make the Pi more useful for his hobby in the future, Dave has been working on refining a long-range radio (LoRa) module for the Pi. It was on board the balloon used in *Stargazing Live*, but the

> # The Pi is an ideal device, allowing the telemetry to be automatically uploaded

was good practice and I can't wait for that one."

While thinking up and taking part in numerous headline-grabbing events, Dave has been able to refine his methods, regularly coming up with new and more efficient ways of 'exploring' life beyond our planet. "The first Pi I sent into the air used

media activities surrounding the launch meant Dave didn't get a chance to set up the tracking. Had he done so, he would have been able to eliminate the need for a PC, since LoRa devices are transceivers – they receive as well as transmit. The hard work of demodulating the signal is done

Behind A view over Cornwall taken from a high-altitude balloon carrying a Raspberry Pi

Below Dave Akerman being interviewed on TV by Dr Lucie Green

inside the LoRa chip. "The Pi is an ideal device, allowing the telemetry to be automatically uploaded to the internet for display on a map," says Dave. "It also becomes possible to upload messages to the balloon tracker."

LoRa will replace the traditional RTTY (radioteletype) balloon tracker for Dave, even though the older system is very easy to program and has been used for around 95 percent of amateur high-altitude balloon launches in the UK. "It's essentially the same as RS232 serial communications, with the ones and zeroes being denoted by two slightly different radio frequencies," explains Dave. "On the Pi, all that's needed is to connect the serial port to a small radio transmitter via a few resistors, and then send the data out of the serial port. The

Below The potato in space, as filmed from a GoPro

receive end is a bit trickier, and is generally done with a ham radio receiver and a PC."

Dave has carried out four LoRa test flights so far, the first of which landed on a golf course during a competition. "The payload was collected by one of the golfers, who wrapped it round his trolley, which explained the fact that the landing position kept moving!" Another test flight had two LoRa trackers, one receiving data from the first and then relaying to the ground over an RTTY link. "Most impressive, though, was a trial of high-data-rate images, where the incoming packets managed to saturate the uplink on my admittedly slow ADSL internet," Dave adds. "More work is needed, but this does look promising."

Yet even though LoRa modules are being introduced, some aspects

of Dave's flights will remain, most notably the Pi Camera Module which replaced the original webcam on the balloon's payload. "The Pi camera quality was a big improvement on the webcam," he tells us. "It was lighter too, which helps. Previously, I used Canon compact cameras for stills, or a Kodak camcorder for video."

Video capture

Such video-taking capabilities have proven to be very useful, especially during some of the publicity-generating stunts that Dave has pulled. His favourite involved taking a 20cm-tall teddy bear – the Raspberry Pi mascot, Babbage – to an altitude of 39 kilometres and dropping it from the sky. He wanted the toy to rival human daredevil Felix Baumgartner, who had set the world record by skydiving from a height of 38,969 metres in October 2012.

For the 2013 Babbage flight, the teddy dropped at speeds of up to 200 miles per hour as a fitted camera filmed what the toy 'saw'. Landing four hours later in a field near Shaftesbury, the teddy – which contained a Pi and a tracking device in its stomach – was intact, and its endeavours eventually came to be watched by more than 160,000 YouTube users. "I wanted that downward video of the [Baumgartner] jump, but with a slightly lower budget and rather less seriousness,"

Stills of Earth as the Pi is sent into near space, as part of filming for the solar eclipse

CHEF ENJOYS A SPUD LAUNCH

In October 1995, the potato made history when top scientists working for NASA developed a special kind of spud: one that could be grown in space to feed hungry astronauts. This amazing fact was not lost on English celebrity chef Heston Blumenthal when he was creating his Channel 4 series, *Heston's Great British Food*.

For the 'Pie' episode, Heston decided it would be a good idea to use Dave Akerman's high-altitude Pi in the Sky balloon to launch a potato. "My first question was 'are you expecting anything physical to happen to the potato?', thinking that Heston probably wanted it freeze-dried or something," says Dave. "But no, it was just to put it into near space and get it back again. No problem then."

To achieve this, Dave built a payload with a Raspberry Pi doing the tracking and live imaging, plus three GoPro cameras – one up, one down, one sideways – for video. There was a second AVR tracker in a separate payload as a backup. Dave then had to find a day when the wind predictions were suitable and Heston was available. "That was not an easy task," he adds.

But how receptive was Mr Blumenthal? "Heston, as you might imagine, is basically a ten-year-old adult, so he and I got on just great," Dave replies. "We started chatting and the producer stopped us, explaining that he wanted cameras to record Heston's reaction when he learned things for the first time. We then had to drive up and down the road for some footage, during which Heston kept starting sentences like 'So, when the balloon bursts...' and I'd reply with 'Sorry, can't tell you yet!' It was obvious that he'd been looking forward to the day for some time."

The flight was straightforward, with the crew following the live images in the chase car. Quite fittingly, the landing was in a muddy field and lots of coverage was gathered for the TV programme. "It was great to see that when it eventually got broadcast, and it was a lot of fun to then see the flight ridiculed a few days later by [English comedian] Alan Carr."

Even so, it piqued a lot of interest. Following the show, Dave had a noticeable increase in the number of emails received from people who wanted to follow in his footsteps. "Flights like these do encourage others to get involved," he says.

explains Dave. "I'd bought a Babbage soon after he went on sale, with the hope that I'd be able to fit a Pi Model A inside him, and was pleased to see that it just fitted. The hardest part was replacing Babbage's eye with a Pi camera – those eyes are very, very well fixed in." Babbage beat the world record by 31 metres.

This 'mission' showed Dave's eye for detail, even though there were problems. At one stage he

moon landings, it was easier to do it than fake it," laughs Dave. Not that the launches are actually simple. He says anyone wanting to replicate Pi in the Sky flights would need to spend a good few months researching first, and even he has had his fair share of mishaps. "I did manage to lose a couple of payloads to the sea: one early on, when I was unaware of the effect of wind on gauging the amount of gas in

> ## For the 2013 Babbage flight, the teddy dropped at speeds of up to 200 miles per hour

was going to build a replica of Baumgartner's capsule, until it appeared it would be too heavy. Tests had also shown a reluctance for Babbage to jump. Even when it transpired all had gone to plan, Dave's attempts to track the toy were hampered by the SIM card in his MiFi (mobile WiFi hotspot) running out of credit. "I also had a call from the BBC asking about the progress, just as I was trying to find Babbage in a field. I managed to walk straight past him."

However, as with Dave's other exploits, publicity followed. Two journalists from Austria even accused him of faking the flight as a publicity stunt for the Raspberry Pi Foundation. "Well, like the

a balloon, and one later on, when the predicted flight path was completely wrong because the Met Office didn't fly its own balloons the day before."

But with the top four flight records for live images at around 40 kilometres altitude, Dave's hobby is, he adds, a thrill that never leaves him. "On the very first flight, the thrill was to hold something in my hand that had, to all intents and purposes, been to space," he says. "Prior to that flight, that was all I wanted, plus images that I had taken from near space. For many people this is enough, but like a few others in this hobby, I like to find new things that I've not done before."

SKYCADEMY
Aided by Dave, the Raspberry Pi Foundation's Skycademy event introduced 24 teachers to high-altitude ballooning, enabling them to help schoolchildren launch Pi-equipped balloons.

LAURI HAKKARAINEN

Lauri and his friends founded Esmes Digital, a web and mobile application business that sometimes has spare time to make crazy projects.
sneek.co/blog/candypi

CANDYPI

Use your Raspberry Pi to satisfy your sweet tooth with an old-school candy dispenser and new-school technology

Delicious jelly beans, kept tantalisingly out of reach inside their glass prison

Using a coin and physically twisting it is so last century: now there's a motor that does it automagically

Behind the scenes, a Pi allows you to press a button on a web browser to dispense some tasty beans

Quick Facts

> The project uses a Raspberry Pi Model A+

> It took the team a day to build the whole thing

> The USB port was removed and attached via wires

> The project's components are wrapped in duct tape to protect against power surges

> Their next project is a Pi-powered 3D printer

We remember going to the shops as kids and looking at the sweet-dispensing machines. We only needed ten pence to try to get some! Unfortunately, our mother had our health in mind (and probably better sweets in a hidden location anyway), so it was a very rare occasion to actually get any sweets from one of these dispensers. While these machines seem to have all but disappeared, mini versions of them are now popular, offering gifts and trinkets. Inserting coins, though, is old-hat, which is where Lauri and his team at Esmes come in:

"We are huge fans of Jelly Bellys, and a while back we ordered ourselves a small candy machine. We needed to use coins to give us candy, and putting the coin in the slot became boring after a while. So we decided to modify the machine so that we could use a mobile phone to trigger the mechanism, since using coins is so 2014. Complete overkill, but why not! With Raspberry Pi, we could host the mobile front-end on the device itself and interface with a stepper motor controller."

With that, the CandyPi was born: the mobile-phone controlled candy dispenser, with no need to nag your mum. They thought about the concept for a while, but it wasn't until they came across the right gears and screws and other components needed that they decided to actually give it a go.

HOW TO GET A JELLY BEAN

>STEP-01
Find Candy Pi
With CandyPi set up and connected, all you need to do is navigate to the browser interface for the actual machine itself: it makes sense to do this via your smartphone.

>STEP-02
Push the button
No complicated controls or levers to push: all the machine can do is dispense random jelly beans when asked. So there's a single button to press to get to your sweets.

>STEP-03
Eat your sweets
The Raspberry Pi and technological part is done. Before you lies a bounty of sugared and/or sweetened goods. Grasp them with your hand and feast on your victory.

> When we run the motor, it makes the original dial rotate. Rotating that dial moves the mechanism, which drops the candies to the 'chute'

Lauri explains how the CandyPi works: "The motor is attached to the rotary dial via gears. When we run the motor, it makes the original dial rotate. Rotating that dial moves the mechanism, which drops the candies to the 'chute'. We decided not to reinvent the wheel and it seems that it was a good idea, since the mechanism is quite stable."

The setup includes the original machine, a stepper motor, some specific gears to get the mechanism working, and a connected Pi (with Wi-Fi) to power the whole thing and provide the web interface. Why, specifically, did they use a Pi?

"Raspberry Pi is the favourite embedded platform for us," Lauri says. "Many available tutorials, GPIO, small form factor, cheap price, [and the] possibility to run Linux are huge pros. With Linux, we could host the web front-end easily on the device itself (nginx), and the stepper motor interface was easy to do in Python."

While Esmes won't be selling the CandyPi, pre-assembled or as a kit (it was just a fun little project, after all), the build process is well documented on their website (**sneek.co/blog/candypi**) if you want to give it a go. As for the future of the project, they might add a more powerful motor to make the CandyPi work a little better, but otherwise they'll probably just use it to get sweets whenever they're a bit peckish in the office.

Below left
Everything is such a tight fit that the protruding USB port had to be removed and reattached via wire

Below A slight tear-down of the device reveals that it's mainly the candy dispenser and the Pi

MCMASTER FORMULA HYBRID

Members of the McMaster Formula Hybrid team worked together for over 18 months to build a racing car capable of competing in the competition. **formulahybrid.ca**

Instead of using traditional dials, McMaster's Pi-powered racing car uses an LED display to give the driver information about his speed, revs, and lap time

The Raspberry Pi 2 is housed behind the dashboard, where it is sealed in to protect it from the elements. Telemetric data is sent wirelessly to the team in the pits

The front wheels are powered by 15kW electric motors; the rear wheels by a 250cc petrol engine. Sensors throughout the car provide data on how well the hybrid engine is performing

MCMASTER
FORMULA HYBRID

McMaster University needed a smart telemetric system to get its hybrid racing car onto the winner's podium, and the Raspberry Pi 2 provided everything the team could ask for...

Quick Facts

> The car is quarter the size of a regular Formula 1 car

> The front wheels are powered by an in-hub 15kW electric motor

> The rear wheels are powered by a 250cc KTM SFX motorbike engine

> It can do 0-100 km/h in three seconds flat

> It has a top speed of 150km/h

When the engineering students from McMaster University in Canada started working on their entry for the 2015 Formula Hybrid and EcoCAR 3 competitions, they knew they'd need more than raw muscle to get a podium finish. Not that their race car lacks muscle: it packs a 15KW in-hub motor for the front wheels, and a 250cc motorcycle engine for the rear wheels.

The challenge was bringing all the technology together and keeping the car going. McMaster's secret weapon was a Raspberry Pi 2, used to gather telemetry data and send it to the team on the trackside.

We caught up with Jonathan Moscardini, LV lead for the

electrical division of McMaster University's Formula Hybrid and EcoCAR 3 teams. He tells us that the Raspberry Pi has been crucial to the car's success. "We're a pretty big team, between 70 and 90 people. But our project is entirely student designed, built, and tested. The students do everything."

McMaster has been entering the Formula Hybrid and EcoCAR 3 competitions for several years now and had pretty much perfected the physical car: "It has a very clever monobox," asserts Jonathan. "It's one big fibre tub."

Physically the car was fine, but that's not enough to win a race. "We do a lot of electronics in the car," says Jonathan, "a lot more than we need to" and that's where

the Raspberry Pi steps in. "What the Pi does for us is handle all of our communications. Essentially, it's both the dashboard computer and our team radio. It also gives us a few new features along the way, simply because it's so powerful."

Good telemetric data is essential when building a race car. "We have live up-to-date information about everything that's happening in the car," says Jonathan. "We use a wireless adapter known as a Bullet [BULLET WirelessHART Adapter], which is built for a variety of outdoor uses. We have one at either end: one in the car and one in the pits."

The telemetry data enabled McMaster students to analyse the car as it raced around the track, which helped them fix a variety of

Above The Raspberry Pi 2 sits behind the dashboard and powers the display. When the car is racing, it automatically sends telemetric data to the team in the pits

engineering challenges. "We were having reliability issues," divulges Jonathan. The team used the Raspberry Pi with various sensors to analyse parts of the car as it went around the track. "When we installed a Raspberry Pi 2 it made life a lot easier."

While they initially installed a Raspberry Pi 2 to gather telemetry data, its use soon expanded to other aspects of the car. McMaster engineering students quickly

the steering wheel, to keep it well protected. "You really need to be able to seal and waterproof the computer," Jonathan tells us. "You need to keep it away from the elements".

So what if you want to start integrating your Raspberry Pi with a track car? "Planning and testing is one of the biggest things," advises Jonathan. "Race cars are not the place to be trying things out. As far as

> We use a wireless adapter known as a Bullet, which is built for a variety of outdoor uses...

realised they had enough power to build an electronic dashboard. "We also installed the PiCam [Raspberry Pi Camera Module]," says Jonathan, to get first-person video recording from the car. The Raspberry Pi was sealed behind

implementing goes, planning and testing is really important because it's a lot easier to work on things when you're not in the car. So you really need to have everything installed before you start."

Above The car is much smaller than a Formula 1 car, but with a top speed of 150km/h it is much more than a standard kart

INSTALLING A RACE-CAR COMPUTER

>STEP-01
Raspberry Pi
The Raspberry Pi is connected to custom PCBs built by Advanced Circuits (**4pcb.com**), and a stock video display (picked up from eBay). The Raspberry Pi Camera Module is also added (to provide video recording of the race circuit).

>STEP-02
Sealed in
The Raspberry Pi electronics kit is located behind the steering wheel and is sealed in using Loctite 243 and Henkel (**henkel.com**) adhesives, sealants, and functional coatings. This protects it from the elements. The display is mounted on the dashboard behind the (detachable) steering wheel.

>STEP-03
Trackside telemetry
The Raspberry Pi is hooked up to a BULLET WirelessHART Adapter, which communicates with another Bullet at the trackside. Data captured by the Raspberry Pi is sent wirelessly to the team working on the car.

AMAZING PI PROJECTS

8 imaginative creations that *innovate* and *inspire*

While the Raspberry Pi is to all intents and purposes a simple Linux-powered PC, it's sometimes difficult to convince people on the street that they merely need to connect a standard TV or monitor and keyboard and mouse to use it like any regular computer or laptop. They struggle to comprehend that something so small and strange in appearance is anything other than alien in origin. The difficulty is usually intensified when you talk to them about all the incredible things people do with the Pi. Sending Raspberry Pis to the edge of space to take pictures of the curvature of the Earth, configuring them to adjust the temperature or control the lighting in their home… how can they hope to even turn it on, let alone take control of their home?

Amazingly, turning on a light is usually the first step for anyone wanting to make use of the Raspberry Pi's extensive physical computing repertoire. All it takes is a few lines of code and a basic grasp of elementary electronics (if that). Once they've cracked it, though, everything else is common sense and trial and error. One minute a tiny LED light is blinking; the next, your robot is deciding whether to turn left or right.

Once that light bulb moment occurs and the initial culture shock has subsided, the final blocker is usually indecision. What do you do with a credit-card-sized PC that can go anywhere and do anything? That's the focus of this feature – ideas, inspiration and advice from some of the community's best hackers and makers.

Project Aquarius

Two brothers recreated the Amazon rainforest in their home, including indigenous flora and fauna. Weather, sound, and lighting effects produce accurate day and night cycles…

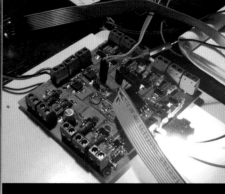

Above **It uses a custom PCB to aid control**

Above **It simulates light, sound, and weather**

Simulating
THE AMAZONIAN RAINFOREST

Poopi and Piter's paludarium is controlled by Raspberry Pi and four ATmega 168Ps. Here is its extensive feature list:

- 6× independent sections of halogen lights
- 27× independently controlled 1W LEDs for various effects
- 3× independent 3W RGB LEDs for ambient colour effects
- 3× independent 3W LEDs for thunder and moon simulation
- 3× independent 10W LEDs for paludarium lighting
- 2× independent fans for wind simulation
- 3× fog generators
- 2× independent solenoids for rain control
- Temperature monitoring

All lights are fully dimmable, and Poopi and Piter also have full control over fan speed.

Wojciech 'Poopi' Lazarski is a technology evangelist from Poland. Poopi was once a developer in the demo scene, way back when the ZX Spectrum and Amiga were the best show in town. These days Poopi and his brother-in-law Piter are more concerned with recreating the Peruvian rainforest – specifically, a region called Rio Tahuayo – in their home with their custom-made paludarium.

"One day my brother-in-law showed me a video on YouTube and said it would be cool to have something like this," explains Poopie. "He said that making the tank wouldn't be a problem, but creating [the project] would be impossible for him. I asked him to give me time to digest it and a week later I said yes, but that I'd like to do it my way. I didn't just want to add lighting effects so I started thinking about a more sophisticated solution."

At the start, it controlled lights to create the illusion of night-time with the phases of the moon, and sunrises and sunsets with all the associated colour effects. Everything is accurately calculated based on the target location. Later, wind simulation was added using two fans, and then mist and rain effects using solenoids. Since delicate flora are present, careful temperature monitoring is also of utmost importance.

You can see Project Aquarius in action on YouTube (**youtu.be/FeS5zqL8frk**), simulating various times of day and weather conditions.

One Controller to Control Them All

Retro gaming is a popular avenue for the Raspberry Pi, but few have done it with as much flair and precision as Brian Corteil...

Brian Corteil is a Cambridge Raspberry Jam regular and founding member of the Cambridge Makespace (**makespace.org**). Brian is well known in the Raspberry Pi community for the remarkable quality of his projects and their stunning attention to detail.

"I wanted to make something my two boys could set up and play with, without me being around," he tells us about his distinctive retro gaming project. "It's also a great honeypot to draw people in to my table when I show off at Maker Faires and Raspberry Jams [see sidebar on the next page]."

Brian's retro gaming console-cum-arcade controller is certainly that, and it should be of little surprise that it's just as neatly presented on the inside as it is on the outside.

"I used one of the laser cutters at the Cambridge Makespace to cut [and] engrave the box and back-plate. I also used Inkscape (**inkscape.org**) to design the back-plate and modify the box design from Steve Upton's box-generating script (**officeoffairetrade.com**). The RetroPie SD card image takes care of the software side of things

(**bit.ly/1lYZkDg**)." digitalLumberjac's arcade joystick driver (**bit.ly/1xHKQCz**) also proved to be the best way for Brian to interface the joystick and buttons to the Raspberry Pi's GPIO pins.

Brian keeps an excellent log of his many Raspberry Pi projects, including the building of robots, on his website: **corteil.co.uk/Blog**.

All images courtesy of Alex Eames **www.raspi.tv**

Make it HAPPEN

Brian is one of the founding members of Cambridge Makespace (**makespace.org**), which gives him full access to the tools and equipment (like 3D printers and laser cutters) he uses in his projects, not to mention the expertise of fellow members.

While trailing its US equivalent, the UK maker scene is growing fast, with new locations popping up all the time. Try searching online for 'maker spaces' or visit **hackspace.org.uk**.

There are also numerous online services that will do the 3D printing or laser cutting for you and send the results by post.

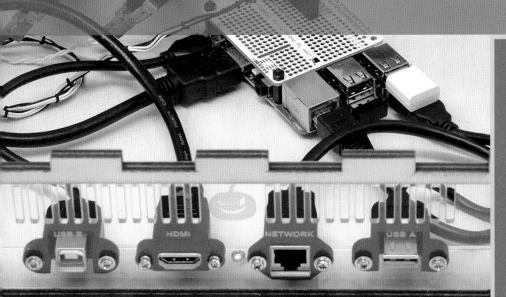

Digital Zoetrope

Brian's second project is a deliciously modern take on a pre-film animation device that produces the illusion of movement with still images…

"I started the Digital Zoetrope over Christmas 2014 and I'm still refining it," Brian Corteil tells us about his remarkablae animation device. "I was inspired from the work of Eadweard Muybridge, an early pioneer of high-speed photography [who] was the first person to show that a horse takes all of its feet off the ground when it's running. Researching his work led on to Zoetrope and I thought it would be a wonderful project."

As with his retro-gaming console, Brian utilised the laser cutter at Makespace, and Inkscape for the computer-aided design work. Despite bundling a wealth of technology, his Digital Zoetrope is moved by hand. Like the original designs, you spin the device and look through the slats to see movement in the still images as they rotate.

Since his project uses 12 OLED displays with the Raspberry Pi, it's actually possible to update the frames in real-time, so you could watch an entire film if you wanted. Moreover, using the technological trickery, it's possible for two people to view entirely independent animations when looking into the Digital Zoetrope from different angles.

Organise YOUR OWN JAM EVENT

Raspberry Jams are a great way to get together with like-minded hackers and makers. They're also the best place to find inspiration and help to build amazing Raspberry Pi projects. You can find a Raspberry Jam near you by pointing your web browser to **raspberrypi.org/jam**. Can't find an event near you? Don't worry – it's easy to set up your own! Here are a few tips from Cambridge Raspberry Jam (**camjam.me**) organisers Mike Horne and Tim Richardson:

1. **Find a partner and team:** Don't try to organise everything on your own. Find a core team of two or three people who can meet regularly and gather helpers on the day.

2. **Get a venue:** It must be accessible with good parking and transport links, and have the space you need to do what you want. It could be as small as your kitchen table or as large as a local community or sports hall.

3. **Get talking:** Everyone likes 'show and tells' and talks, so start with those. You can add things like workshops, sponsorship and vendors later.

4. **Walkthroughs:** In the run-up to every Jam, put yourself in an attendee's shoes. Imagine walking in through the front door for the first time. What do you see? What do you need to do?

5. **Questionnaires:** Just after the end of the event, send out a questionnaire to all attendees to find out what was good and what could be improved. Use it to make your next Jam even better!

Internet of Things Chessboard

16-year-old Ben James spent two months designing and building his IoT chessboard, and three months developing the software. The results speak for themselves…

Ben James is a home-educated Raspberry Pi enthusiast who plans on becoming a robotics engineer when he's older.

"The inspiration for this project came about one afternoon when I felt like playing a game of chess, but there was no one to play with. I would have gone online and played, but that's a 2D diagram view that feels really unintuitive, so I decided to make a real physical chessboard that could play online."

To play, your opponent requests a new game on the chessboard's own website. "When they make a move by dragging a piece on the web interface, the relevant piece and square will flash on the IoT Chessboard. Whoever's sitting in front of it will move that piece to update the board, then will make their own move. The board detects this, then sends that move back to the opponent's web UI, where the piece is moved on the screen."

According to Ben, the biggest challenge of the build was desiging the circuitry. "Each of the 64 squares on the chessboard has to have an individually addressable LED on its surface, an LED on the piece sitting on top of it, and a detection circuit to determine whether there is a piece on it."

Instead of controlling an unwieldy 192 input/outputs, the project utilises multiplexing. "Each group of four squares is handled by a PCB, then the 16 PCBs are connected horizontally and vertically in groups of four." While it makes I/O much more managable, it required over 2,000 solder joints and made troubleshooting issues a gargantuan task. "It was more efficient in the end, though, cutting the I/Os down to under 60, and it meant the software was a lot easier to write."

See it in action at **youtu.be/bWeObKths-I** and learn more at **engineercheer.wordpress.com**.

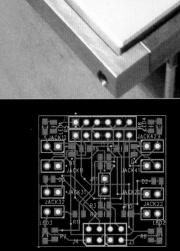

Above The circuitry is impressive

Above Ben had to solder 2,000+ join

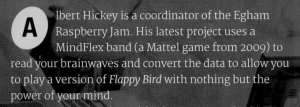

Flappy Brain

Control a Flappy Bird clone with your brainwaves? It's mind-blowing stuff…

Albert Hickey is a coordinator of the Egham Raspberry Jam. His latest project uses a MindFlex band (a Mattel game from 2009) to read your brainwaves and convert the data to allow you to play a version of *Flappy Bird* with nothing but the power of your mind.

In a recent interview with Alex Eames on RasPi.TV (**bit.ly/1FEvmNK**), Albert explained more: "The headband features a little piece of metal that you put against your temple and it reads your brainwaves." It's connected to an Arduino that converts this information into usable data that's then passed over to the Raspberry Pi and used as controller input for the game. "Just search online for 'MindFlex Arduino Hack' and you'll come up with a page that explains how do it."

Albert used Pygame to create *Flappy Brain* on the Raspberry Pi and, much like the game on which it's based, you need to move the protagonist (in this case a tiny brain) past a series of obstacles.

Unlike *Flappy Bird*, though, the brain automatically moves up the screen – to move it down (and past the obstacles), the user needs to concentrate; Albert demonstrates by doing mental arithmetic to move it down. To allow it to move up again, Albert blinks repeatedly to break his concentration. Amazing! Learn more at **winkleink.blogspot.co.uk**.

Images courtesy of Alex Eames www.raspi.tv

Pi Wars COMPETITION

If you're looking to find amazing Raspberry Pi robots, look no further than Pi Wars (**piwars.org**) – it's an annual UK-based competition organised by the makers of Cambridge Raspberry Jam (**CamJam.me**) to bring home-made Raspberry Pi robots together to compete in a number of challenges and categories.

You don't need to be a robotics expert to attend, but check out this excellent video by RaspberryPiIVBeginners from the 2014 event to get your creative juices flowing: **youtu.be/PQyoDZzQJIY**

Above One of last year's smallest bots

Crowdfunding SUCCESS

As we're seeing in this feature, Raspberry Pi projects come in all shapes and sizes. If you've got a really big idea and you'd like to take it to the next level, you might want to try crowdfunding it on a platform like Kickstarter. Here are two examples we've got our eyes on…

NATUREBYTES WILDLIFE CAM KIT

The Naturebytes Wildlife Cam Kit incorporates a Raspberry Pi and a Raspberry Pi Camera Module that's triggered by a PIR motion sensor, to help just about anyone take candid shots of birds and animals in their natural habitat. The team's Kickstarter campaign (**kck.st/1Ndsg99**) proved a great success. Find out more about this heat-sensitive camera trap at **naturebytes.org**.

BIGBOX-3D

BigBox-3D incorporates two of our favourite things in the world – Raspberry Pis and 3D printers – so we're naturally rather excited about the project, the subject of a successful Kickstarter campaign.

It's the brainchild of E3D, a British engineering company with extensive 3D printing experience, and LittleBox, which has previously found success on Kickstarter with the MicroSlice mini laser cutter.

The idea of the BigBox-3D is to make it easy and affordable to achieve high-quality 3D prints. The project uses OctoPi (a cloud-based print solution) and the Raspberry Pi Camera Module for a remote live view of your prints as they happen. Learn more at **bigbox-3d.com**.

FERRAN FÀBREGAS

A Spanish computer scientist who works at a consultancy for urban ecology by day, by night he is an active member of the Barcelona maker community.
lifebox.ferranfabregas.info

LIFEBOX

Creating artificial intelligence on the Pi may sound like the start of the robot uprising, but the LifeBox isn't taking any chances, and has imprisoned them in lights...

Quick Facts

> The project took two months to complete

> Ferran learnt how to laser-cut wood for the project

> It is apparently not inspired by Conway's Game of Life

> The code is available on GitHub: bit.ly/1T8VKtC

> There's a mini version in development

T here are so many different type of light-display projects on Raspberry Pi that you could be forgiven for thinking that the LifeBox was just another neat little programmed series of LEDs. This would be a huge mistake to make because the little lights are a lot cleverer than you could imagine: they're alive. Well, sort of. At the very least, they have been programmed with behaviour. Instead of launching into a thesis on when artificial intelligence can be classed as alive, we're going to concentrate on the LifeBox itself. Here's what it says on the side of the box:

"In this box live two pixelic entities, the blue and yellow species. These two species compete to survive and reproduce, feeding with the white mana that grows under [their] feet.

"Each species has eight configurable variables that can change their behaviour. The white mana also has five parameters that determine their behaviour and also rule the future of the two species that feeds.

"Learn the basic concepts of programming and biology being the god of these entities, varying all the parameters and seeing the consequences of your actions in the LifeBox!"

Powered only by a Raspberry Pi, the AI isn't quite able to take over the world, but it makes for a really cool experiment

Two species fight it out for limited resources on this ever-changing LED display

Laser-cut wood creates this sharp, intriguing-looking box that houses the components

Its creator, Ferran Fàbregas, explains it to us in a less poetic manner, but one that makes more technical sense.

"LifeBox, in short, is a virtual ecosystem simulator on a 32×32 RGB led panel," Ferran tells us. "It's composed of two species that compete for the resources (mana) to get energy, survive, reproduce, and grow.

"Both species and the mana (which actually acts as a different species itself) have a user-defined

cheap 32×32 RGB LED panel at a fair and I decided to create the LifeBox. I was captivated by the idea of seeing the evolution of a programmable ecosystem on a beautiful box on my dining room [table], like other people can enjoy with a fishbowl."

Inside the box is just a Pi, the LED panel, and a driver to connect the two. Because of this, the code is split up into two sections: one part to control the driver, and one part that controls the simulation.

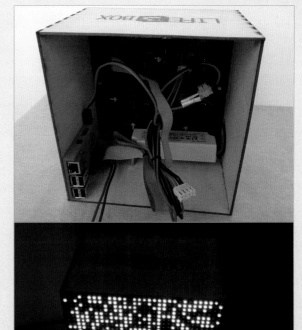

> ## Learn the basic concepts of programming and biology being the god of these entities

parameterization that allows [the user] to change their behaviour and see the consequences on the panel, acting as a god of the virtual ecosystem."

Ferran's god complex has been with him a while, as well as the interest in simulating these kind of ecosystems:

"Since I was a child, I was attracted to robotics and the possibilities of simple life simulations. I programmed some basic life simulators software before, but one day I found a shiny, beautiful, and

"The driver is based on the great work of the original C++ driver by Henner Zeller and a reimplementation in C by Peter Onion with slight modifications," Ferran explains.

"The simulator is build in C and the main goal is to maintain it as simple as possible, so anybody can change not only the species parameterization but also the simulation algorithm itself (although this is not the objective, because it can result in an unusable LifeBox situation)."

The whole thing is configurable via specific files, and you don't need to recompile it each time either. The code is still being improved, and you can find it on GitHub (**bit.ly/1T8VKtC**), or, if you really like the project, you can look at getting one of the LifeBox kits by checking out the crowdfunding page at: **lifebox.ferranfabregas.info**.

Top It looks messy inside, but it's generally quite a simple setup once you break it all down

Above The most interesting night light you've ever used: maybe it will be this decade's lava lamp?

BRING YOUR RASPBERRY PI TO LIFE

>STEP-01
Set the parameters
Delve into the config files and define how your life forms and mana work: life expectancy, energy requirements, reproductive rates, and so on.

>STEP-02
Start the experiment
Power on the LifeBox and the simulation begins. The simulation will run for as long as you supply it with power, and any resets will start it from the beginning.

>STEP-03
A new beginning
Once you've completed the experiment, it's time to start again. Go back into the parameters and reprogram the life forms and mana.

ROBERT DOERR

Robert Doerr runs Robot Workshop and has built robots that compete in *BattleBots* (the US version of *Robot Wars*).

robotworkshop.com/robotweb

> Rectangles are cut into the base, and servos with wheels are glued beneath

> The Raspberry Pi board is clipped into the case, with a RoboPi board mounted above

> Two furniture gliders are screwed to the front and back to provide stability

PIPLATEBOT

Drawing inspiration from the turtle robots of old, **Robert Doerr** created a Raspberry Pi robot with the components hidden inside a Bud Pi Plate case. Say hello to PiPlateBot...

R obert Doeer is no stranger to building robots. He's the owner of Robot Workshop, an organisation dedicated to restoring classic robots, and has entered two robots into *BattleBots* (the US version of *Robot Wars*): Crash Test Dummy and Crash Test Junior.

But this is no battle droid. When Robert saw a Bud Pi Plate case (**budind.com**), he was struck by how similar it looked to the turtle-style robots used to train computer science students. It was "definitely [like] the early turtle robots like the Terrapin Turtle [ones] and the early Tasman Turtle robots," says Robert.

The Pi Plate's circular design enables easy access (you twist off the top) and there is space inside for additional components. Robert immediately decided to see if he could place a Raspberry Pi, along with all the parts required to build a moving robot, inside the case. "It is the only Raspberry Pi-based robot that I know of built using an off-the-shelf Raspberry Pi case," he claims. "I tried to use as many Raspberry Pi-type products in the construction as I could."

"Getting everything to fit was the biggest hurdle," says Robert. He cut two rectangular holes in the base of the Pi Plate enclosure, and glued servos to the bottom of the

case. An EZO power bank sits on top of the Raspberry Pi and RoboPi boards, and works as a battery. Finally, a USB WiFi adaptor enables wireless communication via SSH. "Those that have seen it really like the robot and ask where I bought it," Robert says with pride. "The completed robot really looks like a finished project, so they assume it may be sold in stores."

The powerful RoboPi board (**mikronauts.com**) is an important component. "The Raspberry Pi is great at the high-level thinking, while the Parallax Propeller chip on the RoboPi board is a great I/O controller for offloading all the real-time tasks."

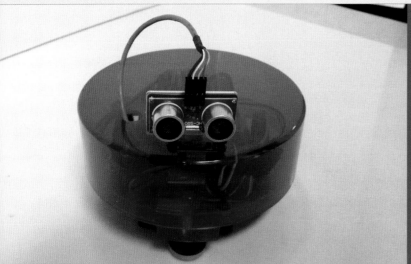

Above The finished product is a friendly-looking turtle-style robot that can sense objects in front of it

> ❝ If you have an idea for a project, just go for it! You'll never get it done just thinking about it ❞

"I have been programming the robot in C," Robert tells us. "The RoboPi controller has libraries available for both C and Python. Eventually it would be fun to write a Logo interpreter so it could also use Logo and emulate the early turtle robots."

Finally, Robert added an HC–SR04 sonar sensor (ultrasonic transducer) so the PiPlateBot could measure objects directly in front of it. "[It] was built over the course of a couple weeks during my spare time in the evenings," he says. "It could have been built in a few evenings, but I had to wait for some parts to come in." There is still a bit of room left on the robot for additional sensors like contact bump, IR line following, or even a I²C compass.

Having created, and rescued, countless robots, Robert has good advice for budding robot builders: "If you have an idea for a project, just go for it! You'll never get it done just thinking about it. Even if the first iteration doesn't work out, you can always change it along the way and you'll learn a lot as you go."

Above A standard smartphone battery pack is squeezed on top of the boards and inside the case

BUILDING THE PIPLATEBOT

>STEP-01
Cutting and mounting
Holes cut in the base allow the wheels to fit, and glue sets the servos in place. Furniture gliders attached to the front and rear stop PiPlateBot from wobbling.

>STEP-02
Assembling the components
The Raspberry Pi is fitted and a USB WiFi adaptor is connected. The RoboPi board is stacked on top of the Raspberry Pi board. A smartphone charger provides power.

>STEP-03
Power and motion
The RoboPi comes with libraries for both C and Python that are used to control the servos. An HC-SR04 sonar sensor is fitted: this enables PiPlateBot to sense its surroundings.

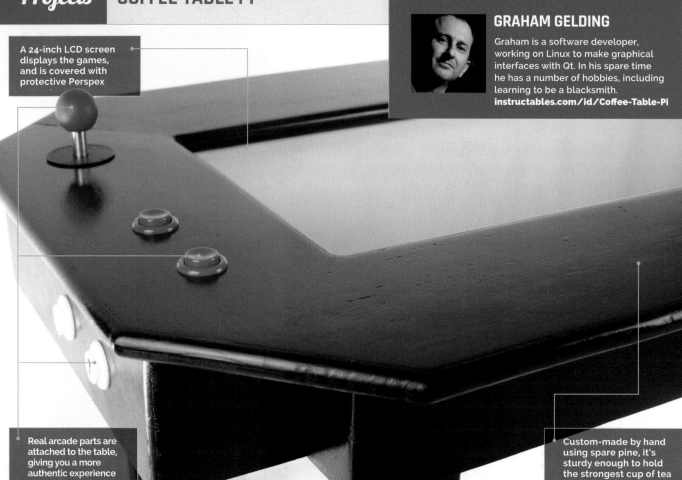

A 24-inch LCD screen displays the games, and is covered with protective Perspex

GRAHAM GELDING
Graham is a software developer, working on Linux to make graphical interfaces with Qt. In his spare time he has a number of hobbies, including learning to be a blacksmith.
instructables.com/id/Coffee-Table-Pi

Real arcade parts are attached to the table, giving you a more authentic experience

Custom-made by hand using spare pine, it's sturdy enough to hold the strongest cup of tea

COFFEE TABLE PI

This fully fledged cocktail arcade cabinet, apparently masquerading as a coffee table, is one of those Pi projects everyone wants to do…

Quick Facts

> The project took a few weeks to complete

> The Perspex over the screen can get scratched easily by kids

> *Donkey Kong* is Graham's favourite game to play on it

> It does actually get used for resting cups of coffee on

> There will be no kit, so use the Instructables guide

As you probably know, the Raspberry Pi, while an excellent educational tool, is big among the maker community. The kind of folks who like to create machines are always on the lookout for a tiny computer controller, one that can power their project with the smallest footprint. Along with the makers, any tiny computer released to the market also tends to attract a great deal of attention from the arcade gaming community, looking for the next thing to power their work-in-progress MAME cabinet. With this cross-section of interests for one device, it's a wonder why we haven't seen full-size arcade cabinets powered by a Raspberry

Pi in every single issue of the magazine. Graham Gelding is one of the few to take on this task. Not only that, he's gone a step further and created the ultimate in classy, grown-up arcade gaming apparatus: a cocktail arcade cabinet (although it has a slight twist, as he likes to refer to it as his 'coffee table').

"It was an attempt to recreate the classic arcade cocktail cabinet," Graham tells us, "but in a way that can fit into a lounge room. It's also a way of introducing my kids to the games that I had growing up.

"I also wanted to try some woodworking and needed a project for my Raspberry Pi. The idea of

Above The insides are neatly arranged and very chunky, just like any good arcade machine should be

USING GRAHAM'S COCKTAIL CABINET

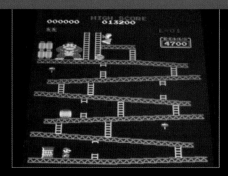

>STEP-01
Table or arcade machine
When the coffee table is off... it's still a table. To turn it into its true arcade machine form, you need to switch it on.

>STEP-02
Select your game
Like a lot of Pi emulation software, you're met with a selection of pre-loaded games that you've added yourself. Selecting a game will launch it.

>STEP-03
King of Kong
Play your game and have fun! Try not to put your coffee cup directly on top of the screen, and try not to knock it off while screaming at Mario.

mixing the two projects seemed perfect. I could make use of my experience with Linux, but also learn about woodworking."

He's not joking about the woodwork either. While you might think it was just a table that had been modified, or an existing cocktail cabinet that had been gutted, Graham made the whole table from scratch using pine from an old bookshelf, as well as installing the screen, arcade controls, and the Raspberry Pi itself that powers it. This made the most expensive parts of the project the LCD screen and some of the controls.

As well as those main components, Graham gutted some old PC speakers for their drivers and transformers, installed a sheet of clear Perspex over the screen to protect it, and did a lot of custom wiring and powering.

As for the future of the project, Graham is just happy with what he's made. However, he has plans for his next Raspberry Pi thing, telling us: "I would like to do something combining the Pi with the Oculus Rift virtual-reality headset."

The headset is finally coming to the consumer market, so marrying the two, if possible, would be a big leap in Raspberry Pi projects.

> " It was an attempt to recreate the classic arcade cocktail cabinet, but in a way that can fit into a lounge room "

Above The table is set up for games that use a vertical screen, so most arcade games during and before the 1980s

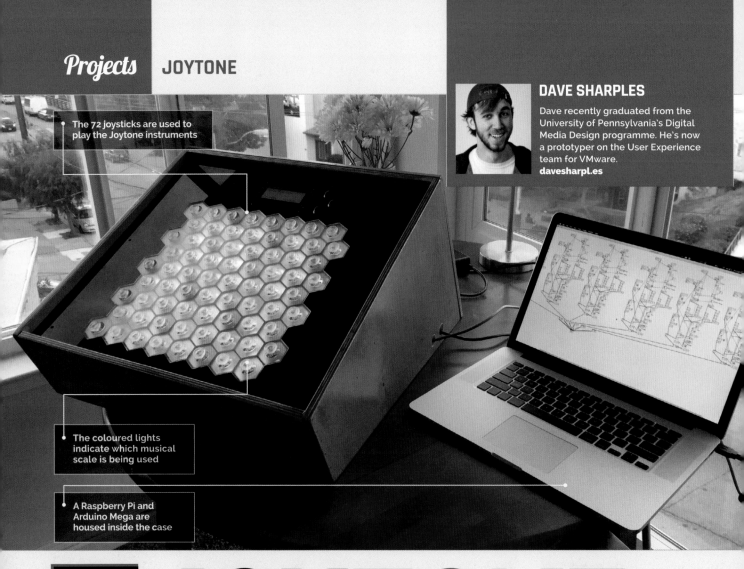

The 72 joysticks are used to play the Joytone instruments

DAVE SHARPLES
Dave recently graduated from the University of Pennsylvania's Digital Media Design programme. He's now a prototyper on the User Experience team for VMware.
davesharpl.es

The coloured lights indicate which musical scale is being used

A Raspberry Pi and Arduino Mega are housed inside the case

JOYTONE

A unique musical instrument made from joysticks, lights, and powered by the Raspberry Pi. We talk to the Joytone's maker…

Every so often we come across a project so spectacular we have to share it. Joytone is one such creation. Designed and crafted by engineering expert Dave Sharples, the Joytone is a unique musical instrument played using an array of mini-joysticks.

"I've always wanted to be able to play a musical instrument," says Dave, "and a couple years ago I took a music theory class to see if that could help me learn piano."

Rather than learning the piano, Dave had a revelation about musical structures. "I became fascinated with the patterns associated with musical structures and realised how beautifully simple music can be," he reveals.

"Acoustic instruments are designed around the physical phenomena that produce sound," says Dave. "A violin is smaller than a cello because shorter strings make higher notes, not because it's convenient for the player."

Electronic instruments, like synthesizers and electric guitars, don't have to reproduce these limitations. There's no inherent reason for an electronic instrument to resemble the acoustic tool it is derived from.

So Dave set about creating a unique new musical instrument that made sense. "Joytone is a unique new musical instrument that features a hexagonal grid of 72 joysticks," he tells us. "The

Joytone's hexagonal grid exposes musical patterns that are normally obscured by the quirks of common acoustic-style interfaces, like the white and black keys of a piano.

"Each joystick plays one note and the motion of the joystick affects the volume and character of the note," explains Dave. "The way the notes are distributed across the perfectly hexagonal grid means that all kinds of musical patterns become clear.

"Every major chord has the same finger shape, no matter what note you start on," he continues. "This is true of minor chords, scales or any other kind of musical structure, making [the Joytone] much easier to learn and play."

Above A laser cutter being used to cut the piece of acrylic.

> " There's no inherent reason for an electronic instrument to resemble the acoustic tool it is derived from "

Building the Joytone

The 'keys' of the Joytone are created using 72 joysticks. These are Xbox-style thumbsticks and were replacement parts that Dave found on eBay. They have clear plastic grips to let the LED lights shine through.

The lights (also sourced from eBay) are used to indicate which notes belong to the selected musical key. They are connected to NeoPixel (WS2812) strands from Adafruit (**adafruit.com**).

"Each joystick is really just a pair of potentiometers connected to a little plastic post," Dave explains. "One measures movement along the X-axis; the other measures movement along the Y-axis."

These are connected to an Arduino Mega via a series of custom circuit boards designed by Dave himself. "With two signals per joystick and eight joysticks per row, there are 16 analogue signals generated by each row of joysticks – a grand total of 140 for the whole instrument," he calculates.

"The Arduino only has 16 analogue inputs, so the Joytone makes use of multiplexers to handle all those analog signals. I designed custom circuit boards for the rows of joysticks, and at the end of each board is a 16-channel multiplexer.

"A multiplexer is like a big switch," says Dave. "The output wires from the multiplexers are connected to analogue inputs on the Arduino, [which] can set all the multiplexers to forward channel 0, then read all nine inputs. It then sets the multiplexers to forward channel 1, then reads all nine inputs again, and so on. Once it knows the positions of every joystick on the board, it can go through and figure out which ones are being moved.

"For each active joystick," continues Dave, "the Arduino looks up the MIDI note it represents, then bundles that information up with the two values coming from the joystick sensor and sends a little MIDI message to the Raspberry Pi."

WHAT PARTS ARE USED?

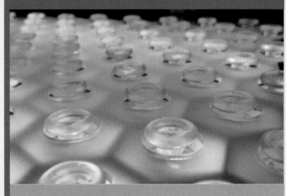

>STEP-01
72 joysticks
The interface of the Joytone comprises these mini-joysticks (picked up from eBay). The clear plastic grips enable light from LEDs to shine through.

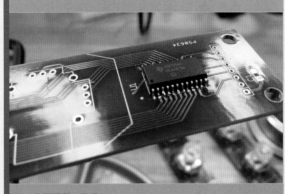

>STEP-02
Multiplexer and Arduino Mega
An Arduino Mega and multiplexer are used to assess the stick positions. The Arduino only has 16 analogue inputs, so the multiplexer enables it to handle all 72 joystick signals.

>STEP-03
Screen and Raspberry Pi
The screen is an RGB backlight positive LCD 20×40 from Adafruit (**adafruit.com**). The screen provides feedback to the user. The Arduino Mega sends MIDI information to the Raspberry Pi (which plays the audio).

PUTTING JOYTONE TOGETHER

>STEP-01
Custom circuit boards
At the heart of the Joytone are nine printed circuit boards (PCBs). These make the Joytone more reliable and easier to fix than earlier models. Dave signed up for TechShop in San Francisco to learn how to design PCBs.

>STEP-02
Fitting the joysticks
The clear joysticks and lights are fitted into the PCBs. Rather than use individual lights, the Joytone employs a strand of 25 Digital RGB LED Pixels (**adafruit.com**). These are easier to fit and more reliable than individual LEDs.

>STEP-03
Arranging the boards
Nine PCBs, each containing eight joysticks, are arranged into a square in this offset pattern. With two signals per joystick, there are 16 analogue signals generated by each row.

>STEP-04
Multiplexer and Arduino
Multiplexers are used to connect the PCBs to the Arduino Mega. They enable the Arduino to examine the position and movement of all 72 joysticks at once.

>STEP-05
Raspberry Pi
The Arduino looks up the MIDI note it represents and sends that information up to the Raspberry Pi, which then uses it to create the audio sound.

>STEP-06
Played with sticks
A sheet of acrylic is laser-cut into a honeycomb shape to hold the joysticks. A box holds all the equipment, and the device is ready to play. A single finger is used to play each stick and you can play up to six notes at once.

The software
The Joytone depends on PureData (**puredata.info**): "You can connect blocks with lines to direct the flow of data through a series of mathematical operations, to produce all kinds of strange and delightful behaviour."

Dave built a PureData patch for the Joytone. "[It] receives MIDI messages, then unpacks them and passes the values inside into a group of blocks that produces a synthesized note," he explains.

"The pitch is controlled by the joystick the user chose to push," says Dave. "One axis of the joystick controls the kind of waveform produced. It fades from a bright trumpet-like sawtooth wave to a darker triangle wave that sounds like a bell." The other axis of motion controls how flat or wide the note sounds by making a small tuning difference between the pair of oscillators that produces the note.

"All of that expressive potential is represented in the group of blocks in PureData," Dave tells us. "There are six of those groups in the patch, meaning the Joytone can play up to six notes simultaneously."

Playing the Joytone
While the idea behind the Joytone is complex, playing it is surprisingly easy. "My friend who helped me build the first one in school is a very talented musician," affirms Dave, "and the first time we got it working, he played with a couple of the joysticks, then paused and thought for a second, then immediately played a Bach fugue he was familiar with. It was an awesome moment of success after a string of very long nights."

Playing the Joytone is remarkably straightforward. The joysticks are played with a single finger. "It's easy to hold your hands as if you were typing on a keyboard," advises Dave, "and play many notes at once. The joysticks are pretty close together, so the player has access to a large musical range with pretty limited hand motion."

Integrating the Raspberry Pi

This build is the second iteration of Joytone and is the one that introduces the Raspberry Pi to the design. "The first Joytone had to function though a nightmarish rat's nest of wires inside," Dave recalls.

"In the two-brain design I used for the Joytone, the Arduino does all the analogue-to-digital conversion and the Raspberry Pi does all the audio synthesis. I like to use it on a Raspberry Pi because I can just tuck it inside the enclosure and focus completely on the instrument. I taught myself a little bit about PCB routing, and with the help of some friends they came out perfectly," he says.

Showing off the Joytone

Part of the inspiration for building a more powerful iteration of the Joytone was the Toronto International Film Festival (TIFF). Dave was asked to provide Joytone for part of the digiPlaySpace exhibition at the show.

"I had to design it to run continuously and withstand thousands of visitors over a period of six weeks," Dave says, "so I did some research at the Exploratorium in San Francisco to see how they build their exhibits.

"[The Joytone] saw about 16,000 visitors this year and I've been showing it around to my friends. Everyone seems to have a good time with it, and I'm curious to see what could happen with some serious practising. My favourite moment so far was a write-up from a six-year-old blogger who visited the TIFF exhibit.

"I'm glad that the Joytone is back from the TIFF exhibition because I can practise on it now. I only finished it a day or two before I had to ship it out! Even with the relatively short amount of practice time I've had, I can play almost any scale or chord with ease."

Despite the apparent complexity, Dave claims that the Joytone was pretty simple to build. It was "extremely tedious because there are so many joysticks."

It isn't a cheap project to make, either: "The parts for the Joytone cost about $600, most of which is for the lights and joysticks." Dave also spent an additional $450 on the custom PCBs, though he tells

us he's got enough leftover parts to build another instrument.

"I have lots of plans for other musical inventions," he says. "I'm going to iterate on the joystick idea but investigate some other form factors. I'd also like to make something more compact and portable."

Making musical instruments

If you are interested in following in Dave's footsteps, it's worth knowing that you don't have to build a device as complex as the Joytone. "Anyone could wire up a joystick to an Arduino and start sending MIDI notes to their computer," says Dave, and "you could make a simple musical instrument in an hour or two."

Budding musical creators should just "go for it," he tells us. "There's a great community of people building new musical instruments, and lots of inspiring work already documented. PureData is a wonderful tool to experiment with quickly, and the Raspberry Pi is a friendly platform for musical inventions. Learning a little music theory is also really helpful."

Above Pushing a stick up controls the kind of waveform produced; left to right controls how flat or wide the note is

Top left The Joytone is a spectacular-looking modern musical instrument

Left A sturdy wooden case is used to house all of the components

RASPBERRY PI
NOTEBOOK

uit's star makers, the **Ruiz brothers**, are back
another stunning handheld Raspberry Pi project...

Here's a brilliant project for you or your family to test your hacking and making skills with this weekend. This beautiful retro-styled mini-notebook, built by Adafruit's Ruiz brothers (**bit.ly/1MkrxGe**), is powered by a Raspberry Pi 2 and an Adafruit 3.5″ PiTFT touchscreen rechargeable battery, which sits sandwiched between the Pi 2 and the screen, is managed by a PowerBoost 1000C, a load-sharing DC/DC boost converter capable of doling out 5.2V and charging the battery while your gadget is in use. Finally, a small amp is connected to a tiny speaker for audio output.

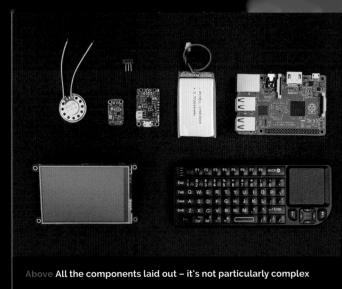

Above **All the components laid out – it's not particularly complex**

> ## The project comes hot on the heels of the Ruiz brothers' excellent Pocket PiGRRL

and, frankly, not a great deal more! The project comes hot on the heels of the Ruiz brothers' excellent Pocket PiGRRL – as covered on page 46 – a home-brew Nintendo Game Boy build we're still swooning over a few months after discovering it.

Besides the Raspberry Pi 2 and PiTFT display, for control the project features a mini-chiclet keyboard with built-in trackpad. It's a widely available wireless input device that's both affordable and easy to use. The 200mAh

While the hardware is the really exciting bit, the 3D-printed chassis is a work of art, too. Take, for example, its totally modular hinged design. While it works really well on this Raspberry Pi mini-notebook, you could reuse it for 101 different hardware projects.

Like all of Adafruit's excellent Raspberry Pi projects, you can find a full shopping list of parts, software and 3D printing files for the Raspberry Pi Notebook on the Adafuit Learning system at **learn.adafruit.com**.

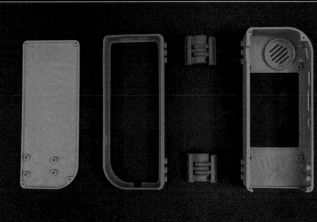

Above **The 3D-printed case, complete with modular hinges**

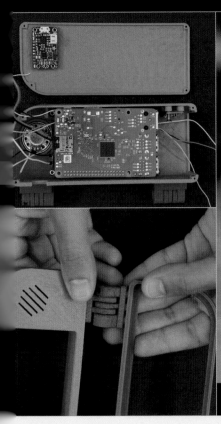

Above **It's a thing of beauty and a cracking weekend build, assuming you have access to a 3D printer**

DANIEL SPIES

A Dutch magician who likes to build his own tricks, and has taken to more advanced electronics and microcontrollers to improve his shows.
facebook.com/raspberrynin10do

NIN10DO

A 3D-printed Raspberry Pi-powered Nintendo Entertainment System that can also play Sega games

Quick Facts

> The first version took about two months

> The case is made of XT-CO-Polyester instead of the normal ABS plastic

> Daniel now has plans and the confidence to develop his Pi box of tricks

> A future version will be made with laser-cut acrylic

> It's not a trick, it's an illusion

When you're a magician looking to make your tricks – sorry, *illusions* – better, you have several paths to go down. You could start buying or recreating other people's work; however, that's not entirely original, and you risk other people having seen it already. What truly great magicians do is to create their own illusions – original tricks that wow an audience with a wonderful show. Creating tricks and illusions for people-sized magic sounds similar to another hobby: that of being a maker. Makers love the Raspberry Pi, and this is where professional magician Daniel Spies found himself at the end of 2014.

"I wanted to start learning how to program in Python so I could integrate a Raspberry Pi in complex magic acts," Daniel tells us. "The Raspberry Pi would be great for starting special music

Below A 3D modelled and printed chassis allows for the perfect fit for the project

The Nin10do keeps the flap, but repurposes it for human interface input

A small NES-style case that contains the Raspberry Pi and many other electronics

The RetroPie software allows you emulate over 20 years of systems, and allows for USB controllers of many kinds

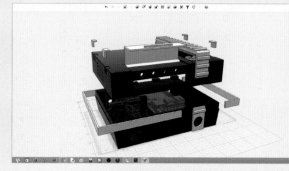

or sound effects, operating small smoke machines or even electromagnets. After I mastered the basics (servos, LEDs, etc.) it was time to build something as a practice project. It had to include as many different skills as possible, like CAD drawing, 3D printing, mechanical engineering, programming, and electronics. Then I saw guys on YouTube using their Raspberry Pi to emulate classic games on their TV. The idea was born."

Daniel decided to 3D-print his own custom NES case for

professional game console; it must run my Python script in the background but *not* sacrifice any speed or usability; it must have a option to be turned on and off without damaging the software or the SD card; and the cover must not damage itself if, for some reason, it is opened twice by the stepper motor."

With this in mind, Daniel went to work. He created full schematics for the electronics, making use of a series of LEDs, stepper motors, driver boards, timing belts, and lots of extenders

Daniel designed and 3D-printed a case reminiscent of the NES that could house his Raspberry Pi and electronics. The important question, though, was whether or not he succeeded...

"The latest version runs very stable!" Daniel reveals. "I added some parts a while ago (small capacitor in the second momentary switch) and changed the USB hub to a better version. This solved the last (minor) bugs."

The full build process, printable 3D models and code are all available online from Daniel, so if you want to give it a go yourself, the tools are there. There may even be a kit coming in the future...

Above The flap is motorised, revealing the USB ports when turned on, thanks to a custom Python script

> ## " Daniel designed and 3D-printed a case reminiscent of the NES that could house his Raspberry Pi "

the Raspberry Pi; it was smaller, sleeker and with a few more tricks than the 30-year-old console, including motors, lots of flashing lights, and the ability to play N64 games. There were some rules for the project to make it worthwhile as a test run for bigger things, though. "[These] rules included the Nin10do must look like a firm

to reach the I/O ports to make it actually usable. All of the components used were basic ones, so while there was a lot of soldering involved, he wasn't gutting any existing devices to make the project work.

With this and the coding in place (which you can find on his GitHub page – **bit.ly/1RkBirf**),

HOW TO CREATE A NIN10DO

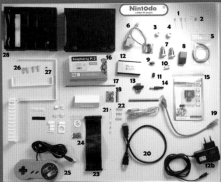

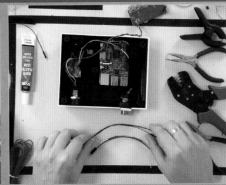

>STEP-01
Electronics
Put together all the necessary components you need for the project. Apart from the Pi, this includes the LEDs, the other controllers, USB extensions, and the motors necessary for the mechanics section.

>STEP-02
Programming
The main emulation is done by the RetroPie software. However, you also need to create a Python script that controls the buttons, motors and LEDs, depending on the situation.

>STEP-03
Mechanics
Finally, fit everything into a custom, 3D-printed case. This step includes assembling the mechanised flap, along with installing the USB ports and physical buttons.

DENIS PAPATHANASIOU

Denis Papathanasiou is a managing director at Banrai LLC, an analytical technology firm that he co-founded in 2001.
denis.papathanasiou.org

PISCAN

One project builder turned a Raspberry Pi into a home-made Amazon Dash scanner. The maker of PiScan tells us more…

Quick Facts

> It uses the Open Product Data database to match products

> Unlike Amazon's Dash, you can order any product from Amazon with it

> It cost around $70 to build (including the cost of the Raspberry Pi)

> All the software and installation instructions are on GitHub

> A similar project called Oscar served as the initial inspiration

Wouldn't it be amazing if you could just scan a barcode and get another one of that particular product through your door the next day? Amazon clearly thought so; that's why it built a mini device called Dash that did just that. No more online shopping, just scan and go…

PiScan is an open-source version of Amazon Dash created by Denis Papathanasiou. With it, you can scan products using a Raspberry Pi and order them directly. It's great fun and incredibly practical, and it's even more powerful than Amazon's official device.

"It's the ultimate in lazy-person shopping," says Denis. "PiScan will read the barcode on any consumer product and order it for you from an online vendor."

The inspiration came from another Raspberry Pi project called Oscar. That just converted "product barcodes into a grocery list," explains Denis, "but I thought it would be nice to take it one step further."

PiScan converts scanned items into a list that you can use to order products, using Amazon's API.

Right A list of recently scanned products. Placing a tick next to the product enables you to shop for that item

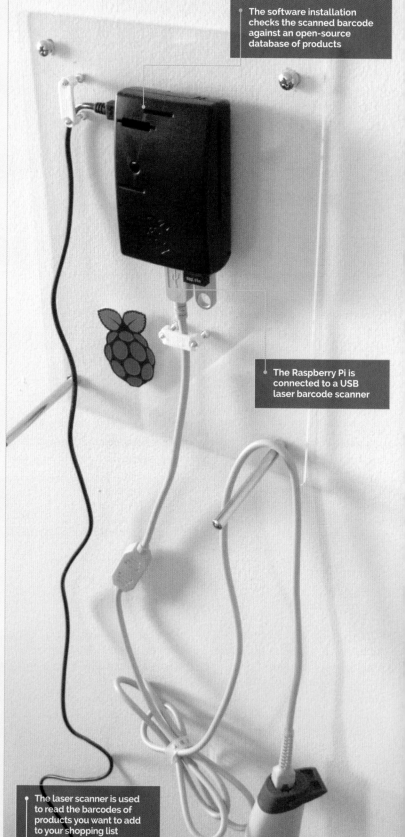

The software installation checks the scanned barcode against an open-source database of products

The Raspberry Pi is connected to a USB laser barcode scanner

The laser scanner is used to read the barcodes of products you want to add to your shopping list

SETTING UP PI SCAN

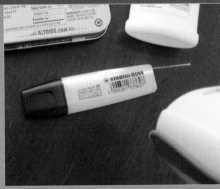

>STEP-01
Laser USB scanner

The main piece of hardware is a USB laser barcode scanner. This is used to read barcodes on products and send the digital information to the Raspberry Pi (which then matches it to a database).

>STEP-02
Software installation

With the scanner connected, you install the software. Denis has put a pre-built ARM binary on GitHub (plus the source code). He's hosting an open barcode database (**saruzai.com**), or you can create one of your own.

>STEP-03
Scan and shop

Use the barcode scanner to scan products. An open-source database of products is used to match the barcodes. You can then tick products in the list and shop for them automatically on Amazon.

In terms of hardware, PiScan is pretty basic. "I used a Raspberry Pi Model B with a WiFi dongle and a USB laser barcode scanner," says Denis. The scanner is the only extra hardware requirement to a regular setup, and you can pick one up from Amazon for less than £20.

"I wrote software for the Raspberry Pi to listen for input from the barcode scanner," adds Denis. "The scanner works just like

I didn't need to use any of the Pi's GPIO pins... Most of the work went into the software design, to make sure that the input from the barcode scanner was being read correctly.

"It's great," he tells us. "The dedicated scanner device reports barcode numbers with high fidelity.

"I've been using it to buy staple products regularly."

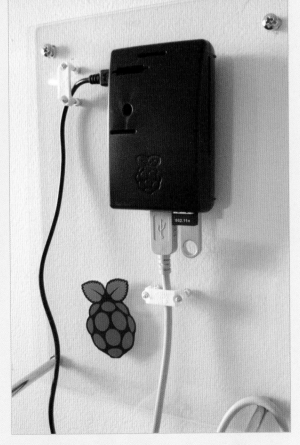

> ❝ PiScan converts scanned items into a list that you can use to order products using Amazon ❞

a keyboard, except its input comes in short bursts of characters."

The input is a 10- to 13-digit number matched to the Open Product Data database (**product-open-data.com**).

"If there's a match," explains Denis, "it will put the name of a product into a list." The Raspberry Pi delivers the list to you as an email, or you can tick items to add to your Amazon shopping cart.

Building the PiScan "was simple and straightforward," says Denis. "There was nothing to solder and

It's even better than Amazon's Dash scanner, claims Denis. "Dash only works with certain brand products, and it doesn't give you any say about quantity or price."

The only vendor so far is Amazon, but Denis is looking to expand to other retailers.

"Tesco in both the UK and Korea supposedly offer similar APIs," says Denis, "and there are probably other vendors out there that I'm not aware of."

If you fancy making your own PiScan personal product scanner,

the software is freely available to download from GitHub (**github.com/Banrai/PiScan**), along with installation instructions.

"I've tried to make them simple to understand," says Denis, "but feedback is welcome."

Above The finished PiScan device is attached to a wall and orders products online when you scan them

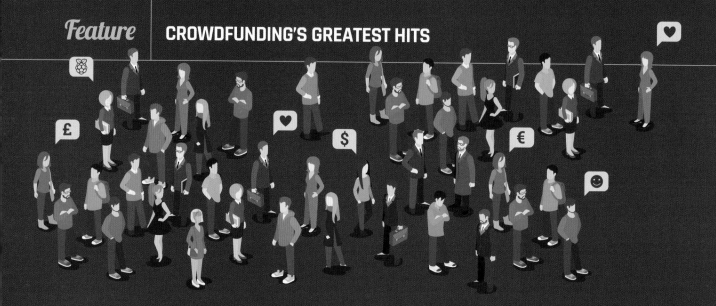

CROWDFUNDING'S GREATEST HITS

The Raspberry Pi is the perfect maker tool, so it makes sense that it has played a pivotal role in some of the best crowdfunding stories ever told...

The low cost of the Raspberry Pi, coupled with its appeal to hackers and tinkerers, has launched an explosion of hardware projects – from simple plastic cases, to entire spin-off devices powered by a Pi at their heart. For many, the only thing stopping them from taking their project from the workbench to market is a lack of funds, something crowdfunding sites like Kickstarter and Indiegogo aim to solve.

Crowdfunding serves several valuable purposes for smaller businesses and individual makers: it allows them to raise funds to bring a product to market without having to go through traditional funding channels, like bank loans or venture capital; it enables them to quickly gauge the demand for a particular product and receive feedback on its design ahead of mass-production; and it can help build buzz around a product launch.

For customers – 'backers,' in crowdfunding parlance – it provides access to hardware that would otherwise not be readily available, along with a feeling of being part of the journey to market that doesn't come from simple pre-orders

or registrations of interest on a corporate website. While only around two in five Kickstarter campaigns reach their funding goal, the right idea at the right time can earn a fortune, as proven by our rundown of the biggest successes from the Raspberry Pi community.

It's a heady mixture that has featured some stunning successes, along with a perhaps surprisingly small number of failures. If you've ever wondered about the secret of crowdfunding success, we've spoken to those who have been there and done that, to bring you the advice you need to know in order to succeed, while avoiding the pitfalls that have caused others before you serious upset along the way.

KANO

The top-grossing crowdfunding campaign in Raspberry Pi history by quite some margin, Kano raised nearly £1 million in November 2013, with a premise that at first seems laughably basic: a Raspberry Pi starter kit bundle.

Positioning the project as 'a computer you make yourself', Kano bundled an off-the-shelf Raspberry Pi with carefully selected accessories, including an eye-catching orange keyboard and trackpad, and a customised operating system. Its real potential came with the unveiling of Kano Blocks, a bundled graphical programming language inspired by MIT's Scratch and Google's Blockly, along with built-in lessons to walk the user through everything from assembling the kit to programming a game.

Despite its record-breaking funding run, Kano – as is common with crowdfunding projects – ran into some trouble during production. The first Kano units were due to ship in June and July 2014, but problems with the HDMI cables, keyboard battery, flashing the SD cards, the power supplies, and even the plastic case, meant that the first kits didn't ship until September and it was October before the majority of backers received their rewards.

Since shipping Kano, the team behind it has continued to build on its success with the creation of Kano Challenges, educational contests designed to further encourage children to get involved with programming and computing.

HDMIPi

The HDMIPi campaign raised £261,250 – far in excess of its £55,000 goal – from 2,523 backers to produce a low-cost high-resolution display. HDMIPi is notable for another reason than its sky-high funding, though: the project was a joint venture between electronics professional Dave Mellor of Cyntech and Alex Eames of review and tutorial site RasPi.TV, who acted as the public face of the campaign.

"I'd been doing RasPi.TV full-time for 18 months, with no income from it, before HDMIPi," Alex explains. "It was Dave Mellor of Cyntech who approached me about the project in the first place, after talking to the guys at the Milton Keynes Jam. "It was obvious to all of us that a small, inexpensive, portable screen was needed for the Pi – we all wanted one – but there wasn't anything out there under £100. We thought it ought to be possible to make that happen, and we were right, but it wasn't easy."

While the crowdfunding campaign was a great success, the project hit difficulties during fulfilment, which led to some backers receiving their displays almost a year late – a common theme in hardware campaigns. "The actual driver board design came partly from ideas [that] backers suggested during the campaign," Alex recalls. "We liked them because they made the product unique, but they were probably the biggest cause of the delays; in hindsight, we could have probably delivered months earlier if we hadn't listened."

SLICE

The creation of FiveNinjas – a group comprising members of Sheffield-based Pi accessories maker Pimoroni, the Raspberry Pi Foundation itself, and music producer and technology trainer Mo Volans – Slice raised an impressive £227,480 to build a media playback set-top box based around the then new Raspberry Pi Compute Module.

Rather than taking the retail Raspberry Pi hardware as the basis for the project, as many other campaigns have done, the Compute Module – an industrial Raspberry Pi variant based around the SODIMM form factor, designed to act as a plug-in computer-on-module for a custom-designed carrier board – allowed FiveNinjas greater control over the final design and layout of the project.

The result is a sleek aluminium box featuring a smart LED strip under user control, a wireless remote control, and an internal hard drive for storage. The Slice focuses more on playback of local content rather than streaming, although WiFi connectivity was unlocked as a stretch goal when the campaign hit £100,000. It includes a slick user interface and excellent compatibility with various file formats, along with features such as SATA storage connectivity, missing from the standard Raspberry Pi hardware.

Like the majority of crowdfunded projects, Slice has been hit by numerous delays. The rewards were scheduled to be with backers by November 2014, but it took until the end of February 2015 for the first Slice packages to begin shipping.

FLOTILLA

Flotilla, in fourth place with £146,680 raised, is the second Kickstarter campaign to come directly from the Sheffield warehouse of Pimoroni, and takes aim at the educational market with a range of smart input and output modules which can be easily programmed from a Pi.

Pimoroni made a name for itself in crowdfunding circles by launching the first project to go live on Kickstarter UK: the Picade. "We actively wanted to be first. We'd heard that Kickstarter was coming in the UK, so we made sure that our campaign was ready and [that] we were there ready to press the button," explains Jon Williamson. "We just stood there at ten midnight, pressing F5 until the live button became live, and we were the first to press it," adds a laughing Paul Beech.

Despite not having the benefit of being first, Flotilla easily surpassed the £74,134 raised by Picade. The company has a few ideas for avoiding the delays that plagued its original project, too. "We spent a year working on Flotilla before we put it on Kickstarter," Jon reveals. "With Flotilla, we've already been through six or seven iterations of the design of the system; the software has been in development for six months. Really, it's much closer to being finished this time around, and I guess that's what we've learned: the more stuff that you leave unfinished, the more things that can go wrong to trying to finish it."

PI-TOP LAPTOP

The only top-ten grossing Raspberry Pi crowdfunding campaign to use Indiegogo rather than the more well-known Kickstarter platform, London-based Jesse Lozano and Ryan Dunwoody's Pi-Top project looked to encourage people to learn computing by building their own Raspberry Pi-powered laptop. With £112,130 raised, more than double its original goal, the campaign certainly caught the interest of the community.

While much of the publicity surrounding the campaign focused on the hardware side – including the team's decision to 3D-print the chassis' master, then injection-mould for mass-production – Pi-Top promised more: like Kano, the project positions itself as the ideal platform for teaching beginners about computing, but with a focus on hardware rather than software.

The Pi-Top campaign closed in December 2014, and the team behind it worked hard to keep backers informed, as well giving them all a free upgrade to the Raspberry Pi 2 from the planned first-generation model. While the team had hoped to ship the devices to backers in May 2015, there were delays and the first batch was finally shipped in October.

As with most crowdfunding projects, the Pi-Top is going on general sale once the backers who funded its journey from prototype to production have received their rewards. Indeed, visitors to the team's website (**pi-top.com**) can now pre-order a Pi-Top kit, with or without a Pi included.

ATLAS 3D

Atlas 3D, from Kentucky-based Murobo LLC, is an example of the Raspberry Pi providing the power, rather than inspiration, for a project. Raising £141,940 – a record-smashing 7,333% of its modest £1,944 goal – the Atlas 3D is a 3D scanner built around a 3D-printed chassis and the use of lasers to measure the shape of the target object.

"The Raspberry Pi was an easy choice since it has an excellent 5-megapixel camera add-on, is able to drive lasers and motors, and has enough memory and CPU power to perform a 3D scan," project creator Uriah Liggett explained about his creation during its crowdfunding campaign in early 2015. "All of the software runs on board the Raspberry Pi, so there are no required drivers or software packages to install."

Uriah's project promises to provide benefit not only to its backers, but to the community at large, too. The driving software, FreeLLS, is available under the GNU General Public License as an open-source project, while the electronic design files are open hardware.

While Uriah took a risk by promising to release his creation under an open licence, since potential backers could have been put off by the idea of paying for something that others could build themselves from free designs, his impressive funding run proves that crowdfunding and open source are not mutually exclusive.

With the first batches having been shipped to Kickstarter backers, the Atlas 3D is now available to order from the Murobo store (**store.murobo.com**), from $209 plus shipping.

CROWDFUNDING FAILURES

Not every crowdfunding project ends in success, of course. Overall, 61 percent of Kickstarter campaigns fail to make their funding goal; of these, more than half never even reach one-fifth of the way. These, however, are the lucky ones, failing gracefully and without anyone ending up out-of-pocket. More

date but in January 2015, Azorean admitted that it would be August before devices shipped – leaving backers clamouring for refunds.

"The delays were caused mainly by the difficulty moving from the prototype that we had at the time and the need to adapt it to the new tools of mass-

production," Azorean's Cristina Gouveia explained. "We spent more, much more, time than we were expecting."

Those issues may now be resolved, but there's a more serious problem on the horizon: a lack of funds. "That delay has caused us some financial struggles, so we need to get additional investment," Cristina admitted. As to whether Azorean will be able to ship its promised rewards to backers if investment fails to materialise: "If we don't [receive investment], I don't think we can."

> " Projects that reach their goal, collect pledges, then fail to deliver "

notable are those projects that reach their goal, collect backers' pledges, and then fail to deliver on their promises.

Azorean's Ziphius caught the community's attention back in 2013 with the promise of an aquatic drone powered by a Raspberry Pi and controlled from a smartphone app. The campaign ended with nearly £81,000 to produce the device, with a self-imposed deadline of March 2014.

Not going as planned
By March, only the control boards were completed; in May, the company was still working on prototypes of the drone's chassis and control systems. A revised delivery plan suggested an October release

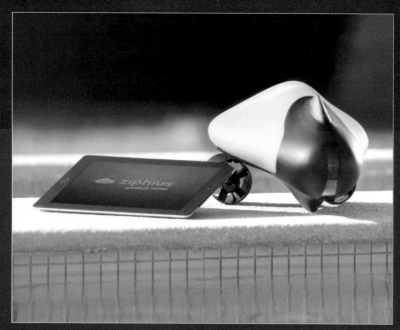

Above **The Azorean Ziphius was a runaway crowdfunding success in 2013, but is still yet to deliver**

Alfredo January 27

I am not happy at all with your last estimations (August 2015). I want a REFUND, as I am sure this product won't be released.

Frank January 30

I would like a refund. This has gone far longer than you estimated.

Justin January 22

I thought we were supposed to get an update in early January? Another deadline missed?

CROWDFUNDING GLOSSARY

Backer Someone who contributes money to a crowdfunding campaign, known as a 'funder' on some sites.

Campaign An attempt to raise funds through one or more crowdfunding sites, usually limited to a 30-day period.

Creator The individual or company behind a crowdfunding campaign.

Early Bird Reward A strictly limited number of rewards offered at a discount, designed to help a campaign build momentum in its early stages.

Fees Crowdfunding sites take a cut of all money raised by a campaign, usually around 10 per cent, in exchange for providing a platform and handling payments from backers.

Flexible Funding A feature of Indiegogo which allows campaigns to receive backers' funds even if the campaign does not reach its goal.

Goal The amount of money required by a crowdfunding campaign to be successful. If this is not raised, the funds are usually returned to backers.

Limited Rewards Campaigns can set limits of the number of rewards on offer, either to boost hype through artificial scarcity, or to meet an upper limit on manufacturing runs.

Pledge The money contributed to a crowdfunding campaign by a backer.

Reward The promised return for a backer's pledge, ranging from an email or T-shirt at the lower levels, to multiple units of the item and even dinner engagements with the creators at the upper end. Known as a 'perk' on some sites.

Story The pitch for the campaign, which typically includes a video presentation, a write-up of the project, information about the creator, a planned delivery schedule, and a section on potential risks.

Stretch Goal A campaign that raises more than its original goal may use the extra money to improve the product, offering a wider choice of colours, free extras, or upgraded features to backers.

Updates A good crowdfunding campaign will post regular progress reports to its page, both throughout the campaign and leading up to reward fulfilment.

Still taking money

At the time of writing, Azorean was still accepting pre-orders for the Ziphius through its own website, priced at $269 plus shipping. There's a disclaimer about possible delays to the shipping date, although it still says 'Estimated delivery: August 2015'. We understand that the company is now planning to launch the Ziphius kit in spring 2016, followed by the ready-made version in the summer.

Azorean's case may be an extreme one, but delays to the schedules originally proposed by crowdfunding newcomers are all too common. "The skills required for prototyping and production at moderate scale are quite different," Saar Drimer, of electronics design consultancy Boldport, explains. "On top of that, the ease by which prototyping is done today can be very misleading. 3D-printing a nice enclosure is pretty easy, whilst sourcing injection-moulded enclosures in volume from China is a completely different matter. Another example is sourcing components: if you're not aware of the many pitfalls of availability and obsolescence of components, you're going to get burned."

Pimoroni's Jon Williamson can certainly attest to the latter, having run into exactly that pitfall during the Picade campaign's delayed fulfilment. "The screens were a nightmare. We picked a screen that was basically end-of-life. It was a great screen, but they were like hen's teeth. We'd get odd batches of them; we might get 20 in Hong Kong one week, and we'd just grab them and we'd have 20 screens, great, but we needed 500. It was not a pleasant experience."

Communicating with a contractor overseas, often the only way a campaign can produce hardware at an affordable level, has its own challenges, too. "The biggest problem we had was communication with China," reveals Alex Eames about the HDMIPi campaign. "Getting things done the way we wanted, meeting our specifications, and being of usable quality was really difficult."

FINDING CROWDFUNDING SUCCESS

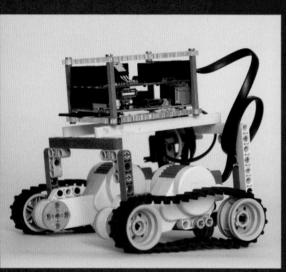

Above **The Dexter Laboratories' BrickPi raised over 67 times its original target**

For those who want to follow in the footsteps of campaigns like Kano, HDMIPi, and Slice, it's all too easy to be blinded by the sums of money on offer and leap in without proper preparation. Convincing people to part with their cash is only the start of the process.

"You [need] to have your plan together for manufacturing, and then have a second one in the waiting if things go really, really well, before you launch your campaign," advises Dexter Industries' John Cole, whose LEGO-based BrickPi robotics kit raised £82,286 – over 67 times its original target. "That should not be an afterthought – that should actually be baked into the campaign. It ties into really concrete things, like what you price your product at and what you promise for a delivery date.

"It also factors into the softer side of developing a product, which is who are you going to be selling it to, what are their tastes, wants and needs? You should understand that clearly before you start the campaign and communicate that with your manufacturer, because they'll play a big role in whether you have a successful campaign or not."

PLEDGING FOR THE SKY

Crowdfunding campaigns typically offer a variety of reward levels, from the pound donation that gets a backer heartfelt thanks, to rewards valued at thousands of pounds. Here are some of the biggest reward levels seen...

Kano Academy
£6,490 to receive workshops for 100 people, bespoke tutorials, guides, and everything an establishment needs to become a Kano Academy, plus a T-shirt. Amazingly, one generous backer snapped the offer up.

BrickPi Namesake
£6,489 to rename the BrickPi's case to anything your heart desires, so long as it's suitable to repeat in polite company. Unsurprisingly, nobody backed the project at this level.

Rapiro Custom Design
£5,000 to have a Rapiro robot customised to your precise requirements. With the base kit priced at just £229, nobody took creator Shota Ishiwatari up on his offer.

Ziphius Prototype
One backer gave Azorean £4,858 to receive a pre-existing Ziphius drone prototype, as used when the company entered the Engadget Expand Insert-Coin Competition.

Slice Full Custom Shop
£2,999 to work with the FiveNinjas design team to construct an entirely custom Slice media player. As with Rapiro, the cost over the £179 standard version was considered too high for anyone to pledge.

Pi-Top One of a Kind
£1,622 to discuss the creation of a custom Raspberry Pi laptop, complete with the promise of automatic hinge and integrated light show. Despite planning for five potential backers, the Pi-Top project was left with no takers for this top-tier reward level.

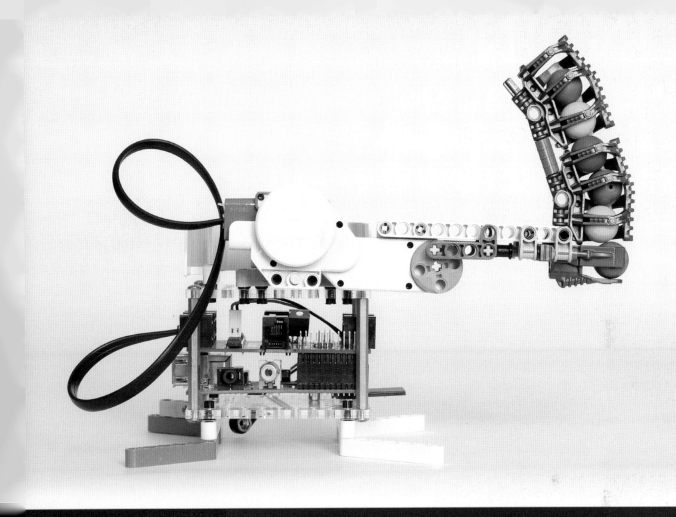

"There have been quite a lot of aspberry Pi-based crowdfunded ojects – even a couple of screens that have not succeeded because e community has never heard the people behind them," adds ex Eames, who was chosen front the HDMIPi campaign ecifically for his recognisability the Raspberry Pi community. he takeaway message from this make sizeable deposits into e community before you try to ake a withdrawal. If you look who's done well in high-value owdfunding projects, there en't many who've managed it thout significant input into the mmunity over a sustained period time before they had their vernight success'. You won't t money out of the community less the community thinks u deserve it and can be trusted th it."

> ## If you've got a hardware idea, keep it simple and true to its core

Minimise complications

The lessons Pimoroni's Jon and Paul are taking into the Flotilla fulfilment process are simple. "Minimise the number of complications. If you're thinking 'should I add this feature?', then I think you should err on the side of caution," Jon advises. "If you start adding features part-way through the design process, you'll risk overshooting by a month, minimum, maybe more."

"If you've got a hardware idea," agrees Paul, "keep it simple, keep it true to what the core of it is, make sure you've got an audience, and make sure you've had lots of good feedback and criticism of it so it's polished."

Experience is key, adds Saar Drimer, and all too often lacking in those turning to Kickstarter to get their project off the ground. "Multiply the time you think it would take by three, then by your level of confidence," he advises, "where one is 'very confident', and three is 'not confident at all.'"

For those on the other side of the table, who are looking to back projects, Saar has a few words of warning. "Your payment is a gamble, and that's what Kickstarter was meant for. If something really appeals to you, support it – and treat the experience of actually getting it at all as a pleasant surprise."

Gareth Halfacree

TUTORIALS

As well as giving you inspirational ideas for projects, our detailed step-by-step guides show you exactly how to make them and learn more about the Raspberry Pi…

90

110

94

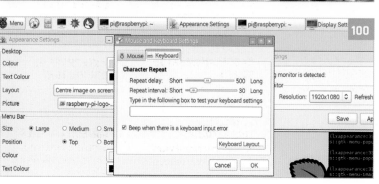

100

114

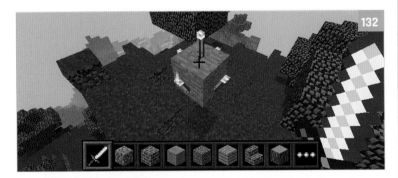

Tutorials

ALEX EAMES

Alex runs **RasPi.TV** and **RasP.iO**, and finds himself between a blog and a hardware business. You can find him as **@RasPiTV** on Twitter.
RasPi.TV

WATCH iPLAYER ON RASPBERRY PI

Download BBC TV programmes as high-definition MP4 files (without any DRM) for offline viewing on your Pi or other devices

You'll Need

> A decent-sized SD card (minimum 8GB)

> A broadband connection

> A few lines of code: **github.com/ raspitv/ get_iplayer**

> A TV, or a monitor and speakers

Get_iplayer is a fabulous, open source utility program which allows you to see what's currently available from the BBC's iPlayer website and download any TV programmes you want. You can choose resolutions between 512×288 and 1280×720, so you can pick one that suits your viewing device and storage capacity. There's no DRM on these files (although the BBC's terms state that you are only allowed to keep them for 30 days), and because they are BBC programmes, there are no adverts either, making it perfect to use for films.

>STEP-01

Update your package lists

We're going to install some software. The first thing you should do when you install software in Raspbian is – at the command prompt – type **sudo apt-get update** (and press **ENTER**), which updates your package lists. Then it's a good idea to **sudo apt-get upgrade** (pressing **ENTER** again) once all your software packages have been updated to their latest versions. It can take upwards of 30 minutes if you haven't done this recently. Then you need to add

Get_iplayer enables you to download films and TV shows from the BBC iPlayer service

As the BBC doesn't use DRM, you can watch shows on your Pi or any other device

```
Matches:
396:     Come As You Are - -, BBC Four, Drama,Films, d
500:     Drive (Radio 1 Rescores) - -, BBC Three, Crim
502:     Drive - -, BBC Three, Crime,Drama,Films, defa
898:     In the Valley of Elah - -, BBC One, Drama,Fil
1784:    Sons of the Musketeers - -, BBC Two, Action &
1785:    Soul Men - -, BBC One, Comedy,Drama,Films, de
1901:    The Devil's Backbone - -, BBC Two, Drama,Film
1981:    The Mummy - -, BBC Four, Drama,Films,Horror &
2093:    The Witchfinder General - -, BBC Two, Drama,F
2209:    Wallace and Gromit - A Close Shave, CBBC, Ani
2210:    Wallace and Gromit - The Wrong Trousers, CBBC
```

Left Here's some example output from the get_iplayer --cat film command. Note the programme IDs (PIDs) on the left

Jon Davies's PPA (Personal Package Archive) to your **sources.list**. Copy and paste the five lines of GitHub code from **github.com/raspitv/get_iplayer/blob/master/code.txt** into a terminal window on your Raspberry Pi and press **ENTER**.

>STEP-02
Install the keyring and software
Once you've done this, you need to repeat the **sudo apt-get update** command in the terminal. You'll likely get an error message about keyrings, so now you need to install Jon's keyring as well, with the following command:

```
sudo apt-get --allow-unauthenticated -y
install jonhedgerows-keyring
```
Then press **ENTER**.

Next, repeat the **sudo apt-get update** command one last time. Now we're ready to go ahead and install the **get_iplayer** program itself (notice the installation name in the command we type is hyphenated, not underscored):

```
sudo apt-get install get-iplayer
```

>STEP-03
Using get_iplayer
Before we start, it's always good to know where to find help, should you need it. To do this, type: **get_iplayer --usage** in the terminal, which should give us a list of the basic options. If you want more options, you can use **get_iplayer --help**, or even more using the command **get_iplayer --longhelp**.

There are a lot of options, so it can be a bit overwhelming, but most of them are not needed for simple searching and downloading of content. Before we can download a programme, we need to collect the index of all the available content. This is done by using the **get_iplayer** command all by itself in the terminal.

>STEP-04
Narrowing down the search
At any given time, there are a couple of thousand items available for download. That's a bit overwhelming, so we need a way to cut it down a bit. You can use categories with the **get_iplayer** command – for example, **get_iplayer --cat film**. You can choose any category from the main list: Arts, CBBC, CBeebies, Comedy, Documentaries, Drama and Soaps, Entertainment, Films, Food, History, Lifestyle, Music, News, Science & Nature, or Sport. You can also use a keyword; if matched, it'll return possible downloads.

>STEP-05
Downloading content
Looking at the list of films available, each item starts with the programme's ID number (PID). Let's choose *Wallace and Gromit – The Wrong Trousers*. This has a PID of 2210. So, to download this film at the best available resolution (1280×720), you would type:

```
get_iplayer --get 2210 --modes best
```
After about 10-15 minutes, the file is downloaded and processed into an MP4 file, which we can view, store or delete at will.

>STEP-06
Watching content
As part of the default Raspbian installation, you have a GPU-accelerated media player called omxplayer. Because it uses the GPU, it's capable of playing HD video, even on a Pi Model A. To watch the film we just downloaded, we would type the following into the terminal:

```
omxplayer [filenamehere].mp4
```
If you're dealing with long filenames, once you've typed **omxplayer** and the first few letters of the filename, you can press the **TAB** key and it will auto-complete the filename for you (then press **ENTER**). You can see the full list of omxplayer controls at **elinux.org/omxplayer**.

DO I HAVE ENOUGH SPACE?

Use the command df -h to see if you have enough space left on your SD card.

WANT SOUND THROUGH THE AUDIO JACK?

Use omxplayer -o local to send sound through the Pi's audio jack rather than the (default) HDMI port.

DISCLAIMER

The BBC's T&Cs state that all iPlayer content is for UK playback only. In addition, any downloads must not be kept beyond 30 days, and must not be distributed in other forms. Neither we nor the Raspberry Pi Foundation condone any breach of these rules. For further details, visit **bbc.co.uk/terms**

RICHARD SAVILLE

Richard runs a popular tutorial and projects blog about an average guy learning the Pi and sharing his less-than-average experiences with the community. **AverageManVsRaspberryPi.com**

SHOOT IN SLOW-MOTION
WITH THE CAMERA MODULE

In this tutorial, the Average Man shows us how to shoot slow-motion videos with the Camera Module and convert them to play on almost any device

You'll Need

> Raspberry Pi Camera Module

> Internet connection

> Something fun to film

Slow-motion video has been used in the film industry for years – think of all those great action movie scenes with people jumping from explosions, or 'Bullet Time' made famous by the Wachowski Brothers in *The Matrix* trilogy.

It's actually really easy to make your own slow-motion videos with your Pi using the Camera Module. We'll get you set up and guide you through a short code listing that will let you record short 30-second videos that will automatically convert to MP4, so you can play it back on just about any device…

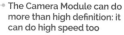
The Camera Module can do more than high definition: it can do high speed too

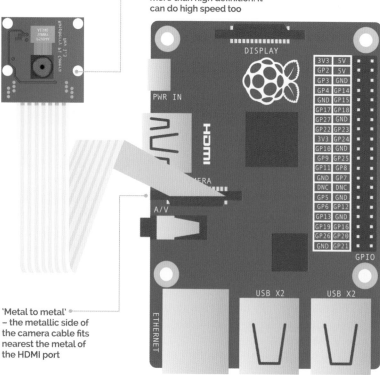

'Metal to metal' – the metallic side of the camera cable fits nearest the metal of the HDMI port

>STEP-01
Connect the Camera Module

The first thing you need to do is connect the Camera Module to your Pi. Make sure your Pi is turned off first. Be careful – the Camera Module is very sensitive to static, so ground yourself by touching something like a radiator before you start.

The Camera Module ribbon cable connects to the socket on your Pi nearest the HDMI port. Use the phrase 'metal to metal' to remember which way round to push it in – the metallic side of the camera cable should face the metal HDMI port. Gently pull up to release the clip and slip the ribbon cable in, then just push the clip back down firmly and check it's secure.

>STEP-02
Configure the Camera Module

If using Raspbian Wheezy, type **sudo raspi-config** in a terminal to enter the configuration menu. Using the arrow keys, scroll down the list that appears and select 'Enable Camera' using the right arrow key. In the next menu, select 'Enable' with the right arrow key to turn on the Camera Module, then hit **RETURN**. If using Raspbian Jessie, select Preferences>Raspberry Pi Configuration from the menu, then enable the camera in the Interfaces tab. Choose to reboot when prompted; or type **sudo reboot** in a terminal to restart the Pi.

>STEP-03
Install a video converter

The Pi records video into raw H.264 files which don't work on most of our devices. We can get the Pi to convert them to a playable format straight after we've recorded them in our script on the right. To do this, we can install a package called gpac. At the command prompt, type the following, then follow the on-screen instructions:

```
sudo apt-get update
sudo apt-get install gpac
```

RECORDING TIPS

Be prepared

Make you have good lighting and a steady mount for your Camera Module. Also, charge your portable power options if you're shooting outside. Finally, don't forget to use an SD card with enough storage space.

What to shoot

How about shooting a remote-controlled car skidding round a corner? Perhaps a ball being thrown or other sports? What about an animation drawn on a notepad, slowed right down?

>STEP-04

Test the camera

Let's make sure everything's working as it should by testing the camera with a couple of terminal commands. With a screen connected, open a terminal window and type **raspistill -o test.jpg**. The picture should appear on the screen for a short time and an image should be saved to your Home directory.

If it doesn't work, check you typed the command correctly, or turn off your Pi and reconnect the camera ribbon cable before trying again.

>STEP-05

Create a Python script

We'll be using Python to create our slow-motion video script. Open your favourite text editor (the Leaf text editor in Raspbian is perfect) and copy the code opposite, being careful not to misspell anything along the way. You don't need to copy the comments (lines starting with **#**) – Python just ignores them. The script uses the OS Python library to carry out terminal commands like you've typed them in directly.

Save your file as **slowmotion.py** in your Home directory (**/home/pi**).

>STEP-06

Run the script

To run the script, simply open a terminal window, type **cd** and hit **RETURN** to ensure you're in the Home folder, then type **sudo python slowmotion.py**.

You will see the status of the script printed in your terminal window as it carries out its commands, and the Camera Module's LED will light up while it's recording.

The script will end when the video has been converted. You can watch the video on your Pi straight away by using omxplayer, which is included in Raspbian. Simply type **omxplayer vid.mp4**.

You could also copy your video onto any other device, like your tablet or smartphone.

The Camera Module has a fixed-focus lens and a wide recording angle

Slowmotion.py

Code Language
>PYTHON

```python
import os
import time

print("Starting program")
time.sleep(2)

##### Record the slow motion video #####
# '-w' sets the width  # '-h' sets the height
# '-fps' sets the frames per second (90 maximum - for slow motion)
# 't' sets the time in milliseconds (30000 = 30 seconds)
# '-o' sets the output filename

print("Recording started - 30 seconds")
os.system("raspivid -w 640 -h 480 -fps 90 -t 30000 -o vid.h264")

print("Recording complete. Please wait...")
time.sleep(2)

##### Convert the raw recorded video file to playable mp4 #####
# '-add' is the name of the raw video we want to convert
# The second filename is the output mp4 file
# (we use the same name followed by '.mp4')

print("Converting video. Please wait...")
os.system("rm -f vid.mp4")
os.system("MP4Box -add vid.h264 vid.mp4")

print("Video conversion complete")
time.sleep(2)

print("Closing program")
time.sleep(2)
```

WILLEM KOOPMAN

Peripatetic sysadmin, providing grumpy solutions to grumpy problems; also maker of **whatcaniseefromtheshard.com**. Stumbled upon the field of computer vision while working in the magical world of visual effects.
secretbatcave.co.uk

FACE DETECTION WITH OPENCV

You've got a Raspberry Pi Camera Module? You've taken a few images? Let's do something really clever and use them to detect faces...

You'll Need

> An internet connection
> Camera Module (or webcam)
> OpenCV

Y ou've set up your motion-triggered webcam, but that pesky dog keeps triggering it. How do you figure out if that alert is someone poking around or Fido searching for socks again? In this tutorial, we'll show you how to get your Raspberry Pi to separate the dogs from the faces, using the computer vision library, OpenCV.

We're going to make a simple Python script that will work its way through a directory of pictures, copying the ones that have faces in them. Not only that, it'll also draw a box around each face.

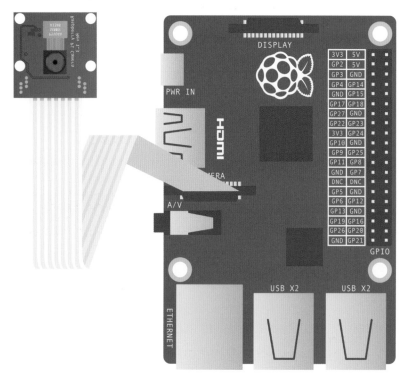

>STEP-01
Install OpenCV

By default, OpenCV isn't shipped with Raspbian. Never fear – everything is a simple **apt-get** away. First, we need to install OpenCV. In a terminal, type: **sudo apt-get update**, press **ENTER**, then: **sudo-apt-get install python-opencv libopencv-dev** and follow the instructions. We'll see if it's installed correctly by running the Python interactive interpreter and loading the OpenCV module. Type: **python** (and **ENTER**), then **import cv** (and **ENTER** again). If everything is installed correctly, you should see an empty prompt. If you see something along the lines of **ImportError**, go back and see if the **apt-get** worked correctly.

>STEP-02
Understanding Haar-like features

We're going to use an algorithm called a 'Haar cascade'. Because computers have no understanding of what a face looks like, we have to give it a rule book. In this case, a Haar cascade describes the 'brightness signature'. A face contains two eyes surrounded by skin. The area surrounding the eye is a different intensity to the eye itself. A Haar cascade describes these patterns to provide us with a way to detect faces (and other objects).

>STEP-03
Begin the code!

Enough chit-chat! Let's write some code. We need to import the various libraries we are going to use and set some sensible defaults for the Haar detector. These defaults provide a trade-off between speed and accuracy. First, we set **minSize** to limit the smallest detectable face to a 20-pixel square. **imageScale** scales the image before we feed it into the detector; smaller

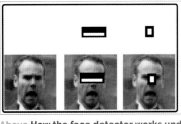

Above How the face detector works under the hood: high-contrast boxes are mapped to parts of the face

images mean faster detect times, but less accuracy. **minNeighbors** tells the detector that a match must be made up of a minimum number. Finally, **haarFlags** are special flags telling the detector what bits to ignore.

>STEP-04
Prepare the image

The first function we're going to create is **detectFace()**. Because the Haar detector only works with greyscale images, we make a greyscale copy; **grey** is resized and copied into the **small_img** container. Lastly, we equalise the histogram (using **EqualizeHist**). This evens out the contrast, making the Haar detector more effective. We pass the variables, **small_img** and **cascade**, along with the rest of the defaults we defined at the very start, into the function **cv.HaarDetectObjects**. It then spits out a list of objects, with attached coordinates, and dumps it into the variable **faces**.

>STEP-05
Mark the faces

We then 'iterate' through all the objects and extract the 'bounding box' (the area where the object detector thinks there is a face.) Now, this is where we do something vaguely confusing. Remember in the previous step, we made a few copies of the original image? Well, we didn't throw away the original. We can mark where we think the faces are on the original, so that we can save full-sized images in full colour!

We've scaled up the coordinates so that we can accurately tell **cv.Rectangle** where the top-left and bottom-right corners of the box should be.

>STEP-06
Final touches

readDirectory() goes through the directory supplied as a command-line argument and extracts files ending with '.jpg'. It then opens the image and passes it to **detectFace()**. If it finds some faces, it'll save out the marked images into a new file using **cv.SaveImage()**. To use your new program, you first need to find a Haar cascade XML file and put the path into **cv.Load()**. They can be found in **/usr/share/opencv/haarcascades/**. Running the program is as simple as storing some JPG files in the folder and typing **python facedetect.py**. With any luck, you'll see something like the following:

```
samples/ has:
   Analysing 292942_10151131251926133.jpg:
        Detected  2  object(s)
        Time = 1268.761ms
```

Facedetect.py

```python
import os, sys, time
import cv2.cv as cv

minSize = (20, 20)
imageScale = 1
haarScale = 2
minNeighbors = 3
haarFlags = cv.CV_HAAR_DO_CANNY_PRUNING

def detectFace(img, cascade):
  # allocate temporary images
  gray = cv.CreateImage((img.width,img.height), 8, 1)
  small_img = cv.CreateImage((cv.Round(img.width /
imageScale),cv.Round (img.height / imageScale)), 8, 1)
  # convert color input image to grayscale
  cv.CvtColor(img, gray, cv.CV_BGR2GRAY)
  # scale input image for faster processing
  cv.Resize(gray, small_img, cv.CV_INTER_LINEAR)
  cv.EqualizeHist(small_img, small_img)
  faces = cv.HaarDetectObjects(small_img, cascade,
cv.CreateMemStorage(0),haarScale, minNeighbors, haarFlags, minSize)

  if faces:
    print "\tDetected ", len(faces), " object(s)"
    for ((x, y, w, h), n) in faces:
      #the input to cv.HaarDetectObjects was resized, scale the
      #bounding box of each face and convert it to two CvPoints
      pt1 = (int(x * imageScale), int(y * imageScale))
      pt2 = (int((x + w) * imageScale), int((y + h) *
imageScale))
      cv.Rectangle(img, pt1, pt2, cv.RGB(255, 0, 0), 3, 8, 0)
    return img

  else:
    return False

# scan all directories and subdirectories for jpg images
def readDirectory(fileLocation, cascade):
  for root, dirs, files in os.walk(fileLocation):
    print root, "has:"

    for name in files:
      if name.find(".jpg") >=1 :
        #sequentially loop, load and detect.
        print "Analysing " + name +":"
        #measure how long it takes
        t = cv.GetTickCount()
        #load in the image
        image = cv.LoadImage(os.path.join(root,name), 1)
        match = detectFace(image, cascade)

        if match:
          #save a new image with a box round each face
          cv.SaveImage( fileLocation + "/face_" + name, match)
        t = cv.GetTickCount() -t
        print "\tTime = %gms" %(t/(cv.GetTickFrequency()*1000.0))

if __name__ == '__main__':
  cdir = "/usr/share/opencv/haarcascades/"
  cascade = cv.Load(cdir + "haarcascade_frontalface_default.xml")

  if len(sys.argv) != 2:
    print 'please provide a directory to read'
    sys.exit(1)
  readDirectory(sys.argv[1], cascade)
```

DAVID HUNT

David has been making projects for the Raspberry Pi since the early days. These include a Camera Controller, TimeLapse Rail, Focus Stacker, and even a Bark-Activated Doggy Door Opener. Oh, and let's not forget the PiPhone!
DavidHunt.ie

WATER DROPLET
PHOTOGRAPHY

Have you ever wanted to capture those split-second photographs of water droplets colliding? Now you can with a Raspberry Pi-controlled solenoid and camera trigger!

**You'll
Need**

> Solenoid valve

> 1× IN4001 diode

> 1× TIP120 Power Darlington transistor

> 1× NPN PN2222 transistor

> 2× approx 2K ohm resistors

> 1× 12V power supply

> Shutter release cable

> Wiring Pi

This tutorial shows you how to build a project that will allow you to capture those beautiful, carefully timed photographs where water droplets are colliding. From assembling the hardware with a solenoid, to writing the code to drive it, you'll be doing your own droplet collision photography in no time. After that, you can have all sorts of fun using different types of liquids, with different colours and viscosities. And hopefully you'll get some shots that you can hang on your own wall!

>STEP-01

The solenoid driver

The solenoid is driven by a GPIO pin through a resistor and a power transistor – see the diagram below. It needs to be a power transistor, as the solenoid can draw up to an amp. The flywheel diode is to prevent any current generated by the solenoid from going back into the NPN transistor. Once the GPIO pin goes high, the current can flow from 12V to GND, enabling the solenoid to open the valve and allowing the liquid to pass through. We only open the valve briefly, just enough to allow a drop through at a time.

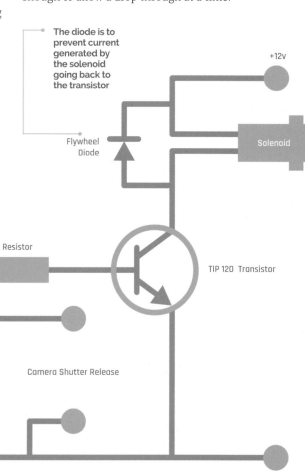

The diode is to prevent current generated by the solenoid going back to the transistor

Flywheel Diode

+12v

Solenoid

GPIO Pin 18

Resistor

TIP 120 Transistor

This is the part of the circuit that drives the shutter cable going to your camera

NPN Transistor

GPIO Pin 17

Resistor

Camera Shutter Release

GND

GND

Code Language
>PYTHON

Above An example of the type of image that can be achieved

Drop.py

```python
# Import the relevant Modules
import wiringpi2 #Learn more about this library at wiringpi.com
from time import sleep

# Set up the GPIO Pins
gpio = wiringpi.GPIO(wiringpi.GPIO.WPI_MODE_GPIO)
shutterpin = 17
solenoidpin = 18
gpio.pinMode(shutterpin,gpio.OUTPUT)
gpio.pinMode(solenoidpin,gpio.OUTPUT)
wiringpi.pinMode(shutterpin,1)
wiringpi.pinMode(solenoidpin,1)

# Release a drop of liquid
gpio.digitalWrite(solenoidpin,gpio.HIGH)
sleep(0.06)
gpio.digitalWrite(solenoidpin,gpio.LOW)

sleep(0.1)

# Release a second drop
gpio.digitalWrite(solenoidpin,gpio.HIGH)
sleep(0.05)
gpio.digitalWrite(solenoidpin,gpio.LOW)

# Wait for the droplet to hit the liquid container
sleep(0.12)

# Trigger the camera (which is set to manual mode)
gpio.digitalWrite(shutterpin,gpio.HIGH)
sleep(0.1)
gpio.digitalWrite(shutterpin,gpio.LOW)
```

>STEP-02

The camera shutter driver

The camera shutter is triggered by a low-power NPN transistor. DSLRs usually have a shutter release input which is shorted to ground, causing the camera to take a picture. In this project we're using a signal transistor to cause that (usually 3.3V) input to short, so we can get the camera to take a picture from the Python script on our Pi. You'll need to get the correct shutter release for your camera, but they can be sourced on eBay for under £5.

>STEP-03

Setting up the solenoid

This is the messy part! A drinks bottle with a small opening is ideal for attaching to the input of the solenoid. This type is often used for sports drinks, and can usually be pushed onto the solenoid input without any leaks. You can cut the bottle in half for easy top-ups. Apply 12V to the solenoid and you should get a stream of liquid through the valve; remove power and the valve should close. Attach it to the circuit you built in step 1.

>STEP-04

Trigger the camera

Now connect up your camera circuit and test it with the Python code. You will need to adjust the timings to get the camera to trigger at the right moment. But initially, you should hear two clicks of the solenoid and one click of the camera. You can adjust the timing in two ways: by changing the Python code, or altering the distance between the solenoid and the liquid container. In the code provided, the timings were good for a 50cm fall.

>STEP-05

Get the lighting right

You'll need to use a flash to freeze the movement of the liquid. Otherwise you'll get blurred images, even if your camera is on a tripod. An off-camera flashgun triggered by a sync cable is a really good idea, as it allows you to move the flash into all kinds of interesting positions. Oh, and keep the flash power low for shorter flash durations, giving you sharper images. And you can always use two or three flash units at lower power for shorter flashes still.

>STEP-06

Adjust the camera settings

You should be shooting on manual setting, with a shutter speed as high as your camera will allow for flash. For Canons this is about 1/160th of a second, and maybe 1/250th of a second for Nikons. Use ISO 100-400 and then adjust your aperture till you get a decent exposure. You can then tweak the flash power down to get shorter flash durations, which will tend to freeze the motion of the liquid more. Open up the aperture more if you need to, but be aware that your depth-of-field will be reduced.

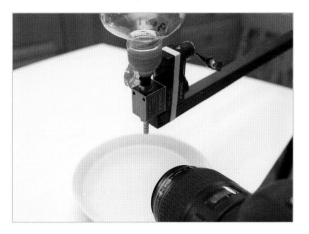

LIAM FRASER
Liam is the creator of the
RaspberryPiTutorials YouTube channel.
He is currently studying Computer
Science at the University of York and has
a special interest in embedded systems.
liamfraser.co.uk

MAKE A PWM
CANDLE LANTERN

Set a romantic mood with your Raspberry Pi by simulating a flickering
candle effect using pulse-width modulation...

You'll Need

- A coloured LED
- Breadboard
- Female-to-male jumper cables
- Resistor (100 ohm to 330 ohm)

This tutorial is intended as a gentle – not to mention romantic – introduction to GPIO (general-purpose input and output) pins on your Raspberry Pi, and how to control them in Python. We'll be creating our romantic candle-like mood lighting using a random number generator to make an LED flicker at different intervals. In addition, its brightness will be varied using a technique called PWM (pulse-width modulation), which effectively controls what percentage of the time the LED is turned on. We will also take a look at the output of the pins on an oscilloscope, so that we can see how the code translates to the electrical signals that make things tick.

>STEP-01
Pick a resistor for your LED
A resistor will limit the current that flows through the LED. Different colour LEDs have different current limits, so you'll need to check the specifications where possible. 100 ohm or 220 ohm will definitely work, though your LEDs might end up being dimmer than usual. The equation for working out resistance is as follows:

R = (3.3V − LED VOLTAGE) / LED CURRENT

Our yellow LED needs a voltage of 1.8V – 2.2V and has a typical current of 20mA, so: **R = (3.3V − 2.0V) / 0.02** (which is 65 ohms). A resistor with a value between 65 and 130 ohms is ideal here, but a lower value will make your LED brighter.

>STEP-02
Setup the breadboard
Unplug your Pi and follow the breadboard illustration setup. Make sure you use the same GPIO pin we have, as only a couple are capable of pulse-width modulation (on the B+). We're using GPIO number 18 for PWM, which is described as **PCM_CLK/PWM0**.

The circuit path, as shown in the illustration, is **GPIO 18 > resistor > LED positive**. Finally, the LED negative leg goes into ground. The positive leg of an LED is usually longer. The negative side will have a flat edge rather than a circular one.

>STEP-03
Get coding!
Once you've wired up the project, power up your Pi and begin coding using an editor of your choice (or opening a terminal and typing **nano candle.py** will do).

Once we've imported the libraries we need, the **setup** function organises our program and starts PWM

A resistor is needed to limit the current going to the LED so it doesn't burn out

A pulse width modulation-capable GPIO pin is used to control the brightness of the LED

Below **This oscilloscope trace shows how LED brightness is controlled**

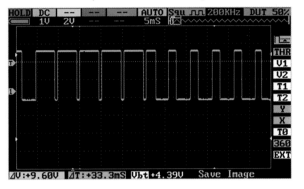

AV:+9.60V AT:+33.3mS Vbt+4.39V   Save Image

for us. The **flicker** function sets a random brightness by calling the **set_brightness** function, then sleeps for a random time. This function is then wrapped up in an infinite **while** loop within the **loop** function, which handles the all-important cleanup of the GPIO library when **CTRL+C** is pressed by the user.

>STEP-04
Test your creation
Exit your editor and run the code by typing **sudo python2 candle.py** into a terminal (unless using Raspbian Jessie, you need root privileges to access the GPIO pins). Now you've tested it, you can exit with **CTRL+C** and we'll make it run at boot. This way, the Pi can run headless and not need any user interaction.

At the terminal, type: **sudo nano /etc/rc.local**, then add the following line: **python2 /home/pi/ candle.py &** (but make sure you put this in the line before **exit 0**). Don't forget to save the changes.

The **&** means the script will go to the background and let the boot process continue. Notice how sudo isn't required because **rc.local** is executed as root. Reboot the Pi with **sudo reboot** to verify that it works.

>STEP-05
Packaging it up
Now that the script is started when the Pi boots, you could package it up into a nice container using a portable phone charger as a power supply. There are plenty of candle holders that can be fashioned out of paper if you search the internet. Paper is ideal, especially with lots of holes in, since the LED probably isn't throwing out much light.

>STEP-06
Presentation, presentation, presentation
The candlelight project is surprisingly effective, but presentation is key in matters of the heart, so you may want to spruce up your project before you use it on a loved one. Pretty lanterns are available very cheaply from most department stores; just make sure you select one that obscures the view of the interior. If the lantern isn't big enough to fit the Pi and breadboard, solder the resistor to the LED and hide the Pi behind it.

Below A candle lantern that obscures the view of the inside is perfect for disguising the LED and hiding your Pi

Candle.py
Language >PYTHON

```python
import RPi.GPIO as GPIO
import time
import random

# Set the PWM output we are using for the LED
LED = 18

def setup():
    global pwm

    # GPIO uses broadcom numbering (GPIO numbers)
    GPIO.setmode(GPIO.BCM)
    # Set the LED pin as an output
    GPIO.setup(LED, GPIO.OUT)

    # Start PWM on the LED pin at 200Hz with a
    # 100% duty cycle. At lower frequencies the LED
    # would flicker even when we wanted it on solidly
    pwm = GPIO.PWM(LED, 200)

    # Start at a brightness of 100%
    pwm.start(100)

def set_brightness(new_brightness):
    # Sets brightness of the LED by changing duty cycle
    pwm.ChangeDutyCycle(new_brightness)

def flicker():
    # We want a random brightness between 0% and 100%.
    # Then then we'll hold it for a random time
    # between 0.01 and 0.1 seconds to get a nice flicker
    # effect. Play with these values to make the effect
    # suit your liking
    set_brightness(random.randrange(0, 100))
    time.sleep(random.randrange(1, 10) * 0.01)

# The wrapper around the flicker function makes sure the
# GPIO hardware is cleaned up when the user presses CTRL-C

def loop():
    try:
        while True:
            flicker()
    except KeyboardInterrupt:
        pass
    finally:
        GPIO.cleanup()

# setup the hardware
setup()

# start the flickering
loop()
```

BUILD A STROBE LIGHT
WITH A TRANSISTOR

Using a transistor, it's easy to control lots of LEDs. In this tutorial, we're creating a strobe to help get the party started with our Raspberry Pi

This tutorial follows on rather neatly from the previous one (pages 96-97), where we emulated a candle using pulse-width modulation. In this guide we'll step things up a bit by throwing push buttons, a transistor, and lots of LEDs into the mix in an effort to create a strobe light that you can manually speed up and slow down. A strobe is a great accessory to any party and, with enough blue tack or duct tape, you should be able to mount this on a wall. For best effect, place it up high in a corner of a room, right where the two walls meet the ceiling.

>STEP-01
Using transistors

An LED typically uses 20mA of current. Since GPIO pins can't provide enough current to light lots of LEDs simultaneously, we're using a transistor to help us.

The 2N2907 transistor can pass 600mA, which is plenty for our needs. A PNP transistor has three pins: an emitter, a base, and a collector. Here, the emitter is connected to 3.3V, and the base is connected to a GPIO pin via a 1K ohm resistor. This pin is used to switch the transistor on and off. When the pin is 0V, current can flow; when it is 3.3V, no current can flow. Hence, this circuit is inverting: this means that when the GPIO is low, the transistor is on, and the LEDs light.

Since transistors have an amplification factor based on the current that goes through the base, we want to limit it with a resistor. Finally, the collector pin of the transistor is connected to the LEDs and eventually ends up at ground.

>STEP-02
The circuit path

Each LED path goes from the transistor, through a 22 ohm resistor to limit the current through the LED, and then into ground. Referring to the LED resistance equation from the previous tutorial, we only need a small resistor because white LEDs have a forward voltage of about 3V and a current of 20mA: **R = (POWER_RAIL − LED VOLTAGE) / LED CURRENT.**

So: **R = (3.3V − 3V) / 0.020** (which is 15 ohms, rounded up to the nearest practical value here).

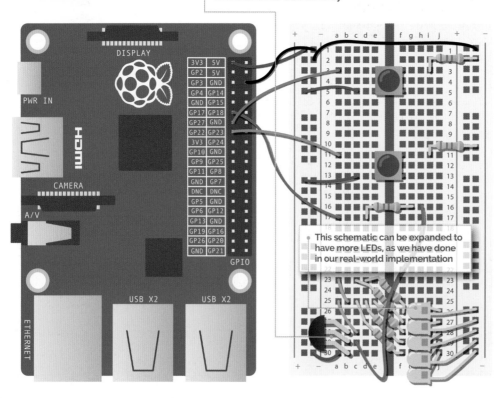

The pins are c, b, e, from top to bottom. The transistor must be inserted this way for the circuit to work correctly

This schematic can be expanded to have more LEDs, as we have done in our real-world implementation

Strobe.py

⚠ WARNING!

This project uses strobe lighting. Do not use it if you or anyone are known to suffer from photosensitivity, never look directly at the LEDs, and never run it for prolonged periods or any faster than four flashes per second.

>STEP-03
Working with push buttons

Electricity always takes the path of least resistance. In the circuit diagram, you can see that a GPIO pin is connected to a leg of each push button. The leg is also connected to ground (0V) via a 1K resistor. This is termed a pull-down resistor because when the button isn't pressed, the signal is pulled down to ground. The other leg is connected to 3.3V. When the button is pressed, the two sides are connected again. There is less resistance to 3.3V and the GPIO input goes high, which we can detect in our code listing on the right.

>STEP-04
Wire up the circuit

Let's get the circuit built, but don't forget to turn your Pi off first. It's important to remember that each LED is connected to the transistor in parallel. This means that they are all effectively connected to the output of the transistor (and not chained in any way). This being the case, you can scale up the design on the breadboard as much as you want, within the specification of the transistor and power supply. In the case of our setup, that would be 20 LEDs or less.

>STEP-05
Event detection

The code for this tutorial is similar to the Candle code in the previous one, with one key difference: we're using events. The functions to speed up or slow down our strobe light will only be called when a rising edge (a transition from 0V to 3.3V) is detected on the button pins. This is a convenient way to handle button presses without having to keep checking them in your main loop.

>STEP-06
Test it out

Create and save the code on the right, then test it out using **sudo python2 strobe.py**. Pressing the button on the right will increase the speed of the strobe. Pressing the button on the left will slow the strobe down. Note that because the delay change is small, you'll have to press the buttons quite a few times. As always, you can start the script when you turn on your Pi, by adding it to **rc.local**:

```
sudo nano /etc/rc.local
```

Add the following line (before **exit 0**) and then save the changes:

```
python2 /home/pi/strobe.py &
```

```python
# Import the GPIO and time library
import RPi.GPIO as GPIO
import time

# First we initialise some constants and variables
TRANSISTOR = 17
BTN_SPEED_UP = 27
BTN_SLOW_DOWN = 22
DELAY_CHANGE = 0.005

# Never use a strobe light any faster than 4 flashes per sec
DELAY_MIN = 0.125 # 1/8 = '4 on 4 off' flashes
delay = 0.2
def setup():
        # Next we initialise setup of the GPIO pins
        GPIO.setmode(GPIO.BCM)
        GPIO.setup(TRANSISTOR, GPIO.OUT)
        GPIO.setup(BTN_SPEED_UP, GPIO.IN)
        GPIO.setup(BTN_SLOW_DOWN, GPIO.IN)

        # This will call a function when the speed up or slow down
        # buttons are pressed
        GPIO.add_event_detect(BTN_SPEED_UP, GPIO.RISING)
        GPIO.add_event_callback(BTN_SPEED_UP, speed_up)
        GPIO.add_event_detect(BTN_SLOW_DOWN, GPIO.RISING)
        GPIO.add_event_callback(BTN_SLOW_DOWN, slow_down)

def speed_up(channel):
        global delay
        # Take away the delay change value from the delay time.
        # Make sure the delay doesn't go less than the minimum
        # safe rate for use of stroboscopic lighting.
        delay = delay - DELAY_CHANGE
        if delay < DELAY_MIN:
                delay = DELAY_MIN

def slow_down(channel):
        global delay
        # Add the delay change value to the current delay
        delay = delay + DELAY_CHANGE

def loop():
        # The try statement makes sure we clean up properly
        # on a keyboard interrupt (Ctrl+C)
        try:
                # loop until the user presses Ctrl+C
                while True:
                        # Turn the strobe on, then wait for the
                        delay time
                        GPIO.output(TRANSISTOR, False)
                        time.sleep(delay)
                        # Turn the strobe off, then wait for the
                        delay time
                        GPIO.output(TRANSISTOR, True)
                        time.sleep(delay)
        except KeyboardInterrupt:
                pass
        finally:
                GPIO.cleanup()

# Now we setup the hardware, and start the main loop of the program

setup()

loop()
```

SIMON LONG

Simon Long works for Raspberry Pi as a software engineer, specialising in user interface design. In his spare time he writes apps for the iPhone and solves *really* difficult crosswords.
raspberrypi.org

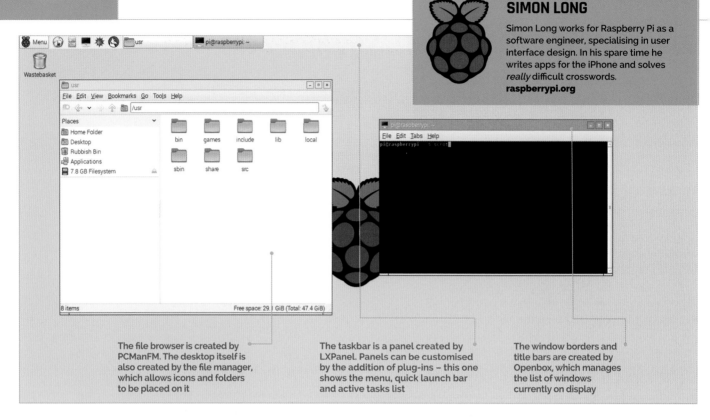

The file browser is created by PCManFM. The desktop itself is also created by the file manager, which allows icons and folders to be placed on it

The taskbar is a panel created by LXPanel. Panels can be customised by the addition of plug-ins – this one shows the menu, quick launch bar and active tasks list

The window borders and title bars are created by Openbox, which manages the list of windows currently on display

HACKING THE RASPBIAN DESKTOP PART 1: WHAT IS LXDE?

In the first part in a series of four, **Simon Long** talks us through Raspbian's desktop environment, LXDE...

Below Openbox manages the appearance of window title bars, including the buttons to minimise, maximise, and close a window

If you've used the desktop environment on Raspbian, rather than the command line, you've seen LXDE. The Lightweight X Desktop Environment is the software which creates the desktop graphic user interface (GUI) that appears when you type **startx** from the Raspbian command line – the desktop, the windows, the taskbar; all are parts of LXDE.

LXDE is a user interface which sits on top of a system called X, a client-server windowing system. When an application starts, it requests a window in which to work from the X server program; the server also takes care of things like detecting mouse and keyboard input, and putting windows on the screen.

But X itself provides only the barest elements of a GUI – there are numerous environments that can sit on top of it and make the result look nicer, and LXDE is one of these. It's a very good fit for the Raspberry Pi because, as the name suggests, it is lightweight in terms of processor and memory usage, and so works on a lower-powered device like the Raspberry Pi.

LXDE itself consists of several different pieces of software, all with specific tasks. The more important of these are described in the 'LXDE key components' box on the next page.

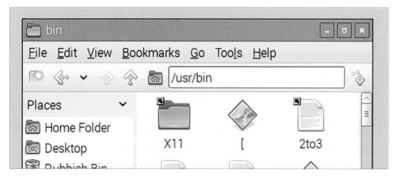

LXDE'S KEY COMPONENTS

Openbox – The window manager

When you launch an application or open a window, the window manager is responsible for providing a window of the appropriate size, in which the application can appear. While the application itself determines what appears inside the window, the window manager is responsible for the overall appearance of the window – the border, the title bar at the top, the buttons to close, minimize, or resize the window – and this is why all windows, from whatever application, look the same in these respects. The window manager is also responsible for the layout of multiple windows on the screen, managing how windows appear on top of others when they overlap, and maintaining which window currently has focus, ie responds to the mouse and keyboard.

LXPanel – The desktop panel controller

This is responsible for creating the taskbar and for managing its contents. In fact, it can create multiple taskbars and put them anywhere on the screen, but that might look a bit confusing! Each taskbar is customisable by the addition of various plug-ins. Some of these – such as the task switcher, the system menu, and the quick launch icons – are standard and are built in to LXPanel, but you can also write and add others yourself.

PCManFM – The file manager

This is responsible for providing the directory windows that allow you to browse the file system on the Pi, as well as things like the ability to drag and drop files from one directory to another. It takes care of associating files with applications, so that when you double-click a file with a certain extension, it opens in the right application. The desktop itself is effectively a file manager window, so the file manager also controls things like desktop icons and the wastebasket.

LXSession – The session manager

When you start LXDE, the session manager is responsible for controlling which applications are launched, including those listed above. Also, the whole of LXDE is written using a graphics toolkit called GTK, and the appearance of every element in the toolkit – buttons, menus, and the like – can be set for the entire system, from what is called a theme. LXSession controls which theme is applied to LXDE, and thus can be used to customise the appearance of every application that runs under it.

Below LXPanel provides a pop-up menu to modify panel settings – more on this in the next tutorial

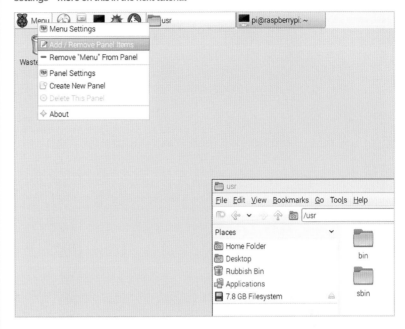

Look under the bonnet

Naturally, like the rest of Raspbian, LXDE is open source and under active development. It is written in C, and the code for all the components can be freely downloaded, modified, and rebuilt, even on the Raspberry Pi itself. If you are a keen hacker, it is worth downloading the code and having a look at it, as much of it is pretty straightforward – have a look at **lxde.org** for all the details, downloads and wiki articles, among other things.

However, before adopting drastic measures, it is worth knowing that a lot of the overall appearance

> " Like the rest of Raspbian, LXDE is open source and under active development "

and behaviour of LXDE is controlled by a set of preference files that sit behind the scenes, and by editing these – they are plain text – you can make quite significant changes to how LXDE looks and works without changing a single line of code. There are dedicated applications to control some of these settings provided as part of LXDE – **obconf** is a controller for the Openbox preferences, and **lxappearance** adjusts the themes used by LXSession – but these don't necessarily control everything you might want to change, and it isn't always obvious where the setting you want to adjust can be found.

So that's what the rest of this series of guides is going to cover: how you can modify the LXDE settings to customise your Raspberry Pi to look the way you want it to.

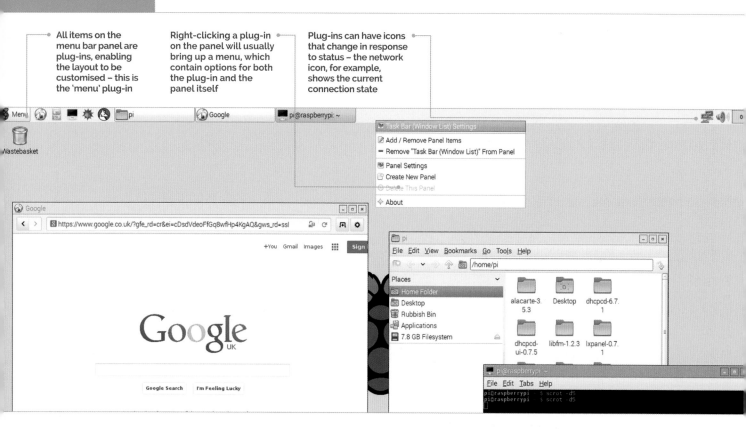

All items on the menu bar panel are plug-ins, enabling the layout to be customised – this is the 'menu' plug-in

Right-clicking a plug-in on the panel will usually bring up a menu, which contain options for both the plug-in and the panel itself

Plug-ins can have icons that change in response to status – the network icon, for example, shows the current connection state

HACKING RASPBIAN'S DESKTOP PART 2:
CUSTOMISING LXPANEL

In part two of his series, **Simon Long** shows us how to change the appearance of the Raspbian desktop by playing with LXPanel

Right The Panel Applets tab on the Panel Preferences dialog allows plug-ins to be added, removed, and rearranged

XPanel is a component of LXDE (Lightweight X11 Desktop Environment), the desktop user interface included as part of Raspbian. As the name suggests, LXPanel is responsible for generating panels – windows that overlay the desktop which can be used for menu bars, application launchers, and other general system functions.

By default, a single panel is displayed on the Pi's desktop, which is used for the menu bar at the top of the screen. LXPanel also allows multiple panels to be used on the same screen, so it is possible to have a second panel displayed at the bottom, to be used as an application launcher, for example. Panels are always attached to one edge of the screen, but the edge can be the top, the bottom, or even the sides.

Each panel can be customised to contain a selection of user interface components. These components are called plug-ins, and there are two kinds. LXPanel includes a number of built-in plug-ins (including the main menu button, the taskbar, and the quick launch icon bar), and standalone plug-ins can also be written from scratch and added to LXPanel. Writing a new plug-in is a fairly complicated programming task and goes beyond the scope of this article, but information on how to get started with writing one can be found at the **lxde.org** site.

In addition to the plug-ins associated with a panel, there are a number of global parameters which control various aspects of the overall display of each panel. Many plug-ins also have parameters which can be set to control their individual appearance and behaviour.

Tweaking the panel

The easiest way to change the configuration of a panel or a plug-in is by using the LXPanel preference dialogs. If you right-click on a panel or one of its plug-ins, a menu pops up. (Note that some plug-ins override this menu, so don't be surprised if this doesn't work in some cases.) The top item on this menu is **<name of plug-in> Settings** – selecting this opens the preferences dialog for that particular plug-in; obviously, the items in that dialog will depend on what customisation is possible for the plug-in.

The menu also contains a number of other menu items for customising the panel itself.

Add/Remove Panel Items opens a dialog box which shows the plug-ins currently on the panel; from here, it is possible to add, remove, or rearrange the plug-ins on the panel.

Also in the menu is **Panel Settings** – this opens a dialog which allows global settings for the panel to be changed, including the edge of the screen to which it is attached, and how much of the screen it takes up. Other tabs on this dialog allow the colour and background of the panel to be changed, and to control whether or not the panel automatically hides when the mouse is moved away, and reappears when it is moved back. Adding or removing panel items can also be performed from a tab on this dialog.

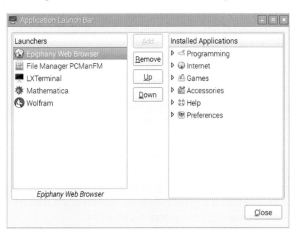

Above Individual plug-ins can be customised – this is the configuration dialog for the application launch bar plug-in

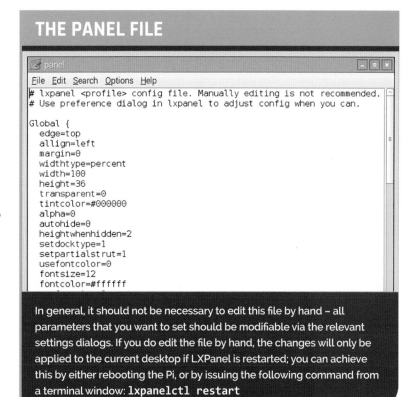

The menu also includes the option to **Remove <name of plug-in> From Panel** – this removes the plug-in you right-clicked from the panel, and is identical in effect to using the Remove button in the dialog box mentioned above.

Finally, the menu includes the option to **Create New Panel** – this creates a new blank panel on a free edge of the screen. This can then be customised by right-clicking on the new panel to bring up the same menu – but in this case, options selected will affect the newly created panel.

Under the bonnet

Changes made in these dialogs are stored in the LXPanel configuration settings file. This, along with various other settings files, is found in the hidden **.config** directory inside your home directory.

Inside **.config/lxpanel** is a directory with the name of your current lxsession profile – this is called **LXDE-pi** on a default installation of Raspbian – and inside this is a further subdirectory called **panels**. Each file in this directory is the definition of a single panel. By default, there is just the one file called **panel**, but if multiple panels are added, there will be multiple files in this directory – one per panel.

The panel file, which can be viewed or changed with a text editor, includes an initial **Global** section in which general panel parameters are stored, followed by a section for each plug-in. Each **Plugin** section contains a line giving the **type** of the plug-in, followed by a **Config** section containing parameters specific to that plug-in.

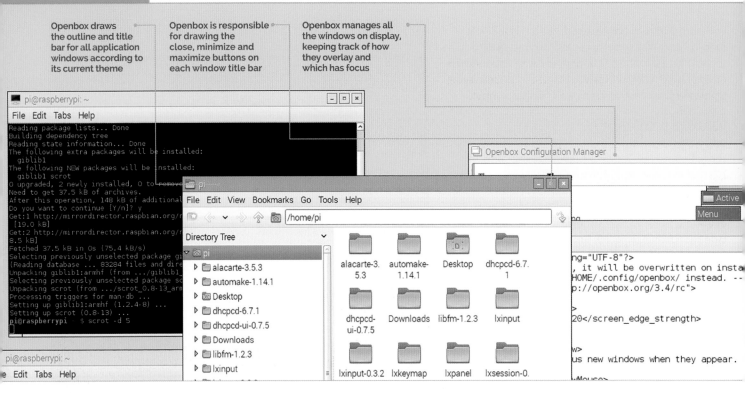

Openbox draws the outline and title bar for all application windows according to its current theme

Openbox is responsible for drawing the close, minimize and maximize buttons on each window title bar

Openbox manages all the windows on display, keeping track of how they overlay and which has focus

HACKING RASPBIAN'S DESKTOP PART 3: CUSTOMISING OPENBOX

In the third part of his series, **Simon Long** talks us through how to customise Raspbian's window manager, Openbox

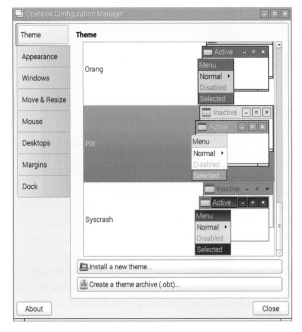

Right The Openbox Configuration Manager allows various aspects of the way a window is displayed to be modified

O penbox is a component of LXDE (Lightweight X11 Desktop Environment), the desktop user interface included as part of Raspbian. Openbox is the window manager – the software which is responsible for drawing the windows in which applications display their contents.

When an application opens, it requests a window from the window manager of the size required for what the application needs to display. The window manager creates the window, and draws the title bar and border. The window is then passed to the application, which draws its contents.

This mechanism may seem complicated, but it means that all windows created in the system will have the same overall visual appearance. The alternative would be for each application to create its own title bar for each window it requires, and the result would be a less consistent appearance, particularly when multiple applications run simultaneously.

The window manager is also responsible for managing the ability to move windows around the screen, for controlling what happens when a window is put on top of or underneath another, and for managing which window receives keyboard and mouse input.

What are themes?

Before looking at how to customise Openbox, it is necessary to understand the idea of theming. LXDE allows the use of theme files for some aspects of operation. An Openbox theme file contains information on all aspects of the visual appearance of a window, such as the title bar colour, what the title bar buttons look like, and how the appearance changes when the window is active or inactive.

Several themes are available in Raspbian – they are stored in **/usr/share/themes**. Each theme has a directory in here, but not all themes include Openbox settings. If a theme does include Openbox settings, its directory includes a subdirectory called **openbox-3**, and in this subdirectory is the Openbox theme file itself, called **themerc**.

It is possible to have themes which are only available to one particular user; these are the same files, but stored in the **.themes** directory in the user's home directory. If a theme file in this directory has the same name as one in the global **/usr/share/themes** directory, the one in **.themes** has priority.

You can install new themes if you don't like any of those installed; they are available for free from numerous sites. You can also create your own, but doing so is outside the scope of this tutorial – by all means, open a **themerc** file with your favourite editor and have a play!

(Note that the default theme is called PiX – this is used to allow the Pi-specific Appearance Settings application to work properly. If you change to a different theme, running Appearance Settings will revert to the PiX theme – be aware of this if you want to customise your desktop in detail.)

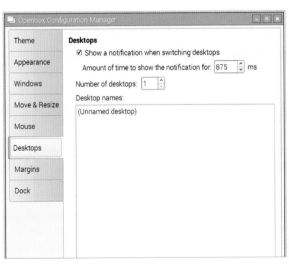

Above The Desktops tab of the Configuration Manager allows multiple desktops to be managed

THE OPENBOX CONFIGURATION FILE

The settings file that controls the appearance of Openbox, including setting the theme used, is found in the **.config/openbox** subdirectory of a user's home directory, and has the extension .xml. If there are multiple files in here, the file used has the same filename as the current session profile name. On a default Raspbian install, this is LXDE-pi, and so the file used by Openbox is called **lxde-pi-rc.xml**.

Making changes

The Openbox XML file is quite large and complicated – you can view and modify it with a text or XML editor, but it is easier to use the Openbox Configuration Manager application. To launch this, type **obconf** in a terminal window.

The configuration manager has a number of tabbed pages. The first page, Theme, shows all Openbox themes installed on the Pi, and you can select from them by clicking in the list – each theme name is shown with examples of the window features it affects, and how they appear when using that particular theme.

The second page, Appearance, sets the fonts used for the window title bar. It also determines which buttons are shown on the title bar, and their order.

These first two pages contain most of the options that affect the appearance of the desktop; the remaining pages are more about adjusting the detailed behaviour of the window manager, and are really for expert users only – by all means play with the settings, but the effect of most of them is fairly subtle.

One tab worthy of particular mention is Desktops. Openbox supports multiple desktops, which can be useful if you want to have many applications open at once; an application's windows will appear on the desktop from which it was opened. If you want to use more than one desktop, simply increase the 'Number of desktops' value on this screen. Clicking the middle button or scroll wheel on the mouse when the pointer is on the desktop brings up a menu which allows you to switch desktops. It is also possible to switch desktops by adding a desktop switcher plug-in to LXPanel – see the previous tutorial for details of how to do this.

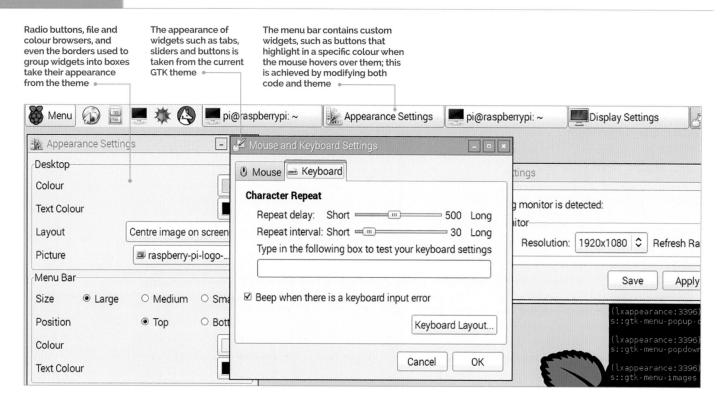

Radio buttons, file and colour browsers, and even the borders used to group widgets into boxes take their appearance from the theme

The appearance of widgets such as tabs, sliders and buttons is taken from the current GTK theme

The menu bar contains custom widgets, such as buttons that highlight in a specific colour when the mouse hovers over them; this is achieved by modifying both code and theme

HACKING RASPBIAN'S DESKTOP PART 4: CUSTOMISING APPLICATIONS

In the fourth and final part of his series, **Simon Long** talks us through how to customise the appearance of applications running on the Raspbian desktop...

A pplications written to run under Raspbian's desktop environment, LXDE, make use of one of a number of user interface toolkits.

A UI toolkit provides reusable code for standard UI elements, such as windows, menus, and buttons. This serves two main purposes. First, it makes creating new applications a lot faster for the developer, as it isn't necessary to create the code for a button from scratch every time one is needed in an application. Second, it ensures that applications look and behave in a consistent fashion – a button in one application will look exactly the same as in every other application, and will display the same behaviour (such as changing appearance when it is clicked) everywhere in the system.

That's in an ideal world anyway. Unfortunately, things aren't quite that ideal, because there are a number of different toolkits out there, and it is up to the application developer to choose which one to use. LXDE itself is written using a toolkit called GTK+ (GIMP Toolkit), and most of the applications included in the Raspbian image also use GTK+. However, there are others – you may see applications written with a toolkit called Qt – and even with GTK+, there is extra complexity due to there being multiple versions in use: you'll find applications which use version 2.x and version 3.x, and they can look significantly different.

All very interesting, but why should a user care? One of the advantages of using a UI toolkit is that it can be themed. In other words, while the toolkit ensures that

Above The first page of the lxappearance application lists the themes installed on the system and shows what each widget looks like in them

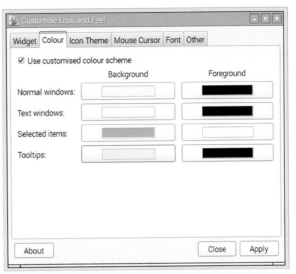

Above Other pages of lxappearance allow colour schemes, icons, fonts, and cursors to be customised

every button looks the same as every other button, the user can change the theme to make buttons look the way they want them to, while keeping them consistent across all applications. By changing the GTK+ theme, you can make everything on your Pi's desktop – including the menu bar – change its appearance at the same time.

Choosing a theme

There are a number of alternative themes already installed in Raspbian – they can be found in the directory **/usr/share/themes** – or you can download and install new themes from various places online. Themes can also be installed for individual users in the **.themes** subdirectory of their home directory. A theme directory contains subdirectories with theming information for different toolkits – most of LXDE is written using version 2 of GTK+, so the **gtk-2.0** subdirectory contains the relevant theme file, which is called **gtkrc**.

The easiest way to change the appearance of your applications is just to change the theme to another pre-installed theme, and there is an application installed in LXDE to do this for you. From a terminal window, run **lxappearance**.

This shows a list of all GTK+ themes installed. Clicking on any of them shows how various UI elements will look under that theme on the example to the right of the screen. Choose one, click Apply, and it will change the appearance of the whole system to match.

The **lxappearance** application also allows you to customise various other aspects of the appearance and behaviour of

the desktop, so feel free to explore the other tabs and options. For instance, the Widget tab also allows you to change the system font, which is used for all text displayed inside a window. (Note that to change the font used for the title bar of a window, you need to change the font used by Openbox – see the previous tutorial for details of how to do this.)

Customising themes

If you really want to change every detail of the appearance of your desktop, you can modify the theme file itself, download one of the many custom themes online, or even create one from scratch. The **gtkrc** files mentioned above are plain text and can be modified with your favourite editor – however, this is not for the faint-hearted, and you can end up with some truly bizarre effects if you don't understand what you are doing. A full tutorial on modifying GTK+ theme files is outside the scope of this guide, but information can be found at the GTK+ website, **gtk.org**.

THE SESSION CONFIGURATION FILE

All the changes made in the **lxappearance** application are stored in a file in the hidden **.config** subdirectory of your home directory. Look inside **.config/lxsession** for a directory with the name of your current lxsession profile – this is called **LXDE-pi** on a default installation of Raspbian – and inside this is a file called **desktop.conf**. Each line in this file corresponds to a setting in **lxappearance**, so you can use a text editor to modify this file instead of using **lxappearance** if you prefer. If you edit the file, you will need to run **lxsession -r** from a terminal window to force the new settings to take effect, or just reboot your Pi.

SAM AARON

Sam Aaron is the creator of Sonic Pi. By day he's a Research Associate at the University of Cambridge and by night he writes code for people to dance to.
sonic-pi.net

IMPORTANT

• Sonic Pi 2.4 is required.

To update to the latest version, type these two commands into the terminal:

• sudo apt-get update
• sudo apt-get install sonic-pi

SONIC PI π)))
TIPS & TRICKS

The creator of Sonic Pi, **Sam Aaron**, shares some of his top tips for budding electronic musicians of all ages...

THERE ARE NO MISTAKES

This is the most important lesson. The best way to learn is to just try. Try lots of different things; stop worrying whether your code sounds good and start experimenting with as many different synths, notes, FX, and parameters as possible. You'll discover a lot of things that make you laugh, because they sound awful, and some real gems that sound truly amazing. Just drop the things you don't like and keep the things you do. The more 'mistakes' you allow yourself to make, the quicker you'll learn and discover your own sound.

USE THE FX

Once you've mastered the basics of making sounds with sample and play, you might be wondering what's next. Did you know Sonic Pi supports over 27 studio FX to change the sound of your code? FX are like fancy image filters in drawing programs, except that instead of blurring or making something black and white, you can add things like reverb, distortion, and echo to your sound. Think of it like plugging the cable from your

guitar into an effects pedal of your choice and then into the amplifier, but Sonic Pi makes it much easier! All you need to do is to choose which section of your code you'd like the FX added to and wrap it with the FX code.

```
sample :loop_garzul

16.times do
  sample :bd_haus
  sleep 0.5
end
```

If you wanted to add FX to the **:loop_garzul** sample, you'd just tuck it inside a **with_fx** block, like this:

```
with_fx :flanger do
  sample :loop_garzul
end

16.times do
  sample :bd_haus
  sleep 0.5
end
```

Now, if you wanted to add FX to the bass drum, go and wrap that with **with_fx**, too:

```
with_fx :flanger do
  sample :loop_garzul
end

with_fx :echo do
  16.times do
    sample :bd_haus
    sleep 0.5
  end
end
```

Remember, you can wrap any code within **with_fx** and any sounds created will pass through that FX.

PARAMETERISE YOUR SYNTHS

In order to really discover your coding sound, you'll soon want to know how to modify and control synths and FX. For example, you might want to change the duration of a note, add more reverb, or change the time between echoes. Sonic Pi gives you enough control to do exactly this, with special things called optional parameters. Copy this code into a workspace and hit Run:

```
sample :guit_em9
```

It's a great guitar sound. Let's change its rate:

```
sample :guit_em9, rate: 0.5
```

What's that **rate: 0.5** bit we just added at the end? That's called a parameter. All of Sonic Pi's synths support them and there's loads to play around with. They're also available for FX:

```
with_fx :flanger, feedback: 0.6 do
  sample :guit_em9, rate: 0.5
end
```

Now, try increasing that feedback to 1 to hear some crazy sounds! Read the docs for full details on all the many parameters available to you.

LIVE CODE

The best way to quickly experiment and explore Sonic Pi is to live-code. This allows you to start off some code and continually change and tweak it while it's still playing. So, if you don't know what the **cutoff** parameter does to a sample, just play around with it. Copy this code into one of your Sonic Pi workspaces:

```
live_loop :experiment do
  sample :loop_amen, cutoff: 70
  sleep 1.75
end
```

Now, hit Run and you'll hear a slightly muffled drum break. Now, change the **cutoff:** value to 80 and hit Run again. Can you hear the difference? Once you get the hang of using **live_loop**, you'll never go back. If you were ever to do a live coding gig in the future, you'd find yourself relying on **live_loops** as much as a drummer relies on their sticks. To learn more about live coding, check out Section 9 of Sonic Pi's built-in tutorial.

SURF THE RANDOM STREAMS

One thing that's really fun to try is cheat by getting Sonic Pi to compose things for you. A really great way to do this is using randomisation. It might sound complicated, but it really isn't. Try this:

```
live_loop :rand_surfer do
  use_synth :dsaw
  notes = (scale :e2, :minor_pentatonic, num_octaves: 2)
  16.times do
    play notes.choose, release: 0.1, cutoff: rrand(70, 120)
    sleep 0.125
  end
end
```

When you play this, you will hear a constant stream of random notes from the scale **:e2 :minor_pentatonic** played with the **:dsaw** synth. It might not sound like a melody, but that's the first part of the trick: every time we go round the

> " You can explore as many melodic combinations as you can imagine "

live_loop, we can tell Sonic Pi to reset the random stream to a known point. It's like going back to a particular point in time and space with the TARDIS. Let's try it. Add the line **use_random_seed 1** to the **live_loop**:

```
live_loop :rand_surfer do
  use_random_seed 1
  use_synth :dsaw
  notes = (scale :e2, :minor_pentatonic, num_octaves: 2)
  16.times do
    play notes.choose, release: 0.1, cutoff: rrand(70, 120)
    sleep 0.125
  end
end
```

Now, every time the **live_loop** loops around, the random stream is reset. This means it chooses the same 16 notes every time, giving you an instant melody. Here's the really exciting bit: change the **seed** value from 1 to another number – 4923, say – and it will give you another melody. So, just by changing one number (the random seed), you can explore as many melodic combinations as you can imagine, and that's the magic of code.

SEAN MCMANUS

Sean McManus is a Code Club volunteer, and wrote the book *Scratch Programming in Easy Steps*. He also co-wrote *Raspberry Pi For Dummies*.
sean.co.uk
twitter.com/musicandwords

MAKE A MULTIPLE-CHOICE QUIZ IN SCRATCH

Dazzle your friends with your own quiz game, containing hundreds of questions! How many can they get right in 30 seconds?

You'll Need

▶ LibreOffice – if not installed, open a terminal and type: `sudo apt-get install libreoffice`

▶ List of capitals by size – **wki.pe/List_of_national_capitals_by_population**

▶ Internet access

Lists are used to remember lots of information, but adding items to them block by block can take a lot of time and Scratch code. In this project, you'll see how you can import (or bring in) large lists from other places, so you can easily make a quiz game with hundreds of questions. As you create this game, you can use your own favourite background and sprites, and arrange them with enough space for the answers to appear. Perhaps you can add your own question list? Anything works, as long as each answer only applies to one question.

>STEP-01
Gather your data
For this game, you'll need two text files: one for the questions and one for the answers. We're going to make a quiz about capital cities, so one file will contain a list of capitals, and the other will contain the countries they are in, in the same order. Start by finding the list of capital cities by population on Wikipedia. Click and drag

over the table to highlight it and then press **CTRL+C** to copy it. It's easier if you highlight from the bottom up. Be patient when the screen scrolls!

>STEP-02
Create your question files
Start LibreOffice Calc and paste in the table using **CTRL+V**. Click OK. This might take a minute or two to work. Click above your cities column to highlight it.

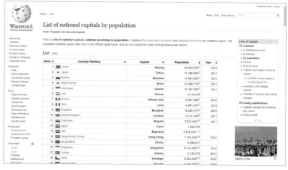

Above You can get a well-organised list of capital cities from this page on Wikipedia

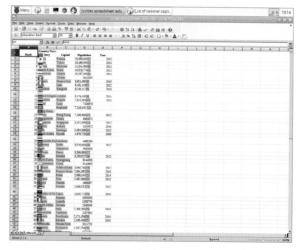

Above Copy the capital cities table from Wikipedia into LibreOffice Calc to make it easy to extract the columns separately

Click to answer; the answer data comes from a list on Wikipedia

The game runs for 30 seconds before it ends

timer 9.5

What is the capital of Vanuatu

Port Vila

Tehran

Mata-Utu

Press **CTRL+C** to copy the column. Open your text editor, Leafpad, which is in the Accessories menu. Press **CTRL+V** to paste. You should now have a text file containing just capital cities, each one on a new line. If you have a heading at the top (the word 'Capital'), delete it, and remove any blank lines at the end too. Save this file as **cities.txt**. Open a new file in Leafpad and repeat the process with the countries column in LibreOffice Calc. This time, save your Leafpad file as **countries.txt**.

>STEP-03
Importing your data into Scratch
Start Scratch. Click the Variables button and make a list. Call it **cities** and make sure it's for all sprites. When the empty list appears on the Stage, right-click it and click **import** in the menu. Browse to the files you just created, and double-click your cities text file. The list on the Stage will be filled with the cities from your file. Repeat the process to make a list called **countries** and fill it with your countries file. Your list files should be the same length. Right-click the list boxes on the Stage and choose **hide**.

>STEP-04
Set up your variables
Through the Variables part of the Blocks Palette, make variables called **question number** (used to remember which question/answer pair we're asking), **score**, **shuffle choice** and **temporary storage** (used for shuffling the list of options), and **wrong answer** (used when making the list of wrong options). You also need to make a variable called **player guessed** to remember which answer the player chooses, and a list called **possible answers**. Make all these variables and the list 'For all sprites'.

>STEP-05
Make the main game code
The main game code uses three scripts (Listing 1). Add them all to the cat sprite. The game uses broadcasts to pass control to the various parts of the program, including on the same sprite. The 'ask a question' section picks a random question number from the list of countries and makes a list of possible answers. It includes the correct answer, and two wrong answers which must be different from the correct answer. The code then shuffles this list to put the answers in a random order, before using a broadcast to make the answer sprites appear and show their answers.

>STEP-06
Make the answer sprites
Import a new sprite to use for showing the answer. We're using Gobo. This sprite has five short scripts (Listing 2). Make the variable **answer choice**, but click the button to make it 'For this sprite only'. If the game shows all the same answers when you run it, you probably made a mistake here! When you've finished this sprite, right-click it and duplicate it twice. In the copies, change the value of the **answer choice** variable at the top to 2 for the first one and 3 for the second one. Happy quizzing!

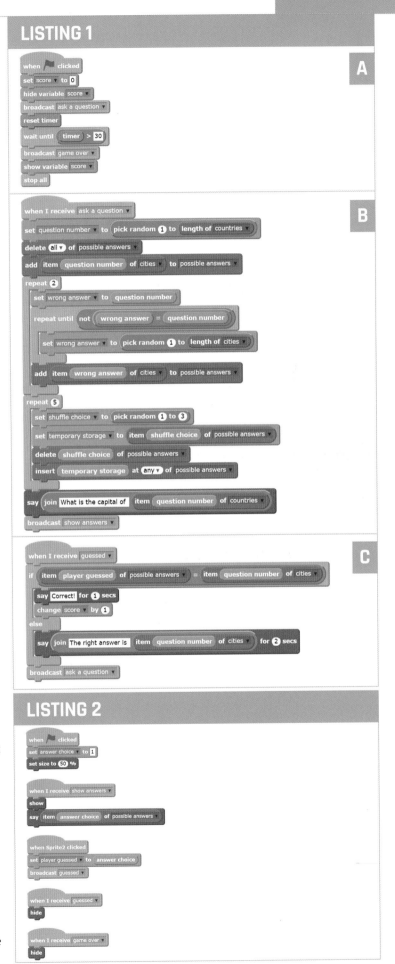

ADD A TITLE SCREEN TO YOUR SCRATCH GAME

To make a professional-looking game, follow these steps to add a title screen with instructions and a fun animation

You'll Need

> One of your own Scratch games, or you can use our simple example here

A book has a cover, a film has its credits, and an album has its artwork. Only with the right presentation do these things feel professional and complete. In the same way, a great game starts with a title screen that draws players in and provides instructions. It's especially important if you want to share your game, as you won't be there to explain it when it's played. In this article, you'll see how you can add a title screen to a basic game. The same techniques will work for most simple games, so why not try adding a title screen to your own games, too?

Add an animated sprite to your title screen and use 'say' blocks to tell players how it works

Black text on hot pink: a timeless background design!

>STEP-01
Write your game
We recommend you try adding a title screen to our example game Cat Catcher before you add one to your own game. To make Cat Catcher, first bring in the sprite Gravity Marble from the Things folder. It comes with some scripts for controlling it with the cursor keys. Add **Listing 1** to your cat sprite. Together, these two sprites make a game where you're challenged to see how quickly you can catch the cat ten times with the marble. We've added the playing field background.

>STEP-02
Create your title screen background
Create a new background image that you will be using for your game's title screen. Ours is just a bright colour with the game title on it, but you could make something more elaborate if you like. On the background, add the scripts shown in **Listing 2**. They change the background between the title screen and the in-game background, and tell all the sprites to go into 'title screen' mode when the green flag is clicked. Ultimately, this should be the only time you use a `when green flag clicked` script.

>STEP-03
Create your title screen sprite
This is the sprite that will tell the player how to play, and it can be animated, too. For our game, we've brought in another cat sprite. Add **Listing 3** to it. There are three parts to this: one part displays the title animation and instructions; another part starts the game when the sprite is clicked; and a third part hides the sprite when the game begins. You'll need to make a variable called `game status`, which all sprites will use

to tell whether the game is running or the title screen is on. You can add more sprites to your title screen. Include the **when I receive play game** script from **Listing 3** to hide them when the game begins. Use a **when I receive title screen** script to show them on the title screen.

>STEP-04
Replace your green flag scripts

Now, you need to go through your game sprites (the game cat and the marble in our example) and change their scripts so they don't start when the green flag is clicked any more. For each sprite and each of its scripts, replace the block **when green flag clicked** with the block **when I receive play game**. Add

> " A great game starts with a title screen that draws players in "

Listing 4 to your game sprites to make them hide when the title screen is on, and appear when the game begins. If a sprite shouldn't be there at the start of the game, you can leave out the **show** script.

>STEP-05
Replace the forever loops

Some of your in-game sprites might have **forever** loops. These will keep running, even when the title screen is showing and the sprite is hidden. To avoid this causing unwanted results, replace the **forever** block on your in-game sprites with the **forever if** block. Give the block the condition **game status = game** (using your variable **game status** and the **=** Operator block). You might also have events that are triggered, such as when there is a key press. To stop these working on the title screen, wrap an **if** block around the entire script after the **when [space] key pressed** block and give it the condition **game status = game**, too.

>STEP-06
Start a new game

When your game finishes, you can show the title screen again by adding a Control block to broadcast **title screen**. For example, you could add it to the end of **Listing 1** in our game. Players can once again start a new game from the title screen. That will keep them in the game and encourage them to keep playing until they've got a score they can brag about! You might need to make some other tweaks for your game (each one is different, after all), but following these steps should enable you to add a title screen to most simple games, to make them look more polished.

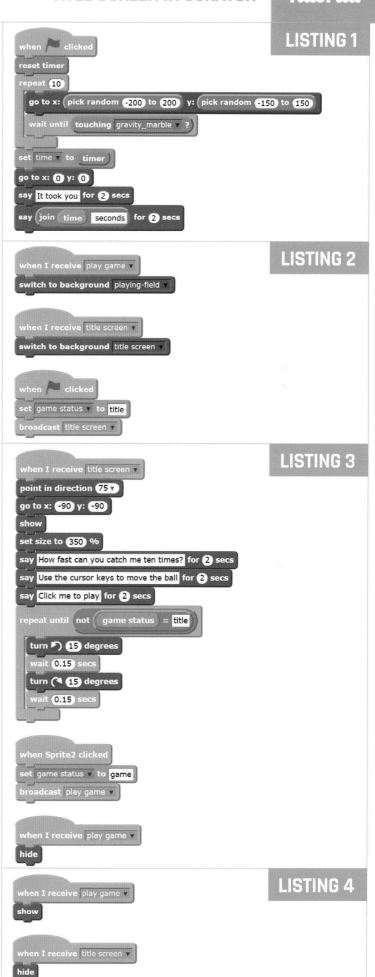

SEAN MCMANUS

Sean McManus is a Code Club volunteer and wrote the book *Scratch Programming in Easy Steps*. He co-wrote *Raspberry Pi For Dummies*.
sean.co.uk
twitter.com/musicandwords

ADD A
HIGH SCORE
TABLE TO YOUR
SCRATCH GAME

Keep players coming back for more by keeping a record of the best scores, and telling them how they measure up

You'll Need

› One of your Scratch games. Pick a favourite!

This project features scripts that enable you to create a high score table, and then add new scores to it if they're high enough. There isn't an easy way to display and hide a list from within your program, so the scripts also tell players how they ranked and what the next highest score is, so they know how close they came to beating it. This code will work with most simple games, but you might need to make some changes if your game invites players to play again, or has scripts that continue when the game has ended.

Tick the box in the Blocks Palette to see the list and edit its values. No cheating, now!

The sprite checks the player's score and tells them how they did

>STEP-01
Make your game

You'll need a game to add this script to – either one of your own, or one that you've programmed from a book or magazine. Try playing the game a few times to work out the likely scores. Some games award a few points, some hundreds, and some thousands. The starting numbers in your high score table should present a challenge to players, but not be completely unachievable. Take care with your own games: if you've spent days playing them in development, they'll be much easier for you than anyone else.

>STEP-02
Add your high score sprite

The scripts for the high score can all go on the same sprite. This sprite will tell players if they got a high score. It could be the main character of your game, the sprite used on the title screen (see the tutorial on pages 112–113), or it could be a new sprite. We've added the sprite **royalperson** for our high score table. You'll find it in the 'people' folder, even though it looks like a dog. It'll be in the way during the game, so add **Listing 1** to hide it when the green flag is clicked.

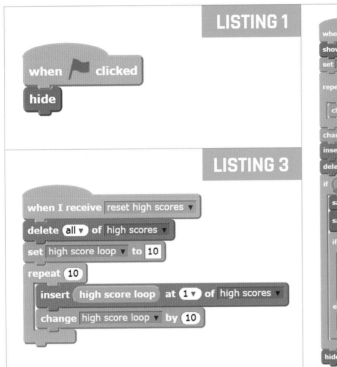

LISTING 1

```
when  clicked
hide
```

LISTING 3

```
when I receive reset high scores ▼
delete all ▼ of high scores ▼
set high score loop ▼ to 10
repeat 10
    insert high score loop at 1 ▼ of high scores ▼
    change high score loop ▼ by 10
```

LISTING 2

```
when I receive check high scores ▼
show
set high score loop ▼ to 10
repeat until item high score loop of high scores > score or high score loop = 0
    change high score loop ▼ by -1
change high score loop ▼ by 1
insert score at high score loop of high scores
delete last ▼ of high scores
if high score loop < 11 then
    say That's a new high score! for 2 secs
    say join You are at position number high score loop for 2 secs
    if high score loop > 1 then
        say join The next highest score is item high score loop - 1 of high scores for 2 secs
        say Can you beat it? for 2 secs
    else
        say Can you get an even higher score? for 2 secs
hide
```

> " This code will work with most simple games, but you might need to make some changes if your game invites players to play again "

>STEP-03
Set up your list

Your high score table will be stored in a list. Click the Variables button above the Blocks Palette, click the button to make a list and call it 'high scores'. In the Blocks Palette, you can click the tickbox beside the list name to show or hide the list on the Stage. This is a handy way to view the whole list, and you can edit the values in it by clicking them and typing on them. The list gets in the way of your game, so we recommend unticking the box.

>STEP-04
Set your starting scores

You can type some starting scores into the list on the Stage, but it's better to use a script to generate your high scores. **Listing 2** does this. It runs if it receives the broadcast **reset high scores**, but you can also click the script once to reset your scores. To change the lowest score, change the value in the **set high score loop** block. To change how much scores go up by, edit the value in the **change high score loop** block. Note: the pointed Operator blocks are shown as rounded in our code because of limitations in the Scratchblocks software we've used for laying out code for this book.

>STEP-05
Add your high score code

Listing 3 checks the score and adds it to the high score table in the correct position if high enough. It also tells the player how well they did. Add it to your high score sprite. Take care with building the script that goes in the hole of the **repeat until** block. You'll need to drag in blocks in a similar order to this: **or**, **>**, **item 1 of high scores**, **high score loop**, **=**, **high score loop**. When the next highest score is announced, add blocks in the order: **say Hello! for 2 secs**, **join hello world**, **item 1 of high scores**, **-**, **high score loop**.

>STEP-05
Patch it in to your game

To finish, connect your high score script to your game. If the game doesn't already use the variable **score**, click on Variables and make that variable for all sprites. You want the high score script to run when your game ends, so you need to add some code at that point in your game. Add a block to set **score** to your game's score variable if you're not already using the variable **score** in the game. Finally, add a block to broadcast **check high scores**. To keep your high scores, simply save your game. When you save a Scratch program, the list values – including your high score table in this case – are saved too.

WILLIAM BELL

Will is a previous contributing editor on *The MagPi* before it became the official Raspberry Pi magazine. Will enjoys solving complicated problems with elegant, bespoke solutions. For him, the bigger the challenge, the bigger the attraction.
whbell.net

BUILD A SPACE SHOOTER IN SCRATCH

William H Bell walks us through how to create an impressive 3D space shooter using nothing more than Scratch and some clever coding techniques…

S cratch is a great programming language for testing out a range of concepts. Scratch programs typically involve controlling one or more sprites on the screen. Computer games where the characters are controlled from a distant view are third-person games. Games can be more exciting when the human player looks through the eyes of the central character in the game, however. This is normally referred to as a first-person game.

In this article, some of the principles of constructing a first-person game are introduced. The player is the pilot of a spaceship that is drifting through a debris field. The main engine has gone offline, causing the spaceship to drift through the debris at a constant speed. However, the spaceship still has working thrusters on the top, bottom, left and right of the craft. The main laser system is also operational. The heroic pilot has to shoot through or dodge the debris. A point is awarded each time a piece of debris is destroyed with the ship's lasers. If the debris crashes into the spacecraft, then the shield of the spacecraft will be damaged. After the shield has been completely broken, the spacecraft will explode.

Perspective

In real life, objects that are far away appear to be smaller. One example of this is a set of railway tracks. Looking down railway tracks and into the distance, the tracks appear to become closer together. This can be applied to a computer game, where objects need to be shown as being in the distance. When an object becomes closer to a player, the object should become larger on the screen.

In this game, a one-point perspective is used. This means that distant objects appear to come from the centre of the screen. Rather than draw a lot of very small images at the vanishing point, it is more sensible to assume a viewing plane. The viewing plane corresponds to the distance at which objects become visible. The two diagrams at the top-left of page 117 show the vanishing point as it appears on the screen, and the position of the viewing plane. In the illustration of the viewing plane, the z-axis points from the centre of the screen straight towards the player and is perpendicular to the x-y plane.

If the spacecraft has no velocity along the x-y plane and an object appears at the viewing plane with a

Right Hit the space bar to fire the ship's lasers to destroy debris; if it crashes into you, your shield (green bar) will deplete

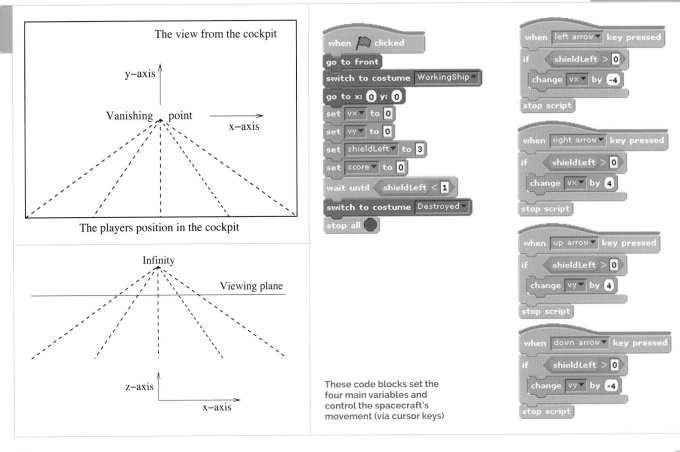

The view from the cockpit

y–axis

Vanishing point

x–axis

The players position in the cockpit

Infinity

Viewing plane

z–axis

x–axis

These code blocks set the four main variables and control the spacecraft's movement (via cursor keys)

> # In the game, the spacecraft is not able to turn. Since the stars in the distance are very far away, they would not appear to move relative to the spacecraft

position that is not in the centre of the screen, then the object appears to have a velocity that is proportional to its distance from the centre of the screen. This is not a real velocity, but is the effect of the perspective used to display the z-axis. This effect can be observed when driving along a straight road: a vehicle that is on the other side of the road, but far in the distance, appears to move to the other side of the road as it approaches.

Spaceship and star field

In the game, the spacecraft is not able to turn. Since the stars in the distance are very far away, they would not appear to move relative to the spacecraft. Therefore, a static star field was drawn on the stage background.

The spaceship cockpit and heads-up display should stay in the foreground. This was achieved by creating a sprite that is as big as the screen. When the game starts, the **SpaceShip** sprite is set to be above other sprites. Therefore, the cockpit edges are displayed as being in the foreground.

The horizontal and vertical velocity components of the spacecraft are stored in the **vx** and **vy** variables. These variables were created as global variables, since

the velocity components affect the motion of other sprites on the screen. The **shieldLeft** variable contains the number of shield points left, and the **score** contains the player's score. The **shieldLeft** variable was created as a global variable, since the other sprites that may hit the cockpit need to be able to change its value; **score** was also created as a global variable, since other sprites need to be able to increment it. The game continues until there are no shield points left. When the game starts, all four global variables are reset to zero and the spaceship is shown to be working as normal. If there are no shield points left, then the ship is shown to be destroyed by changing the costume of the **SpaceShip** sprite. The thrusters on the right, left, bottom and top of the spacecraft are controlled by the cursor keys. Since the spacecraft is in space, there is no friction to slow down its movement. Therefore, firing the thrusters in one direction will build up the velocity in that direction. To make it easier for the player to see the current status of the game, the values of the **vx**, **vy** and **score** variables were selected to be displayed at the bottom of the screen.

Right Each costume is used for one of four shield states

Shield heads-up display

The number of shield points remaining is shown on the left-hand side of the screen. This image is a sprite called **Shield**, which has several costumes that correspond to the different shield states. The different costumes were a copy of the first costume, each with one more green box removed.

Lasers

The lasers were drawn as another sprite. The size of the **Laser** sprite was carefully matched to the **SpaceShip** sprite by copying the **SpaceShip** costume to check where the lasers would appear on the screen.

When the green flag is pressed, the **Laser** sprite is set to appear just below the **SpaceShip** sprite. Therefore, it is in the foreground but not as close as the cockpit. The lasers are fired by pressing the space bar. To make the game a little bit harder, the lasers fire for a second and then recharge for a second. This means that the player should not hold down the space bar, but only fire the lasers when needed. Similar to the **SpaceShip** sprite script, the **Laser** sprite only recognises the space bar when the number of shield points is greater than zero.

Space debris

Two types of space debris were created: **LavaBall** and **Scrap**. The script for the **LavaBall** sprite was copied and modified slightly for the **Scrap** sprite to prevent both sprites appearing at exactly the same time. The two sprites were also given two costumes, to show them as being **normal** or **exploded**.

> The script for the LavaBall sprite was copied and modified slightly for the Scrap sprite to prevent both sprites appearing at exactly the same time

Below These blocks implement the firing of the spacecraft's laser

When the green flag is pressed, the **Shield** sprite is set to be just below the main cockpit but above the other sprites. This means that the shield display stays in the foreground. The script for the **Shield** sprite waits until the number of shield points decreases and then switches to the appropriate costume.

When the green flag is pressed, the **LavaBall** is placed below the cockpit, shield display, and lasers. Then it is hidden from view. The main loop continues while the game is being played. When the **SpaceShip** sprite switches to the **destroyed** costume, it finishes the game by stopping all scripts. This includes the main loops of the space debris sprites.

To show that it is in the distance, the **LavaBall** appears at the viewing plane at 1% of its normal size. To make the game more interesting, its starting position is chosen at random in the x-y plane. Due to the one-point perspective used, objects that are closer to the edge of the screen will quickly disappear from this location. Therefore, objects were chosen to appear within a 100 by 100 box around the centre of the screen. The initial position of the sprite, along the x- and y-axes, is stored in the **initial_x** and **initial_y** variables. Since these variables are only needed for this sprite, they were created as local variables for this sprite only. The initial position components are rescaled to produce an apparent velocity offset associated with the perspective. They are rounded to integers, since the sprite moves in numbers of pixels. The sprite is then shown on the screen. Next, the script enters another loop that continues until the sprite is full-size, has touched the edge of the screen, or has been hit by the laser beams. The point where the two laser beams meet was given a pink colour, so that this colour could be used to test if the laser beams had hit the **LavaBall**. The relative velocity of the debris along the z-axis can be raised by increasing the **change size by 5** (5%) command or by reducing the size of the **wait** within the motion loop.

In this game, the space debris is spinning but is otherwise stationary with respect to the rest of the universe. The spacecraft is drifting through the debris field at a constant speed, and starts the game at rest in the x–y plane. When the spacecraft thrusters are fired, the spacecraft moves along the x–y plane with respect to the universe. However, the game is played from the pilot's point of view, rather than from the point of view of the universe or the space debris. Therefore, when the player's spacecraft is moving to the left, the **LavaBall** is shown as moving to the right. If the spacecraft moves downwards, then the **LavaBall** moves upwards. This can be demonstrated by looking at a cup on a desk: if the person looking at the cup moves to the left, then the cup moves to the right with respect to the person's line of sight. The motion of the sprite is therefore the sum of the relative velocity and the apparent velocity, due to the object being created at a point on the viewing plane that is not in the centre of the screen.

If the **LavaBall** has been hit by the laser beams, then the score is incremented and the costume is switched to the **exploded** version. The program waits for half a second for the player to view the **exploded** sprite. If the **LavaBall** has not been hit by the lasers and it has not touched the edge of the screen, then it has hit the spacecraft. If the **LavaBall** has hit the spacecraft, then the number of shield points is reduced by one and the **LavaBall** costume is switched to the **exploded** version. If the **LavaBall** has missed the spacecraft, then it disappears behind the spacecraft harmlessly. After these logic conditions, the **LavaBall** sprite is hidden and reappears somewhere else on the screen.

Possible extensions

Other features could be added to the game. The spacecraft could collect shield tokens or be able to use a wider laser beam to destroy more than one object at once. Alternatively, the principles demonstrated within this program could be used to create a first-person car racing game.

BRUCE SMITH

Bruce Smith is an award-winning author of over 100 books. He has written five books about the Raspberry Pi. Download his first ever book for free from his website.
brucesmith.info

PRINTING WITH YOUR RASPBERRY PI

In an excerpt from **Bruce Smith's** *Raspberry Pi Insider Guide*, we learn how to install and configure a printer on the Pi

I f you intend to use your Raspberry Pi in a home office or to learn programming, you're sure to want to print out your results. In this excerpt from the book *Raspberry Pi Insider Guide* (**brucesmith.info/?p=14**), we look at the software to use and how to configure it.

One of the few areas where the Raspberry Pi has been a little disappointing is in the use of printers and the associated printer support. Most operating systems attack the issue of printers head-on, but Raspbian is not one of these. Installing and configuring printers is a bit of a black art, as it has been for many years on Linux, not least because there are so many makes and models of printer. Often, the real trick is picking the correct printer from the lists that are presented by the system. It is important that you know the exact make and model of your printer, as the software that translates the information from the page you are printing to ensure the correct output onto paper is dependent on this. This software is called the printer driver.

Fig 1 The CUPS configuration screen, as seen through the web interface

---

CUPS.org | **Home** | Administration | Classes | Help | Jobs | Printers

CUPS 2.0.0

CUPS is the standards-based, open source printing system developed by Apple Inc. for OS X® and other UNIX®-like operating systems.

CUPS for Users

Overview of CUPS

Command-Line Printing and Options

User Forum

CUPS for Administrators

Adding Printers and Classes

Managing Operation Policies

Using Network Printers

cupsd.conf Reference

CUPS for Developers

Introduction to CUPS Programming

CUPS API

Filter and Backend Programming

HTTP and IPP APIs

Developer Forum

Printing with CUPS

Before starting out with your printer installation, make sure your package lists are fully up-to-date by using:

```
sudo apt-get update
```

Then ensure that your printer is switched on and available. There are three possible connection types you could have: through the USB or on the local network, either wireless or cabled. The setup process is the same in each case. In the worked example that follows, we've used a Samsung ML-2580N printer connected via a router on a home network.

You will need to download and install the CUPS (Common Unix Printing System) software. The command to do this is:

```
sudo apt-get install cups
```

The process can take a while. CUPS uses the group **lpadmin** to determine who is authorised to administer printers. You will need to add the **lpadmin** group to your user profile to enable you to administer the printers. This can be done by issuing:

```
sudo usermod -a -G lpadmin pi
```

This assumes that your user name is still the default **pi**; replace **pi** with your own user name if you have changed it.

The rest of the setup can be done through a web browser. In your desktop environment, open your preferred web browser. In the URL bar, enter **http://127.0.0.1:631** and, after a moment or two, the 'CUPS' screen should appear, looking similar to that shown in **Fig 1**.

As this is also the screen that you will need to navigate to if you want to change settings or add new printers in the future, it makes good sense to bookmark it at this point.

There are a number of tabs running across the top. Click on Administration (**Fig 2**) and then select Add Printer. At this stage, you will be prompted for your user name and password – enter your normal Raspbian login name and password.

CUPS will then search for printers that are locally connected, along with any it can see on the network. This may take a few minutes. Select your printer from the results, then click Continue (if you have a printer attached via USB, then it should be listed under the 'Local Printers' option).

The next window allows you to edit the name and location of the printer. If you have only one printer, the fields can usually be left at their defaults, but it's nice to personalise things.

Printer sharing

One field that you may consider if you have a local printer is the 'Sharing' option. This is not normally required for a network printer, where you can connect direct from the computer to a printer, but here it would allow you to share a USB printer across the network if required.

Once you select Continue, CUPS will search through its database and come up with a list of potential drivers for your printer. You should scroll through these options until you find the one for your printer – i.e. the one that exactly matches the name and model number of your printer.

If there is not an exact match, then there are a couple of options. Firstly, if there is a make and model number that is very similar, try this; or if there is a generic driver for your make of printer, this would probably work as well – even if it doesn't support all the printer features. Alternatively, try searching the internet with something like 'Linux printer driver XXX', where 'XXX' is the make and model of your printer.

Once you have selected your printer, click Add Printer. The next page allows you to set the default options for your printer. It isn't really necessary to do this at this exact point, as you'll tend to do this from the application when printing.

Now that you've followed these steps, in any program that you use in future, you should be able to go to the **File>Print** option and select the page or pages you want to produce!

Fig 2 The Administration screen. You'll need to enter your user name and password to make any changes

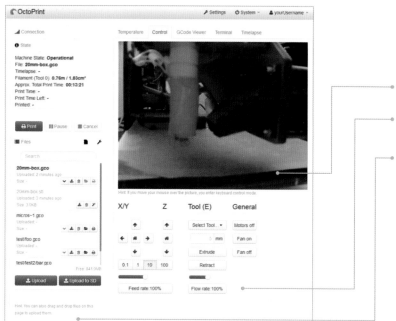

GINA HÄUSSGE

OctoPrint creator, now employed by BQ to work on it full-time! Loves tinkering and playing with both software and hardware in her free time.
twitter.com/foosel

- Get a live view of your printer, right from within your browser
- Manage your printable models and slice them, right on the Pi
- Remotely control all aspects of your 3D printer just as if you were sitting next to it

NEED HELP?

You can find links to the FAQ, the docs, the G+ community and the mailing list at **octoprint.org**

UNCHAINING YOUR 3D PRINTER WITH OCTOPRINT

Gina Häussge shows how to turn your 3D printer into a WiFi-enabled network printer you can control from any web browser, using a pre-made Pi SD card image

You'll Need

- OctoPi image **github.com/ guysoft/OctoPi**
- Camera Module **raspberrypi.org/ products/ camera-module**
- USB WiFi dongle, e.g. **raspberrypi. org/products/ usb-wifi-dongle**
- Compatible 3D printer **bit.ly/1LXZf4b**
- Class 10 SD card (minimum 4GB)

Say goodbye to the cable salad of tethering your desktop PC or laptop to your 3D printer. With OctoPrint, there exists a 3D printer remote control that you can easily run on a Raspberry Pi and use from any web browser, giving you full control and monitoring capabilities. And thanks to the OctoPi distribution, getting this set up and ready to go is as easy as flashing an image to an SD card and booting your Pi from it.

We might try to convince ourselves to the contrary, but let's face it, 3D printers do smell a bit strange and can produce quite a racket while they are working multiple hours on your latest three-dimensional creation.

That's why I sat down a couple of years ago now to create OctoPrint, a free and open-source remote control and monitoring solution for 3D printers that is targeted at the Raspberry Pi. It allows you to control and monitor all aspects of your 3D printer and its print jobs just as if you were sitting in front of it, even if it's on the other side of your house in the garage - or on the other side of the world.

Let me show you how to get this up and running in no time, powered by OctoPi, the customised SD card image created by Guy Sheffer that merits the label 'batteries included'.

Let's get started

First, go to **github.com/guysoft/OctoPi**, click on the download mirror linked there and download the most recent version of OctoPi. This might take a while. While the download is running, let's first prepare your desktop PC or laptop so that connecting to the server later will only require entering 'http://octopi.local' into your browser! OctoPi uses something called 'mDNS' (also known as 'Bonjour' or 'zeroconf') to broadcast this address on the local network and make it discoverable by other PCs that understand mDNS. Since not all systems support this out of the box, we now need to make sure yours will know what to do.

How to achieve that depends on what operating system you are running. Linux users should make sure that libnss-mdns is installed. On Debian and Ubuntu, a simple **sudo apt-get install libnss-mdns** should take care of that. Windows users need to install Bonjour Print Services for Windows, which can be downloaded from Apple at **support.apple.com/kb/DL999.** After installation, you'll need to make sure that your Windows Firewall allows traffic on UDP port 5353 and that mDNSresponder.exe has network access. Mac users are lucky: for them, mDNS should be supported out of the box by the operating system, without the need to install anything else.

Preparing the image

Once you have downloaded the ZIP file, unpack it on your computer and flash it to your SD card. After that's done, don't boot from it yet – we'll first configure your WiFi connection, which we can do quite easily without booting.

Plug the freshly flashed card into the SD card reader so your computer detects it just like it would a USB thumb drive. Open it up in your file manager and take a look there; you'll see a file called **octopi-network.txt**. Open it in a text editor. You'll see a bunch of example configuration snippets for various types of WiFi setups: encrypted with WPA/WPA2, encrypted with WEP, and unencrypted. Choose the one that matches your WiFi setup; if you are unsure, try the first one labelled 'WPA/WPA2', as that's the most common type. Uncomment the three lines by removing the leading '#' and insert your WiFi SSID and password where it says so (**Fig 1**). Let's assume your WiFi has the SSID

Fig 2 Setting up your OctoPrint account on the first run. You should always enable access control if you plan to access your OctoPrint instance through the internet

Final setup

Connect the camera, your printer, and your WiFi dongle to your Raspberry Pi, then plug the SD card in and power your Pi up. The first bootup will take a while,

> # Let's face it, 3D printers do smell a bit strange and can produce quite a racket while they are working multiple hours on your latest three-dimensional creation

'MyWifi', the password 'MySuperSecretPassword' and is WPA2 encrypted; if so, the four lines related to the WPA configuration snippet should look like this:

```
## WPA/WPA2 secured
iface wlan0 inet manual
    wpa-ssid "MyWifi"
    wpa-psk "MySuperSecretPassword"
```

Save the file and securely remove the SD card reader. It's now time to boot up the Pi!

Fig 1 Setting up your WiFi configuration through the octopi-network.txt file. Just enter your WiFi details and save

but sooner or later your WiFi dongle should show some activity and your camera will switch on. If you've entered your WiFi credentials correctly and set up mDNS support properly, you should now be able to just SSH into the Pi via the address **octopi.local** (using the user name **pi** with the password **raspberry**) to perform some final setup steps.

First of all, change the password with **passwd** – don't forget it! Then run **sudo raspi-config** and expand the file system on the SD card. After the obligatory reboot which follows, enter **http://octopi.local** into your browser. Depending on your Raspberry Pi model, this may take a little while to show you a page, but sooner or later OctoPrint's web interface will greet you with a prompt to set up your OctoPrint account. Choose a user name and password, click 'Keep Access Control enabled' (**Fig 2**), and log into your shiny new OctoPrint instance via the Login button in the upper right corner. Then select your 3D printer's serial port and the appropriate baud rate from the Connection menu on the left, and click Connect. Once it says 'Connected' and your temperature graph starts showing your data, you are all set. Congratulations!

You can now fully control your printer from the web interface, upload files to print, remotely watch your print jobs, and create time-lapses. And if you take a look into the Plugin Manager inside the Settings dialog, there are also a bunch of very nice things to be discovered there. Have fun!

CUSTOMISING OCTOPRINT

You can add custom controls or get notified about finished print jobs – take a look at the docs!

EMILE COLE

Fresh out of a Creative Writing degree in Plymouth, Emile is a junior technical author at RealVNC.
realvnc.com/products/vnc/raspberrypi

CONTROL YOUR PI REMOTELY WITH VNC SOFTWARE

Learn how to control your Raspberry Pi from afar, whether you're at the office or stuck using 4G on the train home

A s pocket-friendly as the Pi is, you can't take it everywhere. At some point, you'll find yourself with nothing but a smartphone or computer for company, and it just won't be the same. Fortunately, thanks to RealVNC, there's a way to remotely access your Pi's desktop – even if you're running it headless. This tutorial will talk you through the basics of setting up VNC Server on your Pi and connecting to it from a client device using VNC Viewer. We'll also look briefly at Virtual Mode, and how you can use it to gain visual access to a headless Raspberry Pi.

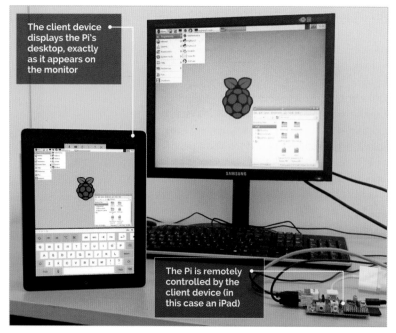

The client device displays the Pi's desktop, exactly as it appears on the monitor

The Pi is remotely controlled by the client device (in this case an iPad)

>STEP-01
Installing VNC Server
Start by opening LXTerminal and running:
```
curl -L -o VNC.tar.gz http://bit.ly/1ILmo8p
tar xvf VNC.tar.gz
```
Once everything's downloaded, navigate to its location and run:
```
sudo dpkg -i <VNC-Server-package-name>.deb
<VNC-Viewer-package-name>.deb
```
Note: You'll need to replace the angle brackets and their contents with your own package names, e.g. **VNC-Server-5.2.3-Linux-ARM.deb**; this will also install VNC Viewer, meaning your Pi can take control of other computers if you wish.

Next, download VNC Viewer to your client device, such as a mobile phone. This can be done for free through either **realvnc.com/download** or the iOS or Android app store.

>STEP-02
Licensing VNC Server
VNC Server must be licensed with a Free, Personal, or Enterprise licence. To obtain one, visit **realvnc.com/products/vnc** and choose the right option for you; while a Free licence will provide you with basic remote control, you'll miss out on features such as encryption, system authentication, file transfer, chat, and dedicated product support. For the purposes of this tutorial, however, a Free licence will be fine. Once you have a key, apply it at the command line with:
```
sudo vnclicense -add <license-key>
```
Note that VNC Viewer will not need to be licensed.

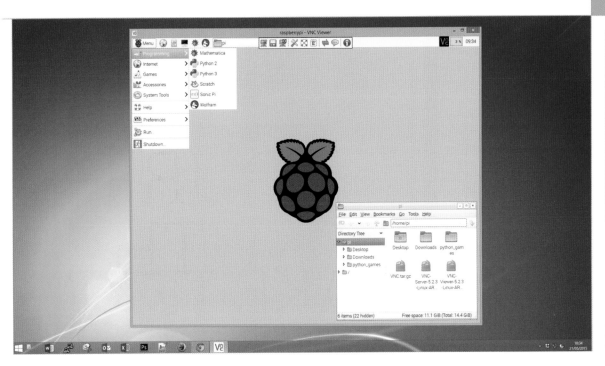

STARTING VNC SERVER IN SERVICE MODE

To automatically start VNC Sever in Service Mode when your Pi is turned on, run: `sudo update-rc.d vncserver-x11-serviced defaults`

Left Controlling your Pi from a Windows desktop

>STEP-03
Controlling your Pi locally

VNC Server is usually run in Service Mode or Virtual Mode; if your Pi is headless, only the latter will work, so skip to step 6. Create a new password for Service Mode with `sudo vncpasswd /root/.vnc/config.d/ vncserver-x11`, then type in a password. Service Mode gives full access to your Pi's desktop. Run `sudo /etc/init.d/vncserver-x11-serviced start`. Now open VNC Viewer on your client device. Type your Pi's private IP address (see VNC Server's dialog box, or run `ifconfig`) and connect. You'll now have visual access to your Pi. For detailed setup instructions, refer to **realvnc.com/products/vnc/raspberrypi**.

>STEP-05
Navigating your Pi on a smartphone

When connecting from a smartphone for the first time, controlling your cursor may feel strange. Instead of navigating your Pi like you would your phone's web browser, you should try to see your phone as a laptop touchpad controlling a cursor. This provides accurate control of your Pi's high-resolution desktop, despite the small screen of your device.

Drag your finger across your screen to move the cursor. The visible desktop automatically scrolls with you. To left-click, tap anywhere once; double-tap to double-click. More gestures are available by clicking the '?' in the app toolbar.

> " Instead of navigating your Pi like you would your phone's web browser, you should try to see your phone as a laptop touchpad controlling a cursor "

>STEP-04
Controlling your Pi over the internet

If your Raspberry Pi's at home and you're not, you'll obviously have to connect to it over the internet. Here, you'll need to configure port forwarding. In a modern router's settings, you should be able to forward the 'VNC' service to port 5900, then select your Pi from the device list.

VNC Viewer can now connect to your Pi from anywhere; just input its public IP address (visit **whatismyip.com** from your Pi). This may only work until your ISP reboots your router if they do not provide you with a static public IP. To ensure you'll always have the right connection information, apply for a hostname using a service such as **noip.com** or **dyndns.com**.

>STEP-06
Creating a virtual desktop

VNC Server can be run in Virtual Mode to create and remotely control as many virtual desktops as your licence allows. In Virtual Mode, the user does not see what they would if sitting in front of the Pi. Instead, they see a virtual desktop that is visible to only the VNC Viewer user. This can provide visual access to a headless Raspberry Pi computer.

Type **vncserver** at a command prompt, then create a password. Note down VNC Server's IP address (including the colon and subsequent display number). Next, you need to input this information into VNC Viewer; you should now be connected to your very own private virtual desktop. To learn more about VNC, visit **realvnc.com**.

STOPPING VNC SERVER

To stop VNC Server in Service Mode, run: `sudo /etc/init.d/ vncserver-x11-serviced stop`. To stop it in Virtual Mode, run: `vncserver -kill :<display-number>`

SEAN MCMANUS

Sean McManus is the author of *Raspberry Pi For Dummies* (with Mike Cook), and *Scratch Programming in Easy Steps*.
sean.co.uk
twitter.com/musicandwords

The code displays multicoloured red, purple, and blue text

A diffuser layer makes it easier to read, and protects your eyes from the bright LEDs!

UNICORN HAT
PIMO RONI

MAKE TEXT SCROLL ON THE UNICORN HAT

The Unicorn HAT provides a compact and colourful way to display scrolling messages on your Raspberry Pi. Here's how it's done...

You'll Need

> Unicorn HAT

> Frosted or Ninja diffuser

> Pibow case (optional)

> Internet access

It's easy to get colourful special effects from the Unicorn HAT, an 8×8 matrix of RGB LEDs. But did you know you can also use it to output text? This project shows you how to scroll messages across it, and could form the basis of any project that needs to display information, such as a robot or Twitter display. Nobody wants to hand-design (or even hand-code) a whole new font for this, so this project uses Pygame to scan a font on screen instead, capturing that font data in a Python dictionary.

>STEP-01
Create your font

The key to this project is to use one of the fonts already on your Pi, **FreeSans.ttf**, and convert it to a useful form for the Unicorn HAT scroller program. Open Python 2 and enter **Listing 1**. It first displays each character in turn and scans it to check the brightness of each pixel. Next, it builds a list of values for each pixel in the letter, and compiles a dictionary of those list values. Finally, it trims the character data back to the minimum width required.

Right The font creator program uses three different shades. On the Unicorn HAT, these shades are multiplied by the colour numbers to create the letters

>STEP-02
Manually modify selected characters

This step is optional, depending on your application. Some of the punctuation symbols (including @) don't render clearly at the size we need to display them for scanning. If you want, you can define them manually. Each character has a list that contains another list of data for each row. Use 1 to plot a point and 0 for an empty point, as shown for @ in Listing 1. Here's a shortcut to save hand-designing the characters first: the Amstrad CPC6128 manual (available at **bit.ly/1AgpY7J**) shows the design for that classic computer's font, which also uses an 8×8 grid (see Chapter 7 of the manual).

>STEP-03
Enter the scroller code

Listing 2 is your scroller code. Enter it into a new window in Python 2 and save it as **scroller.py**. The code assumes you have your Raspberry Pi with the USB ports on the left, so you can stand it up on the side that has no cables going into it. Change the orientation at the start if your Pi is a different way around, to 0, 90 or 270.

>STEP-04
Paste in your font dictionary

Run the font creator program (**python fontmaker.py**), highlight the font dictionary when it's shown in the

Language
>PYTHON

fontmaker.py (Listing 1)

```python
# -*- coding: utf-8 -*-
import pygame
pygame.init()
canvas=pygame.display.set_mode((100,100))
pygame.mouse.set_visible(0)
char_set = "QWERTYUIOP ASDFGHJKL ZXCVBNM \
1234567890-= !$%^&*()_+"
char_set += "[]{} ;'#:@~ ,./<>?\"\\"
font_dictionary = dict()

for letter in char_set: #main dictionary creation loop
    canvas.fill((0,0,0)) #clear the canvas
    fontObj = pygame.font.Font(\
'/usr/share/fonts/truetype/freefont/FreeSans.ttf',9)
    textSurface = fontObj.render(
    letter,True,(255,255,255),(0,0,0))
    textRectObj = textSurface.get_rect()
    canvas.blit(textSurface, textRectObj)
    pygame.display.update() #display the letter

    letter_data = []
    for y in range(8): #check each row of
    # the letter on canvas
        letter_row=[]
        for x in range(8):
            #each x position of letter on canvas
            colour = canvas.get_at((x,y+2))
            if colour[0]>200:
                letter_row.append(1)
            elif colour[0]>100:
                letter_row.append(0.75)
            elif colour[0]:
                letter_row.append(0.15)
            else:
                letter_row.append(0)
        letter_data.append(letter_row)

    for x in range(7,-1,-1): # Trim excess space on right of letter
        column=[letter_data[y][x] for y in range(8)]
        if max(column)==0:
            for i in range(8):
                del letter_data[i][x]

    font_dictionary[letter]=letter_data
font_dictionary[' ']=[[0]*4]*8 #space gets trimmed to empty otherwise
font_dictionary['@']=[[0,1,1,1,1,1,0],[1,1,0,0,0,1,1],[1,1,0,1,1,1,1],\
[1,1,0,1,0,0,1],[1,1,0,1,1,1,1],[1,1,0,0,0,0,0],[0,1,1,1,1,1,0],[0]*7]

pygame.quit()
print font_dictionary
```

shell, and use **SHIFT**+**CTRL**+**C** to copy it all. It starts and ends with a curly bracket and might span more than one screen. Paste it in place of the curly brackets, where **font_dictionary** is defined near the top of Listing 2. Now your scroller program has the font data it needs. Save your program.

>STEP-05
Restart and install software
There appears to be a conflict between Pygame and the Unicorn HAT, so you can't use them both in the same session. If you see random flashing on the Unicorn HAT when you run the scroller program, this is probably the reason why. Restart your Raspberry Pi now. If you haven't already installed the Unicorn HAT drivers, go into the command line and issue the command:
`\curl -sS get.pimoroni.com/unicornhat | bash`

>STEP-06
Run your scroller
You should view your Unicorn HAT through a diffuser layer. You can buy one from Pimoroni, designed for use as a lid on the full-size Pibow case. To run your scroller, open the command-line and go to the folder containing your code in. Enter **sudo python scroller.py**. The program will ask you for text to scroll and then scroll it across the display. When you build this code into other applications, put the message you want to display into the variable **string_to_show**.

scroller.py (Listing 2)

```python
import unicornhat as unicorn
import time
unicorn.rotation(180) #adjust for your Pi's orientation
unicorn.brightness(0.4)
#warning: Altering this value can make LED VERY bright!
font_dictionary={} # paste in your font dictionary here
string_to_show=raw_input("Enter the text to scroll: ")
scroll_rows=[[0]*8]*8 #blank space at start of message

for character in string_to_show:
    if character.upper() in font_dictionary:
        character_rows = font_dictionary[character.upper()]
    else:
        character_rows = font_dictionary['-']
    for i in range(8):
        scroll_rows[i] = scroll_rows[i]+character_rows[i]
        scroll_rows[i] += [0] #gap between letters

for i in range(8):
    scroll_rows[i]+=[0]*8 #blank space at end of message

for scroll_position in range(len(scroll_rows[0])-8):
    for y in range(8):
        thisrow = scroll_rows[y]
        for x in range(8):
            pixel_shade=thisrow[x+scroll_position]
            unicorn.set_pixel(x,y,int((95+x*20)*pixel_shade),\
                int(100*pixel_shade),int((95+y*20)*pixel_shade))
    unicorn.show()
    time.sleep(0.04)
```

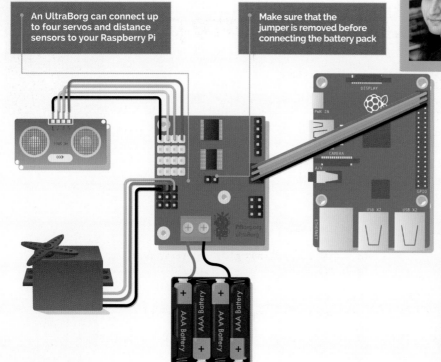

An UltraBorg can connect up to four servos and distance sensors to your Raspberry Pi

Make sure that the jumper is removed before connecting the battery pack

ARRON CHURCHILL

Arron writes the software for the robots at **PiBorg.org**, giving them the ability to chase balls and obey commands. We know what you're thinking, but robots are cheaper and tidier than dogs.
piborg.org

Below The various parts connected to UltraBorg, just missing the Raspberry Pi. The sensor is attached to one of PiBorg's optional mounting kits

MOVE A SERVO
WITH A FLICK
OF THE WRIST

The UltraBorg helps you use servos and sensors with your projects. Here you'll make a servo move by waving your hands like a lunatic...

When building robots, we tend to think of walking or driving robots, but they can take many different forms. Servos are an inexpensive form of robot motor and they're used in many robots, such as planes (UAVs), robotic arms, and even remote-controlled (RC) cars. Ultrasonic sensors are another useful bit of robot-building kit. You can use them to determine how far away things are from the robot, which is ideal for collision avoidance. Both are cheap and easy to obtain, so in this project we're going to demonstrate how you can use both of them together to build a very simple robot that responds to motion.

>STEP-01
Connect the UltraBorg

Start by removing the jumper that is fitted on the two-pin connector in the middle of the board. With the Raspberry Pi powered off, connect the pair of three-pin cables between the UltraBorg and the GPIO header. Make sure the cables are fitted so that the pin marked '1' on the UltraBorg is connected to pin 1 on the GPIO header – that's the pin that is closest to the SD card slot.

>STEP-02
Connect the servo

Next, we connect the servo to one of the three-pin connectors. The servo connections are numbered 1 to 4, with #1 towards the middle of the board. You may use any combination of the four available connectors; for this project, we want to connect the servo up to the #1 connector. Make sure the servo is connected the correct way around: the ground (also called GND, -VE, or 0V) wire should be connected to the pin closest to the edge of the board. Servo cables may vary in colour, but usually the ground wire is black or brown.

>STEP-03
Connect the HC-SR04

The four-pin ultrasonic connections are also numbered 1 to 4; 1 is at the top of the board. Since the sensor has pins instead of a cable, we will need to fit a four-pin female-to-female cable. Connect the cable to the HC-SR04; make a note of which colour wire is connected to the ground pin, marked 'Gnd' on the sensor. Now connect the other end of the cable to the #1 connection on the UltraBorg; the ground wire should be attached to the pin closest to the edge of the board.

>STEP-04
Power the servo and sensor

The UltraBorg uses an external power connection for the servos and ultrasonic sensors. Take the positive wire from the battery holder (usually red) and place the exposed metal into the left screw terminal. Screw the left terminal down until the wire is held firmly. Take the negative wire from the battery holder (usually black) and place the exposed metal into the right screw terminal. Screw the right terminal down until the wire is held firmly.

Now fit four rechargeable batteries into the holder. The four batteries will supply approximately 5V of power, which is fine for the servos and sensors.

>STEP-05
Install the software

Now we need to get our Raspberry Pi running. Connect the power supply and wait for the Raspberry Pi to boot. Open a terminal and use this command to install the software:

```
bash <(curl https://www.piborg.org/install-ultraborg.txt)
```

After the software has installed, restart the Pi. You can check that the servo and HC-SR04 are connected and working by using the demo GUI icon on the desktop. The distance reading should change as you move things in front of the sensor. The leftmost slider should move the servo around. All we need now is the example script to control the servo for us.

>STEP-06
Run the example

First, download the example script from GitHub:

```
git clone https://github.com/piborg/MoveMyServo.git
```

Now, move to the new folder and run the script:

```
cd MoveMyServo
./MoveMyServo.py
```

It works, but we can improve it. Lines 8 to 11 allow us to change how the movement works. By changing the values of **distanceMin** and **distanceMax**, you can change how far you have to move your hand or object. By changing **fastMode** to **False**, you can make the servo slower. Also, changing **updateInterval** slows down the servo response. See what else you can do.

MoveMyServo.py

Language
>PYTHON 2.7

DOWNLOAD:
github.com/
piborg/
MoveMyServo

```python
# Import the libraries we need
import UltraBorg
import time

# Settings
# Minimum distance in mm, corresponds to servo at -100%
distanceMin = 100.0
# Maximum distance in mm, corresponds to servo at +100%
distanceMax = 300.0
# True moves faster, False gives a more stable position
fastMode = True
# Time between updates, smaller is faster
updateInterval = 0.1
# Start the UltraBorg
UB = UltraBorg.UltraBorg() # Create a new UltraBorg object
UB.Init() # Set the board up (checks the board is connected)

# Calculate our divisor
distanceDiv = (distanceMax - distanceMin) / 2.0

# Loop over the sequence until the user presses CTRL+C
print 'Press CTRL+C to finish'
try:
    # Set our initial position
    lastServoPosition = 0.0
    newServoPosition = 0.0
    UB.SetServoPosition1(lastServoPosition)
    # This is the loop which reads the sensor and sets the servo
    while True:
        # Read the ultrasonic values
        if fastMode:
            # We use the raw values so we respond quickly
            distanceMeasured = UB.GetRawDistance1()

        else:
            # We use the filtered values so we get stable readings
            distanceMeasured = UB.GetDistance1()
        # Convert to the nearest millimeter
        distanceMeasured = int(distanceMeasured)

        # Generate the servo positions based on distance readings
        if distanceMeasured != 0:
            newServoPosition = ((distanceMeasured - distanceMin)
/ distanceDiv) - 1.0
            if newServoPosition > 1.0:
                newServoPosition = 1.0
            elif newServoPosition < -1.0:
                newServoPosition = -1.0
        # Display our readings
        print '%4d mm -> %.1f %%' % (distanceMeasured,
newServoPosition * 100.0)

        # Set our new servo position if it has changed
        if newServoPosition != lastServoPosition:
            UB.SetServoPosition1(newServoPosition)
            lastServoPosition = newServoPosition
        # Wait between readings
        time.sleep(updateInterval)

except KeyboardInterrupt:
    # User has pressed CTRL+C
    print 'Done'
```

RICHARD WATERWORTH

Richard makes technology videos on the internet and blogs about technology including the Raspberry Pi. **richardtech.net**

- Modern gaming isn't the first thing that springs to mind when you look at a Raspberry Pi, but you can do it!

- The Pi will be streaming your games from your PC over your home network

STREAM STEAM GAMES TO YOUR RASPBERRY PI

You'll Need

- Nvidia GTX 650 graphics card or higher
- GeForce Experience **geforce.com/ geforce-experience**
- Raspbian
- Internet connection

The Raspberry Pi can do a lot of things, but maybe you didn't know that you can use it to stream your favourite games from your PC

ometimes it's just not convenient to play the latest PC games on your clunky, noisy PC. It's either tucked in the corner of the bedroom or under the stairs, right where it's bound to disturb other people from the moment you press Start to play.

Never fear, though, because it's possible to play your favourite triple-A PC games from the comfort of any TV in the house using nothing more than a suitable graphics card, a Raspberry Pi, and this guide…

>STEP-01
Install dependencies
Before we begin, you will need to make sure that you have all the dependencies installed; typically, these will already be installed with Raspbian. The dependencies are essential for Moonlight, the

application we are using on the Pi to stream, to work. To make sure you have all of the dependencies installed, use the following command:

```
sudo apt-get install libopus0 libasound2
libudev0 libavahi-client3 libcurl3 libevdev2
```

Once this has been done, we can install Moonlight, after we have configured the sound.

>STEP-02
Configuring sound
To make sure that we have sound coming out of the HDMI port, we need to edit the boot configuration file and add a line of text. To edit the boot configuration file, you will need to enter the following command:

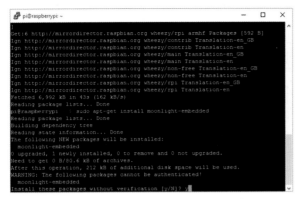

Above Setting up game-streaming is as simple as typing in a selection of console commands

```
sudo nano /boot/config.txt
```

This will then bring up the Pi's nano text editor. You will want to go to the end of the file and enter this line:

```
hdmi_drive=2
```

Once this is done, the sound should be ready to go!

>STEP-03
Downloading and installing Moonlight

Now we're getting somewhere! But just before we can download Moonlight, we need to add its source to the Raspberry Pi's sources list. To edit the sources list, type in this command:

```
sudo nano /etc/apt/sources.list
```

This should open up the sources list in the nano text editor. Now all we need to do is add the following line to our sources list to add Moonlight's source:

```
deb http://archive.itimmer.nl/raspbian/
moonlight wheezy main
```

Once this has been done, we can save and quit the file, and then check for updates on the Pi:

```
sudo apt-get update
```

Once this command has been run, we can finally install Moonlight!

```
sudo apt-get install moonlight-embedded
```

So, now we've finally managed to get Moonlight installed, let's move on to how we can use it.

>STEP-04
Setting up Moonlight

First of all, you will need to get the IP address of your Windows PC on the network. Go to the Command Prompt (in Accessories) on the PC and enter:

```
ipconfig
```

This will obtain the IP address of your PC. If there is a big list, your IP address should begin with '192.168'.

Now we can pair Moonlight with the computer by using the following command on the Pi:

```
moonlight pair YOUR-IP
```

...replacing **YOUR-IP** with the IP address of your Windows PC. Once you've entered this command, a PIN code will appear in the terminal, which you will need to enter into the GeForce Experience box that pops up on your Windows PC.

> " There are many options that can be added to the moonlight command "

>STEP-05
Streaming with Moonlight

Streaming with Moonlight is very simple; all you need to do is type into the terminal:

```
moonlight stream YOUR-IP
```

Steam Big Picture mode will automatically pop up. By default, the stream will be 720p at 60fps, but we've had better luck on our network at 30fps. There are many options that can be added to the command. To stream at 30fps, for instance, you would enter:

```
moonlight stream -30fps YOUR-IP
```

You can find all the options for the **moonlight** command at **bit.ly/moonlight-options**. These include 1080p streaming, changing bitrates, resolutions and much more!

Below Play some of the hottest games on your Pi, by streaming them from your PC's Steam games library

USING ETHERNET VS WIFI

Using Ethernet will allow you to get a better frame rate and resolution compared to using WiFi.

USE A CONTROLLER

Moonlight does support controllers, so you can game as if the Pi were a console. Sadly, we didn't have much luck with our controller, but yours may be more of a success.

MARTIN O'HANLON

Martin 'Minecraft' O'Hanlon is an active member of the Raspberry Pi community, co-author of *Adventures in Minecraft* and keeps an excellent account of his projects on his blog.
stuffaboutcode.com

You'll Need

> Raspbian

> Minecraft: Pi Edition

> Python 2 editor (IDLE)

> Getting started with Minecraft: Pi Edition: **bit.ly/1Ep9LKC**

MINECRAFT: PI CODING TIPS

If you've completed the Minecraft Pi learning resources at **raspberrypi.org**, check out these pro tips and mini programs to learn more about the coding in Minecraft...

BUILD A HOUSE

The quickest way to make a house in *Minecraft: Pi Edition* is to use code and the API. By programming a house rather than building it by hand, it can be any size you want – 10 blocks across or 100!

Create a simple program which will use the **setBlocks()** function, once to create a cube 10×10×10 of wood (17) and then again to create a cube of air (0) 9×9×9 inside the wooden cube.

Below Create massive houses in the blink of an eye using just a few lines of code

```
from mcpi import minecraft
mc = minecraft.Minecraft.create()

pos = mc.player.getTilePos()

mc.setBlocks(pos.x + 0, pos.y + 0, pos.z + 0,
        pos.x + 10, pos.y + 10, pos.z + 10, 17)

mc.setBlocks(pos.x + 1, pos.y + 1, pos.z + 1,
        pos.x + 9, pos.y + 9, pos.z + 9, 0)
```

You can then use **setBlocks()** again to create an entrance by building another block of air (0).

```
mc.setBlocks(pos.x + 4, pos.y, pos.z,
        pos.x + 6, pos.y + 3, pos.z, 0)
```

The limits of coding a house are endless – why not add a stone roof, a wool floor, and some torches to the outside?

Below **Use blocks
affected by gravity
to create your
own** *Minecraft*
mini-game

> # Using the gravity effect of blocks is a great way to add something new to your Minecraft programs

USE GRAVITY-EFFECTED BLOCKS

Sand and gravel block types in *Minecraft* are affected by gravity and will fall down if the block below is air.

The same gravity effect occurs if a block is placed in the world using the API. So if you were to create a block of gravel (13) 25 blocks above the player, it would fall on the player's head. In a new program, type:

```
from mcpi import minecraft
mc = minecraft.Minecraft.create()
pos = mc.player.getTilePos()
mc.setBlock(pos.x, pos.y + 25, pos.z, 13)
```

Using the gravity effect of blocks is a great way to add something new to your *Minecraft* programs. Here is a simple program which loops until it manages to

drop a gravel block onto Steve's head. If Steve wants to stay in the game, he has to keep moving so the gravel misses him. Start a new program:

```
from mcpi import minecraft
from time import sleep
mc = minecraft.Minecraft.create()

pos = mc.player.getTilePos()

while mc.getBlock(pos.x, pos.y, pos.z) != 13:
    mc.setBlock(pos.x, pos.y + 25, pos.z, 13)
    sleep(1)
    pos = mc.player.getTilePos()

mc.postToChat("Got you!")
```

Right Change
the position of
the 'camera' in
Minecraft and get
a different view of
the world

CHANGE THE CAMERA

Bored of always following Steve around? You can alter the position of the 'camera' in *Minecraft* to change how you see the world.

You can change the camera to follow Steve while looking directly down at him, or to look down at the world from any coordinate in *Minecraft*.

The **camera.setFollow()** function will change your view so you are looking down at Steve. In a new script:

```
from mcpi import Minecraft
mc = minecraft.Minecraft.create()

mc.camera.setFollow()
```

To change the camera to look down on any position, you use the **camera.setFixed()** function before using **camera.setPos()** to change the position of the camera. If you wanted to set the camera 25 blocks above the spawn position, you would use:

```
mc.camera.setFixed()
mc.camera.setPos(0,25,0)
```

To set the camera back to normal, you would use the **camera.setNormal()** function...

```
mc.camera.setNormal()
```

Using the camera functions, you could hide a diamond block (57) in the world, then tease the player by changing the camera to show them where it is before challenging them to find it. Try this in a new program:

```
from mcpi import minecraft
from time import sleep
mc = minecraft.Minecraft.create()

mc.postToChat("Here is the diamond ↵
block I have hidden.")
mc.setBlock(100,25,100,57)
mc.camera.setFixed()
mc.camera.setPos(100,30,100)
sleep(10)

mc.postToChat("Go find it!")
mc.camera.setNormal()
```

You could change the program above to drop the diamond block in a random position and use **getHeight()** so the diamond block is always on the top of the world.

MAKE THE WORLD 'READ-ONLY'

Are you fed up with Steve having free rein to destroy your beautifully crafted world? Or would you prefer it if lava didn't burn down your creation?

Using the **setting()** function in the API, you can make your world 'immutable' – something which is unable to be changed. Start a new script with:

```
from mcpi import minecraft
mc = minecraft.Minecraft.create()

#make the world read-only
mc.setting("world_immutable", True)
```

> " Would you prefer it if lava didn't burn down your creation? "

Now, the only way you can change the world is through code – any attempt to place or destroy blocks in the game won't work.

You can make your world writable (or mutable) again by making the setting **False**.

```
#make the world writable
mc.setting("world_immutable", False)
```

You can use this setting to create a new script which will pit your building skills against a friend, giving you 1 minute to make the best building you can before turning the world read-only again.

```
from mcpi import minecraft
from time import sleep
mc = minecraft.Minecraft.create()

mc.setting("world_immutable", True)

mc.postToChat("In a moment you will have 1 ↵
minute to create the best building.")
sleep(10)
mc.postToChat("Go")

mc.setting("world_immutable", False)
sleep(60)
mc.postToChat("Stop - Who's is the best?")
mc.setting("world_immutable", True)
```

LEARN THE HEIGHT OF THE WORLD

If you want to code structures to always be 'on top' of the land, you need to know how high the world is – or, put another way, how far the air comes down!

In *Minecraft* the height is the Y coordinate, while X and Z are the horizontal dimensions – if you pass X and Z coordinates to the API function **getHeight()**, it'll return the Y coordinate. In a new program, type:

```
from mcpi import minecraft
mc = minecraft.Minecraft.create()

y = mc.getHeight(0,0)

mc.postToChat("Height of the world at spawn is")

mc.postToChat(y)
```

If you know the height of the world, you can cover the top layer of world in a different type of block by looping through the X and Z coordinates. What about covering the world in snow?

You can do this in a new script by looping through the coordinates around your player, finding the height for that position and setting the block to snow (78).

```
from mcpi import minecraft
mc = minecraft.Minecraft.create()

pos = mc.player.getTilePos()

for x in range(pos.x, pos.x + 10):
    for z in range(pos.z, pos.z + 10):
        y = mc.getHeight(x,z)
        mc.setBlock(x,y,z,78)
```

What other types of block could you cover the world in? Lava perhaps?!

Below Cover *Minecraft* in snow by using the API to find the height of the world

MARTIN O'HANLON

Martin 'Minecraft' O'Hanlon is an active member of the Raspberry Pi community, co-author of *Adventures in Minecraft*, and keeps an excellent account of his projects on his blog.
stuffaboutcode.com

MORE MINECRAFT
CODING TIPS & TRICKS

You'll Need

> Raspbian

> Minecraft: Pi Edition

> Python 2 editor (IDLE)

Have you exhausted the Minecraft: Pi basics available from **raspberrypi.org/resources**? And completed our tips on pages 132-135? Here are another five tips and mini-programs to experiment with...

BACK UP AND RESTORE MINECRAFT WORLDS

Ever accidentally set off a load of TNT and wished you hadn't? It's at times like these it's a good idea to have a backup of your whole *Minecraft* world so you can restore it back to normal.

Well, you can. *Minecraft: Pi Edition* stores all of your worlds in a directory on your Raspberry Pi's SD card, so by using the terminal and a few commands, you can find your favourite world and back it up to a file. Open a terminal window with:

Menu > Accessories > Terminal.

Next, change directory to the **minecraftWorlds** directory using the following command:

Below **Back up your** *Minecraft* **worlds as a compressed file**

```
cd ~/.minecraft/games/com.mojang
minecraftWorlds
```

Each world is saved in its own directory and named the same as what's displayed in the *Minecraft* 'Select World' screen. Use the **ls** terminal command when you're in that directory to see your saved worlds. To make a backup of **world--**, use the **tar** command to create a compressed file:

```
tar czf world--backup.tar.gz world--
```

tar is the command, **czf** tells it to Create a Zipped File, **world–backup.tar.gz** is the name of the backup file, and **world--** is the directory of the world you want to back up.

Now, the next time you want to restore your world, all you have to do is use the following command:

```
tar xzf world--backup.tar.gz
```

Be warned: once entered, there is no going back!

```
pi@rpi2 ~ $ cd ~/.minecraft/games/com.mojang/minecraftWorlds
pi@rpi2 ~/.minecraft/games/com.mojang/minecraftWorlds $ ls
world  world-  world--
pi@rpi2 ~/.minecraft/games/com.mojang/minecraftWorlds $
  tar czf world--backup.tar.gz world--
pi@rpi2 ~/.minecraft/games/com.mojang/minecraftWorlds $ ls
world  world-  world--  world--backup.tar.gz
pi@rpi2 ~/.minecraft/games/com.mojang/minecraftWorlds $
  tar xzf world--backup.tar.gz
pi@rpi2 ~/.minecraft/games/com.mojang/minecraftWorlds $
```

Minecraft - Pi edition

os: 140, 48.2, 24.3

Above **Use torches like a pro, automatically placing them around a block**

USING TORCHES

If you want to get some light into your *Minecraft* world, you need to create torches. You can do so using the API, but you need to know how to place the torches around the block you want to attach them to.

Torches have their own block type and take up an entire block space in *Minecraft* (even though it looks like they take up a small amount of it), which is

> You could change the code to make a tower of stone

why you can't have more than one torch in a block. When torches are created using the **setBlock()** API function, it automatically connects the torch to the block which is next to it, to the north, south, east, west, or on top.

Use the following code to create a block of stone above the player and place torches all around it, and one on top.

```
from mcpi import minecraft
from mcpi import block

mc = minecraft.Minecraft.create()

pos = mc.player.getTilePos()

mc.setBlock(pos.x, pos.y + 2, pos.z, block.STONE)

# create torches
# on top
mc.setBlock(pos.x, pos.y + 3, pos.z, block.TORCH)
# to the east
mc.setBlock(pos.x + 1, pos.y + 2, pos.z, block.TORCH)
# to the west
mc.setBlock(pos.x - 1, pos.y + 2, pos.z, block.TORCH)
# to the north
mc.setBlock(pos.x, pos.y + 2, pos.z - 1, block.TORCH)
# to the south
mc.setBlock(pos.x, pos.y + 2, pos.z + 1, block.TORCH)
```

You could change the code to make a tower of stone with torches all around, to provide a beacon to help you find your way.

FIND OUT WHEN BLOCKS ARE HIT

When Steve hits a block by right-clicking with a sword in *Minecraft*, it creates a 'hit event'; you can get this using the API and it'll tell you who hit the block, its position, and what face (i.e. top, bottom, left, right) it was hit on.

You use the function **events.pollBlockHits()** to get a list of events that have occurred since it was last called. You can then loop through events using a **for** loop.

```
from mcpi import minecraft

mc = minecraft.Minecraft.create()

while True:
    hitsList = mc.events.pollBlockHits()
    for hit in hitsList:
        mc.postToChat("A block was hit (
who, position, face)")
        mc.postToChat(hit.entityId)
        mc.postToChat(hit.pos)
        mc.postToChat(hit.face)
```

Start up *Minecraft*, run the program above, and experiment with hitting some blocks by holding a sword and right-clicking the block. By using the position and the **getBlock()** function, you can find out the type of block (e.g. stone, dirt, grass) that was hit:

```
blockType = mc.getBlock(hit.pos)
mc.postToChat(blockType)
```

Or even better, change the block which was hit, using **setBlock()** to give Steve the Midas touch and make every block he hits turn to gold:

```
mc.setBlock(hit.pos, 41)
```

Below Give Steve the Midas touch and turn blocks into gold!

Have a think about what other things you can make happen in *Minecraft: Pi* using block hit events.

SAVE AND RESTORE CHECKPOINTS

Checkpoints let you create in-game mini-backups so you can undo changes that have been made. You can use the **saveCheckpoint()** API function to make a temporary copy of your world; when you use **restoreCheckpoint()**, this copy is used to put your world back to how it was when you saved the checkpoint.

```
from mcpi import minecraft

mc = minecraft.Minecraft.create()

mc.saveCheckpoint()

mc.restoreCheckpoint()
```

> " Every 30 seconds, your program will save a checkpoint "

You can use the checkpoint functions to create a program which will allow you to 'undo' any unwanted changes you make to your *Minecraft* world. Every 30 seconds, your program will save a checkpoint and if you ever want to go back to it, just hit a block.

```
from mcpi import minecraft
from time import sleep

mc = minecraft.Minecraft.create()

count = 0

while True:
    #every 30 secs save a checkpoint
    if count % 30 == 0:
        mc.saveCheckpoint()
        mc.postToChat("Checkpoint saved")
    count = count + 1
    sleep(1)

    #if a block is hit, restore checkpoint
    if mc.events.pollBlockHits():
        mc.restoreCheckpoint()
        mc.postToChat("Restoring checkpoint")
```

Measure how far Steve is away from home

CALCULATING THE DISTANCE BETWEEN TWO BLOCKS

When coding *Minecraft*, it's really useful to know the distance between two blocks – and by using some (fairly) simple maths, we can work it out. This can be used in loads of fun ways, such as a hide and seek game where a diamond block is hidden and Steve is told whether he is getting colder or warmer. The maths works like this:

01 Calculate the difference between the x, y and z coordinates of the two positions

02 Multiply the difference by itself (its square)

03 Add all the squares together

04 The distance equals the square root of the total above

This program uses this calculation to display how far the player is from where they started. So the further they move away, the greater the distance. See how it works by copying the following code example into IDLE or your favourite text editor (don't forget to save it with the **.py** file extension):

```python
from mcpi import minecraft
from math import sqrt
from time import sleep

mc = minecraft.Minecraft.create()

startPos = mc.player.getTilePos()

while True:

    posNow = mc.player.getTilePos()

    xDiff = startPos.x - posNow.x
    yDiff = startPos.y - posNow.y
    zDiff = startPos.z - posNow.z

    xSquare = xDiff * xDiff
    ySquare = yDiff * yDiff
    zSquare = zDiff * zDiff

    total = xSquare + ySquare + zSquare

    distance = sqrt(total)

    mc.postToChat(distance)

    sleep(1)
```

Try changing the program to show the distance between the player and a random diamond block you have created.

MARTIN O'HANLON

Martin 'Minecraft' O'Hanlon is an active member of the Raspberry Pi community, co-author of *Adventures in Minecraft*, and keeps an excellent account of his projects on his blog.
stuffaboutcode.com

Left Nintendo's *Splatoon* is a fun multiplayer game where each team has to paint the play area in their team colours

Below *Minecraft Splat* uses *Splatoon*'s brilliant game mechanic to create a fun game for you and a friend

MINECRAFT SPLAT

Create an exciting two-player game in Minecraft: Pi, inspired by Nintendo's recent hit game Splatoon...

You can play *Minecraft: Pi Edition* in multiplayer mode when two or more Raspberry Pis on the same network join the same world. In this guide, we use this technique to create a simple versus game that works along similar lines to Nintendo's *Splatoon*, which sees two teams trying to paint the game area in their team colours.

The objective of our game is very similar: to splat (turn to your team colour) as many blocks as possible for your side, while the opposing team will also be splatting blocks for themselves and claiming your splats for themselves. You will earn points for each block that is still your colour at the end of the game, and the player with the most splats wins!

MINECRAFT SPLAT IS SPLIT INTO 5 PARTS:

01 Create the framework for the program and make sure your code runs.

02 Build the pitch that will appear when the game starts and be the splat battleground.

03 Splat blocks by hitting them with a sword.

04 Game over and displaying the winner.

05 Making a better game.

CREATE THE PROGRAM

Open Python 2 from the Programming menu. The Python Shell will appear; when it does, create a new program using **File>New Window** – it's also a good idea to save your program now, using **File>Save**.

Import the Python modules you will need:

```
from mcpi.minecraft import Minecraft
from mcpi import block
from time import sleep, time
from random import getrandbits
```

You'll need a constant to hold the colour each team will use; it's the colour of the wool block that will be used when a player splats a block. Create a list which holds two values: 13 for green and 14 for red.

```
TEAMCOLS = [13,14]
```

Create the definition for two functions, which you will complete later in this tutorial.

```
def buildPitch(mc, pos):
    pass
def splatBlock(mc, x, y, z, team):
    pass
```

You will need a list to hold the points each team has scored. The first element will be team 1's score; the second, team 2's – they should both be set to 0.

```
points = [0,0]
```

Create the connection to *Minecraft* and post a message to the screen.

```
mc = Minecraft.create()
mc.postToChat("Minecraft Splat")
```

At this point, you can run your program and if everything is set up, you should see the 'Minecraft Splat' message posted to the screen.

Now start up *Minecraft: Pi Edition*. Create a new game and then run your program by clicking **Run>Run Module**.

BUILD THE PITCH

The game needs a pitch where the action can take place; it's a glass 'room' with two glass walls running down the middle.

Find the **buildPitch** function in your program:

```
def buildPitch(mc, pos):
    pass
```

The *Minecraft* connection, **mc**, and a position, **pos**, where the pitch should be built, should be passed to the function.

Delete the **pass** statement and replace it with the following code, which will create a cube of glass blocks. Then create a cube of air inside it before building the central walls of glass.

```
def buildPitch(mc, pos):
    # glass cube
    mc.setBlocks(
            pos.x - 5, pos.y - 1, pos.z - 10,
            pos.x + 5, pos.y + 3, pos.z + 10,
            block.GLASS.id)
    # hollow it out
    mc.setBlocks(pos.x - 4, pos.y, pos.z - 9,
            pos.x + 4, pos.y + 3, pos.z + 9,
            block.AIR.id)

    # add 2 walls down the middle
    mc.setBlocks(pos.x, pos.y, pos.z - 7,
            pos.x, pos.y + 3, pos.z - 1,
            block.GLASS.id)
    mc.setBlocks(pos.x, pos.y, pos.z + 1,
            pos.x, pos.y + 3, pos.z + 7,
            block.GLASS.id)
```

The **buildPitch** function now needs to be called from your program. Add the following code to the end of the program to get the player's position and call the function.

```
pos = mc.player.getTilePos()
buildPitch(mc, pos)
```

Before the game starts, you should also include a delay, to let the players get ready, and a message to let them know the game has started.

```
sleep(3)
mc.postToChat("Go!")
```

Run the program. You should see the pitch appear around your player and the message to 'Go!'.

SPLATTING BLOCKS

The blocks of the pitch's walls and floor can be splatted by hitting them (right-click) with a sword – when you splat a glass block, it'll turn it into a wool block of your team's colour; splatting a block belonging to the opposition will turn it back to glass.

You earn points for each block splatted with your team's colour, and the opposition will lose a point for each block you turn back to glass.

Find the **splatBlock** function in your program:

```
def splatBlock(mc, x, y, z, team):
    pass
```

Change the function so that it splats the block at the position **x**, **y**, **z** for **team**, which are variables passed to the function. When executed, the function will return the number of points scored for each team.

Delete the **pass** statement and create a list which will hold the points scored for each team:

"You earn points for each block splatted with your team's colour, and the opposition will lose a point for each block you turn back to glass"

```
def splatBlock(mc, x, y, z, team):
    pointsScored = [0,0]
```

The variable **team**, which is passed into **splatBlock**, will hold either a 0 or 1 depending on which team splatted the block. Use this value to create a variable to hold the other team:

```
otherTeam = 1 - team
```

Check to see if the block that was hit was a glass block; if it was, turn it into a wool block of the team's colour, and increase the team's score by 1:

```
blockHit = mc.getBlockWithData(x, y, z)
    if blockHit.id == block.GLASS.id:
        mc.setBlock(
x, y, z, block.WOOL.id, TEAMCOLS[team])
        pointsScored[team] += 1
```

If the block isn't glass, check to see if it's a wool block of the other team's colour before turning it back to glass and decreasing the other team's score:

```
elif blockHit.id == block.WOOL.id:
    if blockHit.data == TEAMCOLS[otherTeam]:
        mc.setBlock(x, y, z, block.GLASS.id)
            pointsScored[otherTeam] -= 1
```

The last step in the **splatBlock** function is to return the number of points scored:

```
return pointsScored
```

Now that the **splatBlock** function is complete, you need to add to the code at the bottom of your program which will start the game.

You will find out how many players are in the game, create a loop which will continue until the end of the game, and call **splatBlock** each time a block is hit.

Get a list of players currently in the game, and the time the game started, and store them in variables:

```
players = mc.getPlayerEntityIds()
start = time()
```

Set the variable **gameOver** to False before creating a **while** loop which will continue until **gameOver** is set to True when the game finishes.

Left *Splatoon*
on the Nintendo
Wii U console is
colourful and fun

```
gameOver = False
while not gameOver:
```

Use **pollBlockHits()** to find out if any blocks have
been hit, before looping through each 'hit' with a **for** loop:

```
blockHits = mc.events.pollBlockHits()
    for hit in blockHits:
```

Every player in *Minecraft* has an entity ID and these
are held in the **players** list you created earlier. The
player's position in the list will determine what team
they are on: even = team 1, odd = team 2. Use the
players list and the entity ID of the player who hit the
block to work out what team they are on.

```
team = players.index(hit.entityId) % 2
```

Call the **splatBlock** function, passing the position
of the block which was hit and the team who hit it, and
add the points scored to the total points for the team.

```
pointsScored = splatBlock(mc,
    hit.pos.x, hit.pos.y, hit.pos.z, team)
    points[0] += pointsScored[0]
    points[1] += pointsScored[1]
```

Run your program and, as before, the pitch should
appear around your player. Now, however, hitting
blocks (right-clicking while holding a sword) should
turn the blocks to coloured wool. You could even
get a friend to join your game and test turning your
opponent's blocks back to glass.

As you haven't created the code to end the game,
the program will continue for ever. You can use
CTRL+C or click **Shell>Restart Shell** in the Python
Shell to end the program.

SPLATOON

Splatoon is a refreshing take on team-based combat
games produced by Nintendo for the Wii U console.
While other popular multiplayer combat games
like *Battlefield* or *Call of Duty* centre around war
and destruction, *Splatoon* takes a more colourful
approach to the formula by tasking its players to
paint the playing field in their team colours. The team
with the most paint at the end of the round wins.
The 'Inklings' you control can use splatter guns and
rollers in their quest to conquer their opponents. It's a
brilliant family-friendly game and a great concept that
Martin O'Hanlon has kindly transformed into the fun
Minecraft: Pi game for you to play.

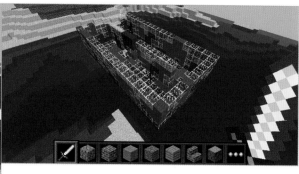

> # Find a friend with a Raspberry Pi, challenge them to a game

GAME OVER

Each match is 30 seconds long and the game is over when the time runs out. Under the **while** loop, you need to check whether the time now minus the time the game started is greater than 30 seconds. Once the game is over, you should post the team's points to the chat window, along with the winner.

```
if time() - start > 30:
    gameOver = True
    mc.postToChat("Game Over")
    mc.postToChat(
"Green Team = " + str(points[0]))
    mc.postToChat(
"Red Team = " + str(points[1]))
    if points[0] > points[1]:
        mc.postToChat("Green Team wins")
        else:
        mc.postToChat("Red Team wins")
```

Find a friend with a Raspberry Pi, challenge them to a game of *Minecraft Splat*, and run your program.

MAKING A BETTER SPLAT

The splat made at the moment is less of a splat and more of a blob. If you want to take the program further, in the next section you will use randomisation to splatter the blocks around the block that was hit as well.

After your code to splat the block, loop through each of the blocks around the one which was hit:

```
for hit in blockHits:
    team = players.index(hit.entityId) % 2

    pointsScored = splatBlock(
            mc, hit.pos.x, hit.pos.y,
    hit.pos.z, team)

        points[0] += pointsScored[0]
        points[1] += pointsScored[1]

        for x in [-1, 0, 1]:
            for y in [-1, 0, 1]:
                for z in [-1, 0, 1]:
```

Using the code **getrandbits(1)**, you can randomly generate a 1 or 0, giving a 50/50 chance of it being 1 – if it is, splat the block for the team and add the points to the total.

```
if getrandbits(1) == 1:
    pointsScored = splatBlock(mc,
            hit.pos.x + x,
            hit.pos.y + y,
            hit.pos.z + z,
            team)
    points[0] += pointsScored[0]
    points[1] += pointsScored[1]
```

Run your program again. Now, each time you splat a block, it should randomly splatter the blocks around it, too.

This is just one improvement you can make to the game; the only limit is your imagination. How will you take it forward and make it your own?

The code for *Minecraft Splat* can be found on GitHub at **github.com/martinohanlon/minecraft-splat**

MCSplat.py

```python
# import modules
from mcpi.minecraft import Minecraft
from mcpi import block
from time import sleep, time
from random import getrandbits

TEAMCOLS = [13,14]

def buildPitch(mc, pos):
    # create the glass cube playing area
    mc.setBlocks(pos.x - 5, pos.y - 1, pos.z - 10,
                 pos.x + 5, pos.y + 3, pos.z + 10,
                 block.GLASS.id)

    # hollow it out
    mc.setBlocks(pos.x - 4, pos.y, pos.z - 9,
                 pos.x + 4, pos.y + 3, pos.z + 9,
                 block.AIR.id)

    # add 2 walls down the middle
    mc.setBlocks(pos.x, pos.y, pos.z - 7,
                 pos.x, pos.y + 3, pos.z - 1,
                 block.GLASS.id)

    # add 2 walls down the middle
    mc.setBlocks(pos.x, pos.y, pos.z + 1,
                 pos.x, pos.y + 3, pos.z + 7,
                 block.GLASS.id)

def splatBlock(mc, x, y, z, team):

    pointsScored = [0,0]

    # who is the other team?
    otherTeam = 1 - team

    # what type of block has been hit?
    blockHit = mc.getBlockWithData(x, y, z)
    # has a glass block been hit?
    if blockHit.id == block.GLASS.id:
        # claim it for the team
        mc.setBlock(
x, y, z, block.WOOL.id, TEAMCOLS[team])
        # increase the team's score
        pointsScored[team] += 1

    # was it a wool block?
    elif blockHit.id == block.WOOL.id:
        # if other team's colour turn it back to GLASS
        if blockHit.data == TEAMCOLS[otherTeam]:
            mc.setBlock(x, y, z, block.GLASS.id)
            # reduce the other team's score
            pointsScored[otherTeam] -= 1

    return pointsScored

# set up points
points = [0,0]

# create connection to Minecraft
mc = Minecraft.create()

# post the message to the screen
mc.postToChat("Minecraft Splat")

# find out the host player's position
pos = mc.player.getTilePos()

# build the pitch
buildPitch(mc, pos)

sleep(3)

mc.postToChat("Go!")

# get a list of the players
players = mc.getPlayerEntityIds()

start = time()

gameOver = False
# continue till the end of the game
while not gameOver:

    # has a block been hit?
    blockHits = mc.events.pollBlockHits()
    for hit in blockHits:

        # which team was it?
        team = players.index(hit.entityId) % 2

        pointsScored = splatBlock(
            mc, hit.pos.x, hit.pos.y, hit.pos.z, team)

        # update the points
        points[0] += pointsScored[0]
        points[1] += pointsScored[1]

        # splat blocks around it
        for x in [-1, 0, 1]:
            for y in [-1, 0, 1]:
                for z in [-1, 0, 1]:
                    if getrandbits(1) == 1:
                        pointsScored = splatBlock(mc,
                                         hit.pos.x + x,
                                         hit.pos.y + y,
                                         hit.pos.z + z,
                                         team)

                        # update the points
                        points[0] += pointsScored[0]
                        points[1] += pointsScored[1]

    # if the time has run out, set game over
    if time() - start > 30:
        gameOver = True
        mc.postToChat("Game Over")
        mc.postToChat("Green Team = " + str(points[0]))
        mc.postToChat("Red Team = " + str(points[1]))
        if points[0] > points[1]:
            mc.postToChat("Green Team wins")
        else:
            mc.postToChat("Red Team wins")
```

REVIEWS & SUPER-TESTS

Discover the best Raspberry Pi add-ons, software, and books by reading our expert reviews and group tests...

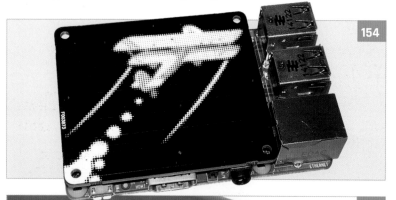

154

155

158

161

Breadboard

164

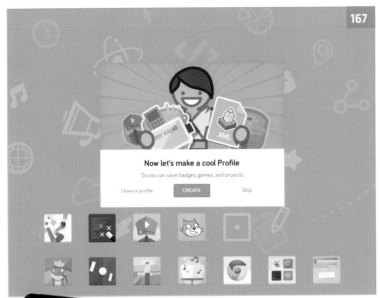

167

172

178

181

Reviews

Hello, World!

SoundIfl

RISC OS specs

MagPi

Snappy Core stuff

MagPi Film

Print Me

Raspberry Pi Desktop
SUPER-TEST

Which operating system should power your Raspberry Pi?
We put four Pi distros to the test…

BLASTER!

Raspberry Pi

Pidora bits

My Stuff

How we tested

We installed the distros on a Pi Model A and Raspberry Pi 2, using an EMTEC 8GB Class 10 SD card and a SanDisk 8GB Class 10 microSD card. We used a Mac Pro 3,1 with SD Formatter 4 to install each OS. We also used a Microsoft LifeCam VX-7000 and Maplin AD-102 breadboard during the test.

The Raspberry Pi packs an amazing amount of power into its tiny frame. But hardware is only half the story; the other half is the software you choose to control it. When setting up your Raspberry Pi, there are a myriad of operating systems (OS) to choose from, most based on different distributions of Linux ('distros' for short).

Raspberry Pi users will be familiar with Raspbian, the operating system based on Debian Linux that is marked as 'Recommended' during NOOBS setup. Raspbian is great to get started with, but it's far from the only OS available.

Every Raspberry Pi owner should take some time out to investigate the other available operating systems. Each has something unique to offer, from the forward-thinking approach to software distribution in Snappy,

to the retro-infused alternative approach of RISC OS.

But which OS is the best to use? There's only one way to find out. In this test we looked at four key OS options: Raspbian, Pidora, RISC OS, and Snappy Ubuntu Core. All are free and have versions designed especially for the Pi.

That's not to say they're all the same: Raspbian and Pidora use different default desktop environments and Snappy Ubuntu Core doesn't yet have a desktop at all – software is installed using a brand new package manager called 'snappy'. RISC OS is an entirely different creature from anything you are likely to have used before.

Each OS offers something unique, and all are interesting and worth exploring. But which distro should be your main go-to operating system? That's what this group test is determined to find out.

Recycle Bin

Raspbian notes

Pidora

All Settings

Packing the power of Fedora into the Raspberry Pi

Compatibility: Raspberry Pi 1
URL: pidora.ca

Pidora is a remix of the popular Fedora flavour of Linux. Currently in its fifth version, the Pidora distro has come a long way since 2012, but it still stands in the shadow of Raspbian. Pidora is part of NOOBS, but adoption and support has been dropping ever since Raspbian became the recommended installation.

Key features:

- Based on the popular Fedora version of Linux.
- Optimised for ARMv6 architecture; doesn't work with the Raspberry Pi 2.
- Default Xfce desktop is good-looking but sluggish compared to LXDE.

Pidora looks every bit as powerful as its bigger brother, but badly needs optimisation

Snappy Ubuntu Core

Fast and futuristic, but may be a little too advanced for most users

Compatibility: Raspberry Pi 2
URL: developer.ubuntu.com/en/snappy

Snappy is the most recent OS for the Pi. Users expecting standard Ubuntu with its Unity desktop will be surprised. Snappy is a command-line affair aimed squarely at developers looking to build web servers and Internet of Things (IoT) devices. The apt-get function is replaced with snappy, which offers some great innovations regarding software deployment.

Key features:

- Command-line interface with no desktop installation available.
- More robust 'transactional' software updates that are guaranteed to work.
- Software packages installed using snappy instead of apt-get.

Snappy Ubuntu Core offers a range of new features that are ideal for server and IoT developers

IMPORTANT!!!

Piano Teach

Raspbian

The recommended distro keeps going from strength to strength

Compatibility: Raspberry Pi 1 and 2
URL: raspbian.org

Raspbian is based on Debian Wheezy/Jessie but optimised for the Raspberry Pi hardware. Technically, Raspbian isn't the official OS and isn't affiliated with the Raspberry Pi Foundation. However, its 'recommended installation' status, along with plenty of documentation and support, make it feel official. Raspbian is definitely the place for newcomers to start.

Key features:

- Largest user base, and most documentation and tutorials reference Raspbian.
- Compatible with all models of Raspberry Pi.
- Lightweight interface is fast and responsive, and it has a built-in Pi Store.

Raspbian is the recommended distro for newcomers

RISC OS

All Settings

Flashback from the 1980s that's still going strong today

Compatibility: Raspberry Pi 1
URL: RISCosopen.org

Created during the heyday of Acorn Computers, RISC OS was designed explicitly for the ARM chipset and has been kept alive by a small team of dedicated enthusiasts. RISC OS is ultra-fast, but hails from a time before the modern GUI metaphor had settled, and its WIMP (Windows, Icons, Menu and Pointers) interface has more than a few quirks.

Key features:

- Ultra-fast thanks to its ARM focus and small footprint.
- Great for low-level programming and getting close to the ARM instruction set.
- Quirky desktop interface and lack of widespread adoption make it difficult to learn.

RISC OS looks normal on the surface, but is radically different to other operating systems

Untitled

Hello, World!

TEST 1

Installation

Pidora
★★★★☆

Raspbian
★★★★★

RISC OS
★★★★★

Snappy Ubuntu Core
★★★☆☆

TEST 2

Hardware support

Pidora
★★★★☆

Raspbian
★★★★★

RISC OS
★★★☆☆

Snappy Ubuntu Core
★★☆☆☆

We started our test using SD Formatter 4 to wipe our SD cards and installed NOOBS (New Out Of Box Software). NOOBS enables you to choose from a list of operating systems, including three on test here: Raspbian, RISC OS, and Pidora.

Raspbian (Wheezy) starts up with a Software Configuration Tool that enables you to reclaim space on the SD card, change the password, choose boot options, and enable support for the Raspberry Pi Camera. Pidora has a more basic Setup Agent, which walks you through creating the user account. RISC OS boots straight into the GUI. Installation was straightforward in all these operating systems.

Snappy Ubuntu Core is the exception in that it has to be installed manually, using the dd tool to copy files from the image file to the SD card.

Upon startup, you're faced with a command line that informs you that apt-get has been replaced with snappy. (The password and login are both 'ubuntu'). Because the Raspberry Pi doesn't sport a clock backed up by battery, the date in Snappy is set to 1970 on start-up, and this prevents snappy software installation, so part of each startup process is using **date -s** to correct the date.

Pidora gets a black mark because it doesn't support the Raspberry Pi 2. Attempting to choose Pidora in NOOBS brings up: 'Warning Incompatible Operating System(s) Detected'. We tried anyway, but got a blank screen for our troubles. So for the rest of this test, Pidora was relegated to our Pi Model A.

Meanwhile, Snappy Ubuntu Core only supports the Raspberry Pi 2, which leaves a considerable amount of Raspberry Pi devices out of the loop.

All of our distros had no trouble recognising the keyboard, mouse, and network connection. Where things became a little more complicated was regarding accessories and GPIO. This is another area where Raspbian is rewarded by being the recommended distro. We had little trouble setting up our webcam and GPIO in both Raspbian and Pidora, but tutorials were easier to source for Raspbian. We couldn't get the webcam to work in RISC OS; GPIO in RISC OS is possible, but it's a confusing setup process.

The RPi.GPIO package isn't present in the snappy list of software, so GPIO access is currently unavailable in Snappy Ubuntu Core.

Print Me

World Map

Recycle Bin

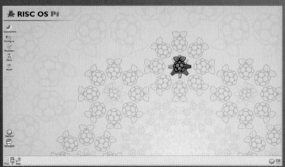

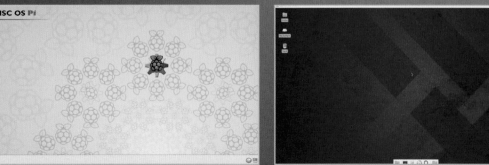

TEST 3
Software support

Pidora
★★★☆☆

Raspbian
★★★★★

RISC OS
★★★☆☆

Snappy Ubuntu Core
★★★★☆

TEST 4
Programming and GPIO

Pidora
★★★★☆

Raspbian
★★★★★

RISC OS
★★★☆☆

Snappy Ubuntu Core
★★★☆☆

Every OS comes with pre-installed software and can download and install additional software via the internet. In Raspbian, software is installed using apt-get or via the Pi Store.

In Pidora, yum is used to install software, but you can install Apt from Yum if you prefer (and then install the Pi Store manually).

RISC OS has a built-in store where you can download new software created by the RISC OS community. However, a heartbreaking aspect of RISC OS is that you have to use BeebIT and ArcEm emulation software to run the rich library of older BBC Micro and Archimedes software, which you could do just as easily from any Linux distro.

Ubuntu Snappy Core replaces apt-get with snappy: programs are split into frameworks and apps (which are isolated like apps on mobile devices). Snappy installs programs using a transactional update system that downloads components before updating or installing (and can roll back programs to earlier versions).

It also supports WebDM, which enables you to connect to your Pi from a web browser and install or remove software. Snappy is very interesting, but very little software is currently available.

Both Raspbian and Pidora make it pretty easy to cover the basics of programming, and accessing the GPIO is a case of downloading the correct library (such as RPi.GPIO for Python or Scratch GPIO).

Snappy Ubuntu Core comes with Python, but without apt-get there was no way for us to install the RPi.GPIO tools. Snappy Ubuntu Core is tremendously interesting to advanced developers though, and is an ideal platform for setting up your own web server, but beyond that it's far from an ideal environment for learning to code.

RISC OS is either a fantastic or dreadful programming environment, depending on what you want to learn. Press **CTRL+F12** and enter **basic** to access BBC Basic, a fantastic starter language that brings tears to the rose-tinted eyes of many a seasoned developer.

Beyond nostalgia, RISC OS is particularly good for low-level programming and learning assembly language (BBC Basic features an inline assembler). Absent are many modern high-level programming languages. That said, RISC OS has its charms for many fun projects.

Distro

Hello, World!

TEST 5

Community and support

Pidora
★★★★☆

Raspbian
★★★★★

RISC OS
★★★★☆

Snappy Ubuntu Core
★★★☆☆

TEST 6

Unique features

Pidora
★★☆☆☆

Raspbian
★★★★☆

RISC OS
★★★★★

Snappy Ubuntu Core
★★★★★

Good community support is vital for getting the most out of your Raspberry Pi. It's unsurprising to learn that Raspbian, as the recommended installation, has the best community support.

All of the projects from the Raspberry Pi Foundation and many other sites (**raspberrypi.org/community**) gravitate around Raspbian.

Having said that, it's worth noting that Fedora, the flavour of Linux behind Pidora, has a large and respectable community. In particular, Linus Torvalds, the initial developer of Linux, is known to use Fedora (even if somewhat begrudgingly).

Of course, numbers and celebrity names aren't everything and the RISC OS community (**RISCosopen.org/forum**) is both dedicated and committed. It's a small clique, though, and outside of the community you'll struggle to find much online documentation. Look instead to decent books like David Bradforth's *First Steps with RISC OS 6* and Bruce Smith's *Raspberry Pi RISC OS System Programming Revealed*.

Snappy Ubuntu Core fares worst in this test with no real community to speak of, but that's only because it is such a newcomer. Give it time.

Each of the operating systems has something different to offer. Raspbian has the most all-round support, the widest range of programs, and is the most nurturing environment.

Raspbian is also noticeably faster and less error-prone than Pidora. While Pidora's lack of Pi 2 support makes any meaningful speed test impractical, we'd put our money on Raspbian and Snappy Core's armhf architecture beating Pidora in any speed test.

Pidora is worth investigating if you work on a Fedora-based main computer, own a Raspberry Pi 1, and want consistency between the two machines.

Snappy Ubuntu Core has much to offer those looking to play a part in the next wave of software development. Developing Snappy apps isn't a game for newcomers, but the transactional deployment techniques seem worth learning. And it's a good OS for setting up a web server. Whether you can make anything out of it currently depends on your skill as a programmer, but we are looking forward to seeing Snappy Ubuntu Core develop as an OS.

RISC OS is nothing if not unique. We've made much of its individuality throughout this group test. Suffice to say it's a fantastic way to broaden your horizons.

Print Me

World Map

Recycle Bin

Spec comparison

All Settings	Raspbian	RISC OS	Pidora 2014	Snappy Ubuntu Core
First release	01/06/12	05/11/12	01/10/12	02/02/15
Latest release	24/09/15	25/04/15	24/07/14	26/09/15
Default desktop	LXDE	Pinboard	Xfce	None
GPIO access	Yes	Yes	Yes	No
Pi models supported	Pi 1, Pi 2	Pi 1, Pi 2	Pi 1	Pi 2
Included with NOOBS	Yes	Yes	Yes	No
OS family	Linux	RISC OS	Linux	Linux
Base	Debian Wheezy	RISC OS	Fedora	Ubuntu
Developer	Raspbian Team	ROOL	CDOT	Canonical
Contact	raspbian.org/RaspbianTeam	riscosopen.org/content	cdot.senecacollege.ca	developer.ubuntu.com/en/snappy
Architecture	armhf	armhf	armv6hl	armhf

All Distros
www.raspberrypi.org

 **BEST ON TEST** Raspbian ★★★★★

 **RUNNER-UP** RISC OS ★★★★

 Pidora ★★★★

 Snappy Ubuntu Core ★★★

Save

THE **LAST** WORD

We expected this to be a much closer race, but Raspbian has – if anything – increased its lead over other operating systems, especially Pidora.

One exception may be Ubuntu Snappy Core, which is a wholly different proposition. This innovative distro's snappy package manager and WebDM interface point to an interesting future for software installation, but without the familiar apt-get installing the usual options is much more challenging.

RISC OS remains great fun in a Monty Python-esque 'now for something completely different' way. It's a good tool for learning assembly, but the absence of many modern high-level programming languages prevent it from becoming more than that for many.

We've always thought Raspbian is best for newcomers, but it's hard to credibly recommend any other OS for general use. Our advice? Use all of them to find a good fit for you, but always have Raspbian on hand.

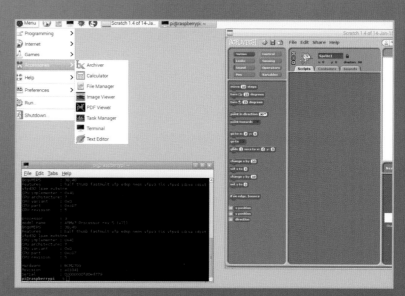
Above Raspbian remains our choice for the best overall OS to install on a Raspberry Pi

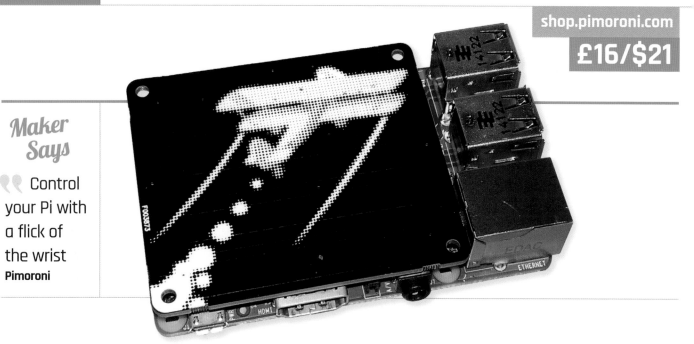

shop.pimoroni.com

£16/$21

Maker Says

❝ Control your Pi with a flick of the wrist

Pimoroni

SKYWRITER HAT

Les Pounder reaches for the sky to uncover the secrets behind this amazing gadget from the Pimoroni 'Pirates of Sheffield'

H ow we interact with technology is constantly evolving – from the early days of clunky keyboards to the sensors we use to capture location and orientation automatically. What remains the most basic interaction is touch and, by extension, gestures. Gesture control can be achieved using technologies such as Microsoft's Kinect or OpenCV, but these are quite resource-intensive solutions. So a cheap, simple, and resource-light solution is needed; step forward Skywriter.

Near-field sensing

The Skywriter is the latest board from Pimoroni, the Sheffield-based maker of a number of quality add-ons for the Raspberry Pi. Designed for the Pi Model A+ and B+, the Skywriter is a gesture controller built around the MGC3130, a 3D gesture recognition and tracking controller chip. It uses near-field sensing to locate the position of your hand in the air

at a range of 5cm. The board can also detect touch input to a number of positions on its surface.

Physically, the Skywriter HAT measures 64mm wide by 56mm tall with a depth of 5mm. On the Raspberry Pi A+, it fits neatly over the top, and with a B+ it fits snugly in the space between the USB ports and the display slot (DSI).

Code control

Along with a neat hardware solution, the team have invested a great deal of time producing a Python API (application programming interface) for both Python 3 and 2.7, installable via the Pip package manager. Examples of how to use this board can be found in Skywriter's GitHub repository (**github.com/pimoroni/skywriter-hat**). We found the contents of **test.py** in the **python/examples** folder very interesting, since it puts out lots of interesting debugging data, as well as helping confirm the Skywriter is working properly.

How can you use Skywriter HAT in your next project? Instantly, gesture-controlled gaming comes to mind. Using Skywriter as a gesture controller for a game of *Pac-Man* perhaps, controlling your Big Trak with just a flick of your hand, or launching a rocket with a tap. We look forward to waving our hands around like Tom Cruise in *Minority Report* to take control of our next project, using nothing more than a gesture and some Python code.

Last word

The Skywriter HAT is a small and well-constructed board that sits neatly on top of your Pi (as any HAT should). It's a really capable and versatile board that adds a novel form of input to any project and the easily understood Python API will benefit coders of all abilities.

★★★★☆

Related

HOVER

Using the same MGC3130 near-field controller chip as the Skywriter, Hover boasts the same I²C interface and compatibility with Raspberry Pi, Arduino and other single-board computers.

£31/$39

hoverlabs.co

anonymebox.com
£142/$219

ANONYMEBOX

With our every online move being monitored, can a Raspberry Pi-based appliance keep you and your family safe online?

Related

ONION PI

It launched the Tor appliance trend, but is designed for the more technically minded of us comfortable working in the terminal.

$85
adafruit.com

Image courtesy of Adafruit.com

Since George Orwell wrote *1984*, the fiction contained therein has become fact in our society. Big Brother is indeed watching you. Your ISP can throttle your speed and governments can get hold of your browser history. One of the tools enabling anyone to stay anonymous online is Tor (The Onion Router), which provides a series of relays that bounce your connection around the world via an encrypted network. Tor is configured per machine, so the Anonymebox's differing approach is more convenient.

Tor made easy

The Pi-powered Anonymebox connects to your home network so anyone can connect securely with any computer. It comes with an Ethernet cable to connect to your router, a Wi-Fi dongle, and a USB-to-Ethernet adaptor. Building the Anonymebox is very easy too: insert the SD card containing the OS, connect the Ethernet cable to your router, and then insert the Wi-Fi dongle before powering up.

Easy configuration

Once it's on, it can be configured via the browser of any device connected to your router. The web interface is sparse, with just an overview showing the devices connected to the Anonymebox, and a settings menu to change the admin password and configure the access point details. Your first post-setup activity involves updating the default password and, optionally, changing the default name of the access point.

Connecting to it over Wi-Fi is the same as connecting to any other router, but the Anonymebox will completely anonymise your online presence via Tor. Visiting a site such as **whatismyipaddress.com** will show that your location is in a completely different country.

Tor needs to be regularly updated to ensure protection, so the developer has created an easy-to-use method for updating. Just download an archive from its website, copy it to a USB flash drive, and insert that into the spare port on your Anonymebox. The software is configured to act if an update is found. The Anonymebox is genuinely user-friendly, requiring little or no technical expertise to set up or use.

For those wanting to create their own Anonymebox, there's even a free download of the OS available from the website, along with instructions about which Wi-Fi dongle to purchase.

Last word

The Anonymebox is a good tool for those who don't have the skills to configure Tor on every machine they use, though its ease belies its true power.

★★★★☆

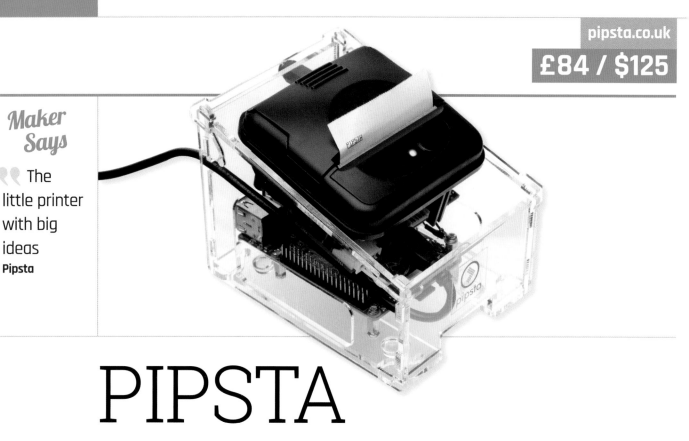

pipsta.co.uk

£84 / $125

Maker Says

" The little printer with big ideas
Pipsta

PIPSTA

Is this tiny, Raspberry Pi-friendly printer what your next IoT project is waiting for? **Russell Barnes** finds out...

It's not unusual for computers to be built into your computing experience. For example, Apple has done a roaring trade putting them behind monitors, and we probably wouldn't have the Raspberry Pi today if it weren't for classic home computers that were built behind keyboards, like the BBC Micro or the Amiga 500. But what about PCs built into printers? Is it taking things a little too far? Well, let's find out, because that's exactly what the Pipsta offers.

It's designed primarily as an Internet of Things gadget – a smart printer able to automagically print weather reports, Twitter feeds, or much-needed travel updates. It's not entirely unlike Adafruit's IoT Printer, though Pipsta is a little cheaper and easier to put together (it also features NFC capabilities). While Adafruit recommends its printer as a weekend project that requires soldering, Able Systems' Pipsta only takes about 45 minutes to put together. Since the printer

workings are completely self-contained, it only takes up a single USB port, so all your GPIO pins are left well alone.

The Pipsta is compatible with any Raspberry Pi, but the mounting holes in the clear acrylic chassis are designed for the current-generation models (B+, A+ and Pi 2 Model B). Every port of the Pi is fully accessible, so there's nothing stopping you setting it up inside the Pipsta for everyday use – even the GPIO and camera expansion ports are easily accessed.

Getting set up

It doesn't come with a printed manual, but it does (on the 12-month warranty card) offer a link to assembly instructions online. To give its maker Able Systems credit, the instructions are very robust and definitive, which is handy, because there's a lot of software cajoling involved.

Print quality is excellent and, like most thermal printers, it's quick and quiet in operation.

It comes with two types of thermal printer rolls to get you started – a standard thermal paper roll and a label roll, which has a sticky back that can be applied immediately (no peeling required).

Overall, it's a great device and the team behind it are certainly doing their best to generate a community around it. There is a growing selection of projects created with the Pipsta at their core on its website, including printing ultrasonic readings, printing via HTML, NFC-powered projects, and more besides: **pipsta.co.uk/projects**.

Related

ADAFRUIT IOT PI PRINTER

Billed as a fun weekend project, this IoT printer kit requires a bit more build time and expertise than Pipsta (including some soldering).

£110 / $165
modmypi.com

Last word

The Pipsta makes a brilliant intelligent print server and offers lots of new ground for Raspberry Pi project makers to explore. It's not cheap, but it is powerful.

★★★★★

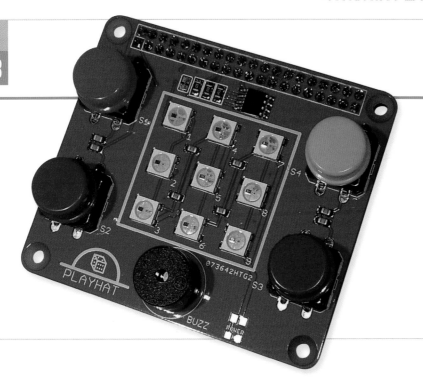

4tronix.co.uk
£12/$18

Maker Says

❝ A great way to learn GPIO, in either Python or Scratch

4tronix

4TRONIX PLAYHAT

Les Pounder looks at an affordable add-on board aimed at introducing physical computing using simple inputs and outputs

Related

PIBRELLA

Pibrella offers LEDs, button, and buzzer just like the PlayHAT, but it also offers four inputs, and four outputs that can be used with external components, such as motors and sensors.

£10 / $15

pibrella.com

4 Tronix is perhaps best known for its range of Raspberry Pi-powered robots, such as Pi2Go and, more recently, the A+ powered Agobo. But 4Tronix is not just about robots. The Derby-based company also develops add-on boards to enable children to learn computing. It started with the PiDie, a 3×3 LED board that enabled users to play dice games and control traffic lights. Then we saw the ultra-cheap Pi Stop traffic-light sticks that clipped onto the GPIO.

The PlayHAT marks 4Tronix's first HAT board; a refinement of those earlier two LED products, it combines them into one neat package. Fitting neatly on top of the 40-pin GPIO present on the A+, B+, and Raspberry Pi 2, the PlayHAT boasts an impressive nine multicoloured NeoPixel LEDs, four push buttons, and a single buzzer. The board is colourful and well built, with components that have been thoughtfully picked with tiny hands in mind.

Setting up

Installation is remarkably easy, requiring only a download of the libraries, along with code examples from 4Tronix's GitHub repository. Upon installation, it is wise to run the strandtest.py script to ensure everything has been installed correctly. A quick word of warning, though: it would be wise to diffuse the NeoPixels with a piece of paper, as they really are very bright.

PlayHAT is programmed using Python, but rather than use a bespoke module, it employs the standard RPi.GPIO library to drive the buttons and buzzer. The NeoPixels, on the other hand, require the Adafruit NeoPixel library, contained in the GitHub download, to be used properly.

4Tronix has included example programs to illustrate how the PlayHAT works. The strandtest script runs various animation sequences on the NeoPixels, while the playhat script has further NeoPixel demos, but also comes with a simple dice game that illustrates how the board can be utilised to create a novel method of output.

This is a simple and easy-to use board, with which much hacking and making can be done.

Last word

Not the most expansive or feature-rich board on the market, but what it lacks in features, it makes up for in its price and ease of use. This is a great 'getting started' board for physical computing with the Raspberry Pi.

shop.pimoroni.com
£18/$30

Maker Says

❝❝ 3x16 character display with three RGB backlights to give you D.I.S.C.O capability

Pimoroni

DISPLAY-O-TRON 3000

Has Pimoroni's art deco-themed Display-o-Tron add-on done the impossible and dethroned the PiFace Control & Display?

T he PiFace Control & Display made quite a splash at launch, offering a simple plug-in board – long before a HAT was a thing – which provided embedded Pi projects with a simple two-line LCD display, a handful of buttons, and a small joystick. Since then, it has remained the king of the hill for any embedded project that doesn't require a graphical display, but Sheffield-based Pimoroni could change all that.

The first thing that strikes you about the Display-o-Tron 3000 is its appearance. As soon as you remove it from the anti-static bag, you spot that it's no ordinary device. The board (also available in HAT form) has been designed with an art deco theme in mind, featuring visual embellishments rarely seen on rival products.

The second thing you notice is the size. Compared to the PiFace Control & Display it was so clearly inspired by, the Display-o-Tron is barely there. Measuring just over 12mm thick including the low-profile GPIO connector on the rear, it adds just 6mm to the height of any model of Raspberry Pi and is designed to stay within the footprint of the compact Model A+.

Despite this, the Display-o-Tron is brimming with features. Although it lacks the extra buttons of the PiFace C&D, the display is a larger three-line, 16-character display with three individually controllable RGB LED backlights. A five-way joystick provides directional control and push-to-click activation for your projects, while the spare GPIO lines are broken out into a nine-segment LED bar-graph along the bottom which illuminates on demand in a retina-searing white.

GPIO out

That feature list does reveal one drawback to the Display-o-Tron, however: it ties up the entire GPIO capabilities of the Raspberry Pi Models A and B.

Those whose projects use the A+, B+, or Raspberry Pi 2 Model B – support for which was added to the RPi.GPIO Python library used by the Display-o-Tron around two weeks after launch – will still retain access to the extended header pins.

Programming the display, LEDs, and buttons is straightforward, with a quickly-installed library and handy example files for everything from controlling VLC to play internet radio, to playing a simple game.

Related

PIFACE CONTROL & DISPLAY

The PiFace Control & Display is undeniably bulkier than Pimoroni's Display-o-Tron, but the extra buttons and cheaper price – in the UK, at least – could prove a worthy trade-off for some projects.

£14 / $29
piface.org.uk

Last word

The Display-o-Tron is mightily impressive for its diminutive size and boasts capabilities better than its far more sizeable rivals. It's not particularly cheap, however, and takes up the entire 26-pin header of older Pi models.

rasp.io/duino

£12/$18

Maker Says

❝ Learn Arduino programming on Raspberry Pi **RasP.iO**

RASPIO DUINO

The Arduino and Raspberry Pi joined into one glorious package?
We grab a box of LEDs and buttons and starts hacking...

A lex Eames is no stranger to Kickstarter: he was part of the team that brought us the excellent HDMIPi in 2014. Fresh from that success, he has launched another product based on a successful crowdfunding campaign. RasPiO Duino enables a Raspberry Pi to work harmoniously with the Arduino microcontroller board. Coming as a kit which requires around 30 minutes to solder, the Duino attaches to all models of Raspberry Pi via the GPIO pins and presents the familiar ATmega328P microcontroller found in the most popular Arduino, the Uno. The digital and analogue pins of the ATmega328P are broken out to a series of male and female headers around the board; providing both types of connection is a nice touch and really goes the extra mile for makers. Another nice touch is breaking out the I²C, SPI, and a

selection of Raspberry Pi GPIO pins, as the Duino covers 26 of the 40 pins present on the Raspberry Pi 2 and the A+/B+ boards.

Installation of the software for the Duino was a little tricky and we did uncover one bug with permissions during installation – but, after a brief chat with Alex Eames, this issue was resolved and Alex has since done some work to refine the install process.

Arduino examples

So you will be thinking, can I use it just like an Arduino? Well, the answer is a resounding yes! We ran two tests that are the most common ones when first dabbling with Arduino: the Blink sketch and Button sketch. We used the Blink example found under Examples in the Arduino IDE and uploaded it to the board, ensuring that we first set up the Board and the Programmer via the Tools menu, and then used the Upload Using

Programmer option in the File menu. After around a minute on a Raspberry Pi B+, the sketch had uploaded and our LED blinked into life. We then wired up the Button example, connecting the button to 5V power, Ground, and finally PD2, which is digital pin 2 on an Uno. Uploading the sketch to the Duino took less than a minute and we had a working push-button-controlled LED. Alex has done a great job of making the Arduino accessible to the Raspberry Pi community.

Last word

The Duino really does provide the best features of the Arduino and shows that the Arduino and Raspberry Pi can work together to make bigger and better projects. Alex has created a lovely-looking and efficient board.

★★★★☆

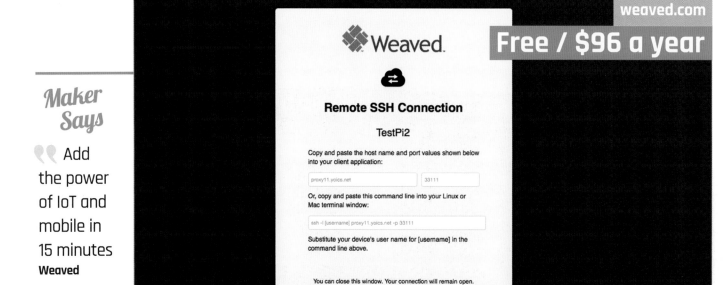

weaved.com

Free / $96 a year

WEAVED IOT KIT

Can a package designed to take the fuss out of port forwarding be just what the Raspberry Pi needs? **Gareth Halfacree** tests the beta...

T he Weaved IoT Kit for the Raspberry Pi is a grand name for a tool which promises to take the pain out of remote connectivity. While the Pi proves an easy platform for running various handy services, accessing these from outside your local network can prove tricky – and securing said access against third-party intrusion more difficult still.

This is, at its heart, the problem Weaved looks to solve. Its free membership tier offers control of ten TCP network ports on one concurrent connection for a maximum session time of 30 minutes (you can just start a new one). $24 a year extends this to 20 ports on two connections, and a 2-hour limit. $96 a year gives you 100 ports on ten connections, with an 8-hour limit.

Installing the Weaved client on your Pi should be simple. During installation, however, we discovered that the password we had generated for the site wasn't supported in the client; sadly,

resetting the password made no difference. We ended up creating an entirely separate account, an issue Weaved tracked down to an obscure bug which should now be resolved.

Configuration

Configuring Weaved is a mixture of simple and awkward. The installer offers four preset services – SSH, VNC, WebIOPi, and web – along with the option to forward any TCP port. Weaved doesn't install any services itself, though: while it'll be happy to forward WebIOPi for you, the service will only work if you've installed it manually. There's also no quick way to forward multiple ports at once beyond running the installer again.

When forwarded, ports become accessible from Weaved's developer portal. Click on a Pi and it will open a new window while simultaneously triggering a proxied connection to your chosen port. While more secure and arguably easier than

traditional port forwarding, this approach has an impact on performance. Our test SSH connections dropped to a tenth of their usual speed – another rare bug, Weaved told us.

An iOS mobile app provides even more functionality: as well as being able to trigger the connections to open while you're out and about, it works with the client software to receive push notifications from your applications.

An Android app is also in development, but is still in alpha testing at the time of writing.

Last word

Weaved is an excellent idea, but there's still work to be done before its final release. We're looking forward to revisiting Weaved once it's out of beta.

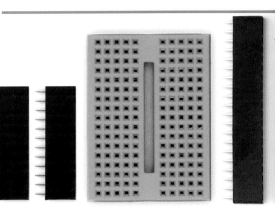
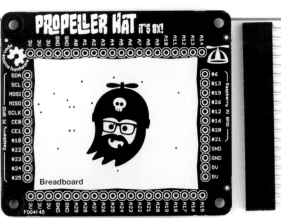

shop.pimoroni.com

£15 / $23

Breadboard

PROPELLER HAT

Les Pounder delves into the world of multi-core microcontrollers, courtesy of Pimoroni's latest board

Quite often, electronics projects require split-second precision. Since this isn't the Raspberry Pi's forte, you'd normally use a small microcontroller, like an Arduino or the Parallax Propeller.

With the Propeller HAT, Pimoroni has placed the Parallax microcontroller on a HAT add-on board, along with a handy 170-point breadboard to help you rapidly prototype projects. The Propeller HAT – a completely open-source hardware and software platform, based upon the Parallax Propeller 1 P8X32A – comes partially built, requiring a little soldering to populate the pin headers that you can see around the board. In total there are 30 pins, labelled A0 to A29. To the left and right of the board, you can see some of the standard Raspberry Pi GPIO pins broken out for use too, including pins for I²C and SPI.

SPIN it

The Parallax Propeller at the heart of the Propeller HAT can be programmed using the PropellerIDE, which creates files in a language called SPIN. Once you have written your project, it is a simple matter of clicking 'Run' in the IDE to create a binary file and then uploading the file to the board. It's a similar process to the Arduino, where code is compiled and then uploaded to be run. Binary files can also be uploaded to the board using the p1load command in the terminal, enabling fast upload of pre-compiled projects. To round off the software, there's also an excellent Python library that enables you to create scripts to control the Propeller HAT with Python.

Elsewhere, the Propeller HAT can emulate the SID chip, commonly found in Commodore 64 and 128 8-bit machines from the 1980s, enabling your projects to output SID music via a 3.5mm jack attached to the breadboard.

Is it right for you?

You might be wondering who this board is for. If you are just starting your journey into the world of hardware hacking and making, then this is not for you. But if you are an experienced hacker, this is a great place to learn more about multi-core microcontrollers, and generally have a lot of fun hacking and making on your Raspberry Pi.

piborg.org

£16 / $25

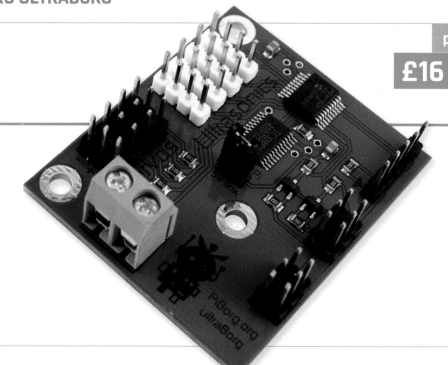

PIBORG ULTRABORG

A combined ultrasonic sensor and servo driving board, is the UltraBorg the all-in-one add-on which roboticists have been craving?

Designed with the Raspberry Pi in mind, but compatible with any microcomputer or microcontroller that can talk I²C, the UltraBorg is aimed at robotics enthusiasts. Built to simplify the building of servo-based robots, the diminutive board provides support for two device types: servos and ultrasonic sensors.

For servos, it provides four channels of 16-bit control on a bank of triple-pin headers on its left. This resolution, provided by a Toshiba pulse-width modulation (PWM) chip and considerably higher than the 12-bit found on most rival devices, indicates that PiBorg has really thought its design through; this is confirmed by the ability to save a startup position, as well as maximum and minimum limits in the controller.

The ultrasonic portion of the board is, likewise, four-channel, supporting the four-pin modules common to most robot kits and hobby supply shops. All

functionality is controlled through an on-board PIC chip, which takes the pressure off the Raspberry Pi's processor and allows for accurate real-time control.

Easy to install

Installation of the board is straightforward using a simple software installation script available from PiBorg's website, although you'll need to provide your own 5V power supply. The board's mounting holes are designed to allow it to be positioned in a variety of orientations, including sharing the Pi A+/B+ and Pi 2's mounting holes and piggybacking above to save space. The UltraBorg takes up the first six pins on the GPIO header, leaving the rest free – and while the limit of just four servos may seem troubling, it's possible to daisy-chain multiple UltraBorgs together to support as many ultrasonic sensors and servos as your project requires.

PiBorg has even thought to include a simple GUI. This makes

tuning the servo limits as simple as possible, with sliders to adjust the positions, and buttons to save a startup position and set max/min rotation limits; these are saved to the PIC processor's EEPROM, which survives power cycles.

The GUI is joined by a basic demonstration program, showing sliders for all four servo channels, along with distance reports from the four ultrasonic channels. Elsewhere, the included Python examples make it easy for new users to get started.

Last word

The UltraBorg is a great choice for robotics projects, offering features rarely seen on servo control boards, but its four-channel limitation – overcome through daisy-chaining – means it can get expensive for more complex projects.

★★★★☆

thepihut.com
£7 / $10

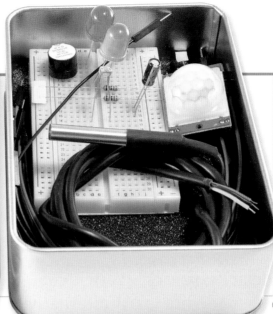

Maker Says

❝ The latest addition to the EduKit family!

CamJam

Image: Alex Eames. www.RasPi.TV

CAMJAM EDUKIT 2

A tin full of tinkering kit, for less than a tenner.
Let's take a look at CamJam's second box of tricks...

The EduKit is a pocket-money project box that's compatible with all models of Raspberry Pi. Rather than produce an add-on board, the CamJam team have packaged all the components needed to build a number of physical computing projects into a rather handy tin.

A follow-up to CamJam's original EduKit, the second edition is entitled 'Sensors' and contains a lot of electronic components – enough to make six starter projects. In the kit you'll find LEDs, buzzers, wires, and a breadboard – as we did in the first EduKit – but there's also a light-dependent resistor (LDR), passive infrared sensor (PIR), and a DS18B20 temperature sensor inside.

Worksheets

So, what can you make with these components? Using the six downloadable worksheets, you can start by controlling the LED and buzzer with some simple Python code. The worksheets also cover creating an alarm based on the PIR sensor, which can detect movement; you could, for example, trigger a sequence of LED flashes and buzzer sounds. One of the more challenging worksheets uses the DS18B20 sensor to read ambient temperature, but it can also be safely placed into liquid for accurate measurements, perhaps a great cross-curricular activity for introducing the Pi into a science lab. Another worksheet focuses on the LDR sensor to measure the light in a room. Since it produces analogue values (something that the Raspberry Pi can't process), the EduKit 2 includes a capacitor, which will be charged and timed using Python code to get the readings. The charge time is dependent on the flow of energy controlled by the LDR, thus giving the user an estimated analogue value. It's nicely done.

Cost-effective

This kit and its predecessor are very cost-effective and well-supported starting points for anyone interested in getting started with the GPIO pins on the Raspberry Pi. While there are plenty of practical project examples included with the kit, it can be applied to countless other projects and ideas and even used with different electronics platforms. The accompanying online worksheets are excellent quality, and provide solid instructions that get progressively more challenging as you learn.

Last word

A very high-quality, yet cost-effective starting point for many physical computing projects. An essential purchase for home and school learners.

★★★★★

RICHARD WATERWORTH

Richard Waterworth is a
15-year-old blogger and video
maker who loves tinkering
with gadgets (and taking really
good pictures like these).
richardtech.net

RASPBERRY PI CASE SUPER-TEST

While the official Raspberry Pi case is cool, blogger **Richard Waterworth** compares four of our favourite third-party alternatives for the B+ and Pi 2...

pi-supply.com
£9 / $14

OVERALL WINNER

SHORT CRUST PLUS

The Short Crust Plus is a fairly minimal Raspberry Pi case. It comes in two different colour options for the base (black and white), and this allows you to alter the overall look. The top of the case is a smooth glossy finish, which can turn into a fingerprint magnet, but it's easily cleaned. The main base of the case is a rougher matte finish, which compliments the top perfectly.

The Short Crust Plus offers plenty of ventilation on the bottom of the case, and the release trigger (also found underneath) allows you to easily remove your Pi. In terms of cost, the Short Crust is reasonable considering the high-quality plastic used. It also comes with non-slip rubber feet and screw holes in the base, should you wish to mount it under a desk or on a wall.

If you're looking for a cleanly designed, modern-looking case with all the mod-cons, you should definitely consider the Short Crust Plus.

Score ★★★★★

modmypi.com
£5 / $8

BEST VALUE

pimoroni.com
£8.50 / $12

thepihut.com
£13 / $20

HELIX CASE

PIBOW COUPÉ

FLIRC PI CASE

The Helix is no ordinary Raspberry Pi case. It's made from MDF and features a flexible 'shell' around its core. The quality of the case is impressive for the price. However, if you are disassembling it you'll need to be careful, as some elements of the case are quite fragile. Once you've installed your Pi in the Helix, though, it looks great, and quite unlike the vast majority of cases on offer elsewhere.

Inside the case, there are some supports that your Raspberry Pi sits on, but there's nothing on the top of the Pi to hold it securely in place. Given the asking price (it's the cheapest on test), we can't be too harsh, but we can't help but think if the pins holding the 'shell' of the case were a bit bigger and there were a few more supports to hold the Pi, this could be a really great case.

The Pibow Coupé offers a very slimline design. Unlike conventional cases, the Coupé does not fully cover the entire Pi, only its sides and bottom, allowing the USB and Ethernet ports to protrude from the top of the case. In typical Pimoroni style, it's constructed from thin layers of plastic and comes in a variety of colours.

While we weren't sure about the look of Coupé at first, it quickly grew on us during testing, though we wouldn't use it for a home theatre setup. For us it'd be much more at home as a second computer or slimline project case, though you might disagree. Most importantly, however, the Coupé provides easy access to all ports, which is especially useful for people who will be using the Camera Module or tinkering with components attached to the GPIO ports.

The Flirc Case has a very solid construction as it's made from a solid aluminium shell with a matte, rubberised plastic top and base. The aluminium finish gives the case a premium feel, too, which is always a bonus. Unlike the other cases on test, it comes with a built-in heatsink. It's easy to put together, using four screws to secure it.

It's certainly not as prone to fingerprints as the Short Crust Plus, but it does smudge, which is only really noticeable up close. The Flirc is primarily advertised as a home theatre case for the Raspberry Pi, but it's likely to be at home in other environments, too. It's the most expensive case on test, but if you can afford it, the cost is easily justified considering the materials used in its construction.

RUNNER-UP

The ModMyPi Helix might not be for everyone, but if you want to set yourself apart and don't have a great deal of money to spend, this is definitely the case for you.

Score ★★★☆☆

The Pibow Coupé has such a distinctive look, you'll probably love it or hate it. Either way, it's a great case for people who want to use their Raspberry Pi for hardware projects.

Score ★★★★★

The Flirc is a very clean and simply designed case for your Raspberry Pi. It looks sleek and feels premium, thanks to its aluminium finish.

Score ★★★★☆

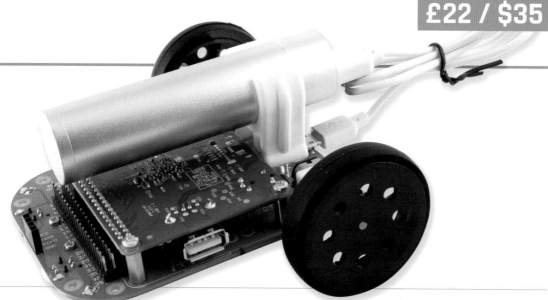

4tronix.co.uk

£22 / $35

Maker Says

❝ The easy-peasy robot for the Raspberry Pi Model A+

4tronix

4TRONIX AGOBO

The Agobo is designed to cut a few corners in its pursuit of simplicity.
Gareth Halfacree puts it to the test...

T he Pi2Go and lower-cost Pi2Go-Lite wheeled robots from UK-based 4tronix have proved popular, but there is still a gap in the market for a no-solder and even lower-cost option suitable for educational use. Enter the Agobo.

Unlike the somewhat bulky kit-form Pi2Go design, the Agobo is a single circuit board which arrives with all the components pre-soldered. That's not to say it's ready-to-go: a small bearing assembly needs putting together and screwing to the front, which can be fiddly when the extended screws and spacers are required. You're well advised to do this over a container that will catch the smaller ball bearings when the cover slips from your fingers.

Trickiest part

The bearing assembly is the trickiest part of the process by far, however. Once that's fitted, there's a single bolt to secure the battery holder in place, then four brass pillars to support the Pi itself. Unlike the Pi2Go, the Agobo is compatible exclusively with the Model A+ – a sensible design choice, given its battery-sipping power characteristics. This attaches upside down and connects to a female GPIO header on the Agobo board, and is then secured in place with four screws and an optional but attractive protective acrylic plate.

The Agobo is billed as a hackable robot, and it certainly is. The GPIO header is replicated at the front of the board for the addition of any extra hardware, and a separate I²C breakout makes the connection of sensors very simple if the on-board line-following sensors aren't enough for your needs. An optional add-on dubbed the PlusPlate provides a large prototyping area, programmable RGB LED, and an nRF24L01-compatible socket for the addition of a radio module.

Despite its low price, the Agobo feels solid and robust. The thin wheels don't offer the traction of its full-sized competitors, but the metal-geared N20 motors are surprisingly powerful for their size. The use of an off-the-shelf lipstick-style USB battery is clever, and it can run the device for a considerable time per charge, although the length of the cable and the need to leave it dangling from the back like a tail is somewhat disappointing. The downloadable Python code examples are clear and work well.

Related

PHENOPTIX MEARM

A desktop robotic arm, the MeArm requires a PWM controller add-on for Pi use, but offers amazing control in an open hardware package.

£33 / $55

phenoptix.com

Last word

While parts of its assembly can be fiddly and it lacks the features of its more expensive competition, the Agobo is a perfect introduction to simple wheeled robotics for owners of the low-power Model A+.

KANO OS BETA 2.0.0

Les Pounder tests a Raspberry Pi distro for kids, designed to teach important computing concepts via a series of games and challenges...

T he Kano first appeared as a crowdfunding campaign in late 2013. The startup sought $100,000 to produce a Raspberry-Pi-powered computer kit that anyone could make. They went on to smash their funding target, raising $1.5m, and have subsequently successfully fulfilled rewards to their backers.

The latest Kano offering ships as a kit consisting of a Raspberry Pi 2, case, speaker, and a rather snazzy wireless keyboard. In this kit you will find a microSD card with a copy of the Kano OS, but you can download the OS for free via the Kano website (**kano.me/downloads**).

Gamification

The latest version of the project's Raspbian-based operating system, Kano OS 2.0.0, provides a slick and child-friendly interface. On your first boot, you are tasked with setting up your Pi via a series of *Matrix*-style challenges. Once set up, you're presented with a fresh interface that offers common applications such as Sonic Pi, Scratch, and *Minecraft*.

What's particularly novel about Kano's approach to learning is the team's use of gamification (learning via a challenge-based system), to encourage the user to stick with it and make more progress. Each of the challenges built into Kano incentivises you to progress via an achievements scheme which tracks your progress and shares your status with the other Kano users via Kano World, an online resource for additional Kano projects created by members of the community. As Kano is based upon Raspbian, it's easy to update your software via the built-in updater, and if you require more applications then you can easily drop into a terminal and use apt-get to install.

Kano's interface is rather lovely, but at times it really did struggle to catch up with us and there were times, such as when loading the apps menu, where we had to wait for a few seconds for the screen to populate. However, Kano is a good choice for small children who want to experience learning for themselves, and could be used as a stepping stone on their learning pathway.

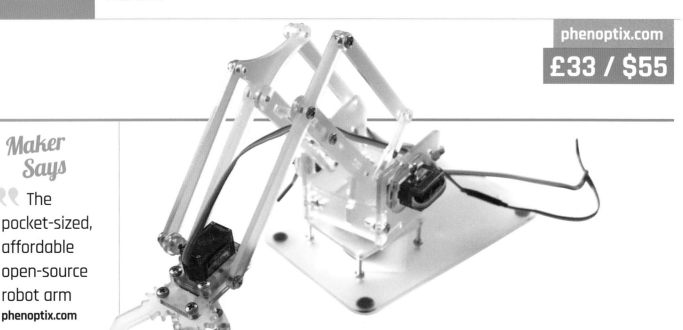

phenoptix.com

£33 / $55

Maker Says

❝ The pocket-sized, affordable open-source robot arm
phenoptix.com

MEARM

Russell Barnes tests an affordable, open-source robot arm designed to get learners started with physical computing

T hey're at the core of industry and they're soon to be at the forefront of modern medical surgery. Robot arms also make brilliant learning tools, especially for those wanting to utilise the GPIO pins on their Raspberry Pi. Historically, robot arms have been just north of affordable for the average bedroom hobbyist, but all that changed with the arrival of the MeArm.

You don't even have to take it out of the box to appreciate its strongest facets. In fact, you don't even need a box. You can build this open source arm from plans available on Thingiverse (you can 3D-print it, cut it from a single sheet of acrylic, or even whittle it from wood). For just £5 / $8, you can buy all the screws and fixings needed from its maker, **phenoptix.com**, or purchase a matching set of four hobby servos for £12 / $18. If you can't 3D-print, whittle wood or laser-cut acrylic,

you can buy a full MeArm kit, including everything you need to build a complete MeArm (minus an add-on board to drive the servos), for just £33 / $50.

The design itself is very clever and over the course of 2014 its creators, Ben Gray and Jack Howard, tweaked the design through four iterations, gradually refining the build, its instructions, and some code examples you can use to control it.

The build process is very hands-on. It has the feel of a 3D jigsaw puzzle when you take the parts from the box, turning the process into a fun afternoon project in its own right. The instructions are picture-led and thorough, but it's not entirely devoid of frustration – there's still some room for improvement.

As well as being a pleasure to look at, the MeArm is surprisingly sturdy. If you're expecting a certain grip strength or pinpoint

precision, you're entirely missing the point of the MeArm. That said, we were happy with its accuracy and its ability to recreate predefined movements.

While there are plenty of options available to drive the four servos (or even the option to buy a fully soldered Adafruit 16-channel servo HAT from **phenoptix.com**), this stands as a missing piece from the MeArm puzzle – meaning it's up to the user to find their way in this regard.

Last word

The creators of the MeArm set out to build an affordable, open source robot arm and the perfect introduction to robotics. They very much succeeded and, despite minor shortcomings, we can't recommend it enough.

★★★★★

Related

4TRONIX AGOBO

See the review of this tiny and affordable Model A+-specific robot on page 166.

£22 / $35

4tronix.co.uk

ubuntu-mate.org/raspberry-pi

FREE

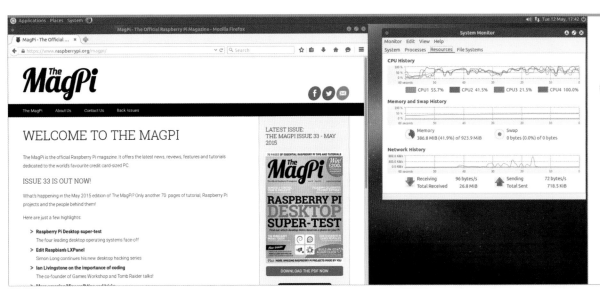

UBUNTU MATE 15.04

A lightweight version of the latest Ubuntu release arrives for the Raspberry Pi 2.
Les Pounder sees how it stacks up against the competition

Ubuntu has long been a frontrunner in the Linux community, but it is only recently that it has been able to enter the Raspberry Pi arena. With the Pi 2 and – more specifically – its ARM7 processor, we are starting to see multiple instances of Ubuntu on our credit card-sized PC.

Ubuntu MATE is a lightweight distribution based on the popular MATE desktop, which is a fork of the more traditional GNOME desktop. Ubuntu MATE is well equipped to work with limited resources and it copes remarkably well with the Raspberry Pi 2 hardware, but since the I/O throughput on the microSD card is something of a performance bottleneck, its makers recommend a class 6 or 10 microSD card. On first boot you are asked to create a user account, and this takes around five minutes to complete. In our test, the installer crashed right at the end, but everything was fine on reboot.

A grown-up distribution
Ubuntu MATE has all the bells and whistles, such as mounting remote file servers, a control centre for system settings, and the Firefox web browser. It also comes with LibreOffice, Thunderbird mail client, and Transmission torrent manager. Media playback is handled via VLC, but for best results we advise using omxplayer in the terminal. On the downside, this first release is missing Pi essentials like GPIO and camera support, which is a shame, but work is progressing to add them via the raspi-config menu system.

Software Centre
Installation of software is handled via the Ubuntu Software Centre or, for those who are comfortable with the terminal, via the Apt package manager (unlike other Ubuntu distros for Pi 2 which use the newer Snappy core). Administration

tasks such as backups and user configurations can be handled via the System menu at the top of the screen, giving Ubuntu MATE a lovely professional feel.

Ubuntu MATE is still in the early stages of development, though the team are making great progress. It will be interesting to see if this popular Linux distro is adopted by the community in a similar manner to Raspbian. If you fancy testing Ubuntu on your Raspberry Pi, this is a good place to start.

Last word

Ubuntu MATE is the best of the latest Ubuntu distributions for the Raspberry Pi 2. It provides a usable desktop, consistent responsive experience, and an easy method to install software.

★★★★☆

Maker Says

❝ Ideal platform for learning and teaching computational thinking

Fuze

FUZE BASIC V3

Just like **Lucy Hattersley,** a whole generation of coders cut their teeth on BASIC; follow in their footsteps with FUZE BASIC V3...

F ew things divide the programming world as much as BASIC (Beginner's All-purpose Symbolic Instruction Code). Once a standard inclusion with all home computers, BASIC was the first language an entire generation of programmers discovered.

FUZE BASIC has quietly earned its reputation as the best version of BASIC for the Raspberry Pi. Part of this success can be put down to sales of the FUZE Workstation (see page 177) to schools – you don't need one to run FUZE BASIC. This provides a huge range of high-quality support materials: Project Workbooks, Reference Guides and Project Cards, all available as free downloads.

Installing FUZE BASIC V3

In previous versions, FUZE BASIC was installed using a preconfigured boot image (based on Raspbian). Now it is installed as a separate download. We did have to dive into the Advanced Options using

`sudo raspi-config` and enable I²C support to get it to work, though, but a preconfigured boot image for newcomers is said to be on the way.

There's a lot to discover in the latest version. It includes new sprite handling tools, enabling rotation, size, and transparency. You can also import, rotate, and scale images, and new audio tools enable music playback and up to four channels of sound effects. These join a stack of comprehensive functions that make programming more fun. FUZE BASIC can control a Maplin USB Robot, draw on-screen graphics, and manage GPIO.

Is FUZE good for you?

FUZE BASIC V3 comes with a text editor and we found it ran programs windowed by default. So it feels more up-to-date than many versions of BASIC. Mind you, it still starts with a command line (known as Direct Mode) where you can use line numbers and good old-fashioned commands like LIST and RUN. Nostalgia

aside, this throwback is faintly ridiculous in the modern world. The mere presence of line numbers and, God forbid, the GOTO function is enough to make most programmers shudder.

While you can define procedures, this isn't an object-orientated programming (OOP) language. The argument that children should move from Scratch directly to another OOP language carries some water. But it could be argued the leap between Scratch and Python is too big for many newcomers, and FUZE BASIC is a great intermediate step that's fun to use.

Last word

The new sprite and sound functions enhance an already creative learning platform, but it's the wealth of support materials that really make it special. Shame you have to sign up to download it, though.

★★★★☆

Related

ARM BBC BASIC V

ARM BBC BASIC V is included with RISC OS (an option in NOOBS). While it's not as feature-rich as FUZE BASIC V3, plenty of manuals and guides are available.

papirus.ws

From £30 / $45

PI SUPPLY PAPIRUS

Les Pounder is keen to build his own e-reader with this low-power E Ink display HAT, but can he?

E Ink screens are an attractive proposition for single-board computers, but the biggest issue generally faced by users is the rather cumbersome array of breakout boards required. To solve this, Pi Supply has unleashed its latest E Ink add-on board, which uses the HAT (Hardware Attached on Top) standard.

PaPiRus is an E Ink display and controller board that has been designed to fit seamlessly onto the 40-pin GPIO found on the Model A+, B+, and Pi 2. It offers a standard connector, to which a range of different-sized E Ink displays may be fitted. For our review, we opted for the largest version, which has a diagonal size of 2.7 inches. Attaching the screen to the board is simple, and uses a latch mechanism very similar to that of the official Raspberry Pi Camera Module. On the reverse you'll find that a battery is fitted, to enable real-time clock functionality.

Software situation

Currently, the software installation is not for the faint-hearted, and there were times when the method wasn't easy to discern. However, with some assistance, we were able to install the necessary software and run the demos to test functionality.

The demos supplied reveal how to use the various functions of the PaPiRus and we were pleased with the inclusion of a temperature sensor and real-time clock, enabling our Pi to retain the correct time without network connectivity. One of the most powerful demos is ImageDemo.py, which uses PIL, a Python image-processing library, to convert images to display on the screen.

The hardware itself is very well developed and built, demonstrating the great care and attention to detail paid by the development team. The software is another matter, but is still a work in progress. We have been assured that the installation and demos will be ready for everyone to hack easily when the final versions are released.

Maker Says

❝ Turn your Pi into a tablet or infotainment system

Raspberry Pi

RASPBERRY PI
TOUCHSCREEN DISPLAY

The official 7″ Touchscreen Display for Raspberry Pi is here, but does it live up to expectations?

It's been a long time coming, but the official Raspberry Pi Touchscreen Display is here. It's the first product to make use of the DSI port at the rear of your Raspberry Pi, meaning you don't need to use the HDMI port on your Pi to get video output. Why is that useful? Not only does this mean that you don't need to use a bulky HDMI cable if you're trying to make a small, self-contained touchscreen project, but it also means you can output two different video signals, via HDMI and DSI, for multi-screen output from one the Raspberry Pi for the first time.

This high-quality 800×480 HD-ready display doesn't connect directly to the DSI, though. Instead, it utilises an adaptor board which handles the power and signal conversion. The DSI cable comes from the Pi and connects to this daughter board, which has exactly the same dimensions and mounting holes as a Raspberry Pi A+. There are only two connections needed: DSI and power. The adaptor board takes care of the latter with a great level of flexibility and allows you to power both the screen and Pi in a couple of different ways. It's possible to either connect it to the Pi with 5V and ground jumper wires, or via a micro-USB connector. This means you can power the Pi and screen with a single micro-USB wall wart, though you'll need to make sure you've got a decent 2-amp supply.

Quality package

You get a lot of technology for £48 / $60. Along with the HD-ready screen and adaptor board, you get all the stand-offs and

swag.raspberrypi.org
£48 / $60

Photos by Alex Eames – www.raspi.tv

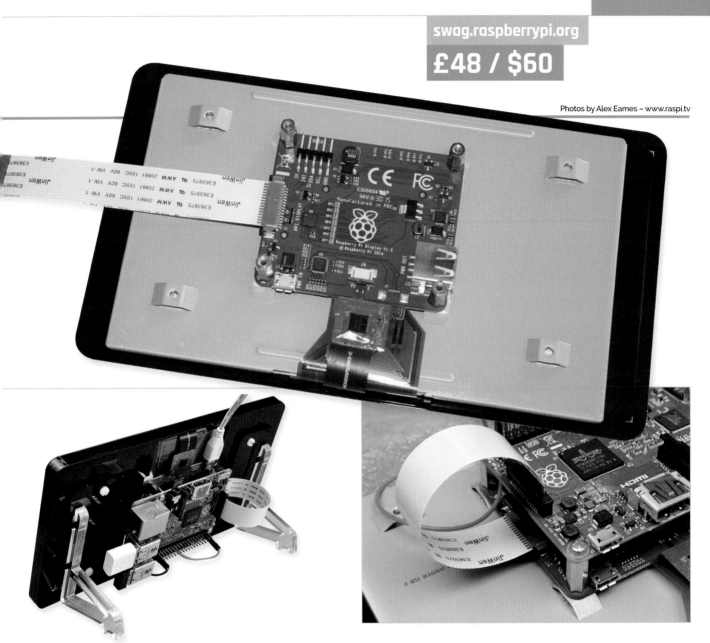

screws you need to safely secure it to your Pi, a DSI ribbon cable, and four jumper wires for both power and communications. Pimoroni has also produced an excellent Pibow-esque bezel with integrated stand in different colours. For a small premium, you can add your chosen colour to the shopping basket so you don't have to worry about propping the screen up or 3D-printing your own solution.

Touch friendly

The real star feature of the new display, though, is its touch capabilities. It's actually capable of ten-point capacitive touch, opening the door to some of the most advanced touch capabilities outside

Apple's new force-touch technology for the iPhone 6s.

In a recent YouTube video (**youtu.be/Eah3Zq18OyM**), Matt Richardson has demonstrated how Kivy, the popular and easy-to-use user interface creation library for Python, can quickly and easily make good use of the touch elements of the Touchscreen Display, while rigging up simple GPIO projects, too.

In his example project, he has created several on-screen buttons and a slider which interact with his GPIO breadboard. Lights can be turned on by tapping the button, and PWM can be adjusted on the fly with a slider to make it pulse faster or slower in response to your touch inputs.

Of course – and by Matt's own admission – this barely scratches the surface of what can be done with the Touchscreen Display and some simple GPIO programming – we've got a great feeling that Kivy is going to help bring a lot of brilliant ideas projects to the table.

Last word

Amazing picture quality, ample connectivity options, and outstanding value for money. Easily the best official Raspberry Pi add-on since the Camera Module.

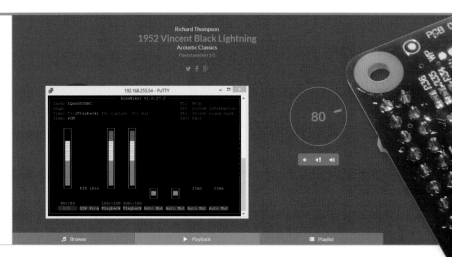

PI-DIGIAMP+
WITH PI-CASE+

Just add speakers: a complete hi-res audio DAC and amplifier in one small board, no soldering required, with an optional stylish acrylic case

A Raspberry Pi makes a great audio streaming device, and with the right add-ons is capable of high-end performance as well as being cheap and convenient. The Pi has its own basic on-board audio, but for the best sound you need either an external USB DAC (digital to analogue converter), or an add-on board. An add-on is preferable, since it will use the Pi's I²S interface, a dedicated digital connection that avoids USB and reduces CPU load. IQaudIO already offers a DAC (the Pi-DAC+), as well as a second board (Pi-AMP+) which provides a 2×20W Class D amplifier on a board that mounts on the Pi-DAC+.

Now the firm has combined the two products into the Pi-Digi-AMP+, a single-board solution which also saves around 30% compared to buying the two previous products. The DigiAMP+ is based on the Texas Instruments TAS5756M chip and supports up to 24-bit/192kHz PCM audio. It is not all gain: you lose the

line out and headphone sockets which you get with the Pi-DAC+. The result is still spectacular, though: a complete audio streamer to which you only need add speakers and your preferred music source, such as Logitech Media Server, Apple AirPlay, Spotify, or simply an attached hard drive full of music.

The Digi-AMP+ can also be used in other projects where you need audio, such as in-car entertainment, custom digital jukeboxes, robotics, and more. The board is HAT (Hardware Attached on Top) compliant, which means it complies with the official Pi recommendation for size and auto-configuration.

The Pi does not supply enough power for an audio amplifier, so the DigiAMP+ requires an additional 15V power supply, such as the XP Power VEH60US15 available from IQaudIO. This also powers the Pi itself, and it is important NOT to connect USB power as well, once the DigiAMP+ has been fitted.

The case is important, too, and IQaudIO also offers a good-looking acrylic case which has cut-outs for the speaker and power connections.

Getting started

Assembling the DigiAMP+ is a matter of screwing four spacers to the Pi, mounting the board, and securing it on the spacers with screws. Note that if you are using the IQaudIO case, you also need four small spacers which fit on the underside of the Pi. We were using the case, so the next thing to think about is fitting the assembled unit into the case and attaching the speaker cables.

This is a slightly tricky operation, the reason being that the speaker cables are secured with small screws that are not accessible once the top of the case is fitted. Just to make this more fun, the case is a jigsaw-like construction that falls apart until the top is fitted, which is why the guide suggests

iqaudio.com

Pi-DigiAMP+ £50/$77 • Pi-CASE+ £15/$23
15V/60W power supply £21/$32

Far Left Volumio running with the DigiAMP+, also showing the AlsaMixer control panel running over SSH

Above The DigiAMP+ assembled with the Pi-Case, showing the attached speaker cables and power supply

> " The Digi-AMP+ can also be used in other projects where you need audio, such as in-car entertainment "

that you use tape to hold the case together temporarily.

It is not too difficult, but we don't really like the way the speaker cables attach in combination with this particular case. The terminals are on the small side (you can forget your chunky audiophile speaker cables), but more importantly, you have to remove the top of the case if you want to change or remove the cables, whereupon it falls apart. A better solution would be binding posts on the outside of the case, though this would add to the cost. The Pi's microSD card is also hard to fit once the case is assembled, so it's best to get this all in place first.

Playing music

On the software side, IQaudIO offers suitable Pi OS images on its site; there is also documentation to configure your existing installation. In our case, we were already using Volumio

1.55, a popular streaming client, which includes IQaudIO drivers. Configuration was a matter of booting the Pi, connecting the Volumio's browser-based user interface, and enabling I²S support with the IQaudIO DAC+ driver.

There was one other thing, which was a slight annoyance. The DigiAMP+ starts up muted, so you do not get any music until you have made an SSH connection to the Pi as root and run a script. The problem is that without this feature, you may get a loud start-up thump to your speakers. You can add the script (which is on the IQaudIO site) to /etc/rc.local if you want it to run automatically. While you are there, you should also run AlsaMixer and set the two Playback volumes to 100%.

With all that in place, we plugged in the speakers (a pair of classic Quad bookshelf models), browsed back to Volumio, and started playing music. The Volumio

volume control worked fine with the DigiAMP+, using the optimal 'hardware' setting.

And how is the sound? In a word, great. This is real hi-fi, not just a cheap and cheerful streamer. We compared it to a Squeezebox playing through a traditional integrated amplifier and felt that, if anything, the DigiAMP+ beat it on clarity, with the Squeezebox sounding slightly soft in comparison. The DigiAMP+ goes loud, too: not enough for a wild party or room-shaking bass, but plenty for day-to-day listening.

Last word

This is true hi-fi in a compact and good-value package. The results are superb, though with a few small annoyances and no headphone socket.

★★★★☆

dime.lo4d.net

$0.10 per download

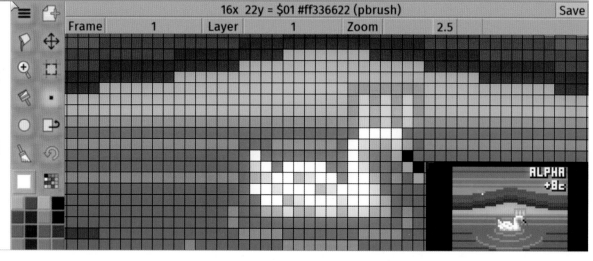

SWANKY PAINT

Designed by and for pixel artists, does Swanky Paint deliver
on its promise of a modern Deluxe Paint? **Lucy Hattersley** finds out…

Digital artists of a certain age will remember fondly the Commodore Amiga and, in particular, Deluxe Paint. More than two decades after it was discontinued, 'DPaint' still has fans who will be pleased to hear that there's a spiritual successor. Developed by Bradford-based WetGenes, Swanky Paint will be immediately familiar to anyone who worked in digital art back in the 1980s and 1990s.

Currently available as a cross-platform alpha build, as well as a Raspberry Pi-compatible executable, the download includes versions for Linux on 32-bit and 64-bit PCs, Windows, and OS X, and there's even an APK file for Android devices. Swanky Paint is certainly flexible. Sadly, the download process isn't straightforward: available exclusively through WetGenes' Dimeload platform, users must register an account, then pay a minimum of $1 for 10 'Dimes.' These Dimes act as

download tokens, each of which can be redeemed for a single download; when a new version is released, another Dime must be spent to download it.

Novel distribution method aside, Swanky Paint is straightforward to install and run. A ZIP archive, weighing in at just shy of 10MB, contains all the versions bar the Android build. Copying the files to a Raspberry Pi acts as the installation; executing the 'gamecake.raspi' application at the terminal loads the software itself. Interestingly, an X desktop session is not required: Swanky Paint can be loaded directly at the console, or the Pi configured to boot directly into Swanky Paint if required.

When it loads, Swanky Paint is attractive and simple. DPaint-inspired keyboard shortcuts make it quick to use, and there's an amazing amount of flexibility for pixel artists, including colour palettes based on classic computers like the Commodore 64 and ZX Spectrum,

and a selection of rendering filters which simulate cathode-ray tube displays. Even animations are handled smoothly, and attractive images are easily created using the various brushes and tools.

The software, in alpha at present, is undeniably a work-in-progress, but the team behind it are releasing improved versions all the time. A pair of bugs encountered during testing – preventing the mouse from being detected, and spamming text to the console – were quickly fixed and a new release issued accordingly.

Last word

Although in the early alpha stage of release, Swanky Paint shows real promise. For fans of Deluxe Paint, it's certainly worth trying out for its low cost and wide range of features.

★★★★★

fuze.co.uk

From £69 - £129

Maker Says

❝❝ Nominated in 2014 and 2015 as a BETT Finalist in ICT tools for teaching and learning
FUZE

THE FUZE

An attractive, robust workstation for the Raspberry Pi, but **Ian McAlpine** wonders if it is more than just a keyboard and case?

The FUZE may appear to be just a case and keyboard, but closer inspection reveals this to be a well-thought-out 'workstation' solution that encourages experimentation. It is excellent for home use and ideal for schools.

The FUZE is available in three main versions: the T2-A, T2-B, and T2-C. There is also the T2-R, which includes the OWI/Maplin Robot Arm kit, and the T2-SE-R, a special edition with the same colour scheme as the original BBC Micro, complete with red function keys. All other FUZE versions have a very pleasing red and black case.

The T2-C is the entry-level workstation and comprises a sturdy, sheet aluminium case, keyboard, powered 4-port USB hub, 2A power supply, and the FUZE I/O board. More on this later.

The T2-B includes everything in the T2-C, but adds an 8GB SD card, mouse and mouse mat, 840-hole breadboard, plus an electronic components kit with jumper wires, LEDs, resistors,

switches, light sensor, and a 7-segment display. There are also numerous breadboard wires of different lengths, which help to avoid the 'bird's nest' appearance of projects. Additionally, the T2-B includes three superb spiral-bound manuals: a 90-page FUZE BASIC tutorial and workbook, a 168-page FUZE BASIC manual, and a "pocket-sized" 126-page FUZE BASIC Programmer's Reference Guide.

Finally, the T2-A is the same as the T2-B, but also includes a Raspberry Pi 2 Model B.

Thoughtful design

All connections to the FUZE are on the back of the case; they include analogue audio, HDMI, SD card, Ethernet, four USB ports, and power, plus a very convenient on/off switch. The case also contains holes, which just happen to be the perfect size for popular building blocks!

The keyboard is high quality, with a size and feel similar to an Apple Mac keyboard. Our only complaint is that the space bar is not long enough for our liking.

The FUZE I/O board is unique to FUZE. It exposes a clearly labelled Raspberry Pi 26-pin header so other add-ons can be installed, but it also breaks out the more common connections: Ground, 5V, 3.3V, PWM, plus eight buffered GPIO ports. As a bonus, the FUZE I/O board also offers four analogue in ports and one analogue out port: these are not standard on the Raspberry Pi. The FUZE I/O board and the 840-hole breadboard fit inside a trough in the top of the FUZE case, making for a very convenient and tidy work environment.

Related

FUZE BASIC

Read a review of FUZE BASIC on page 170. There is also a FUZE BASIC game-programming tutorial in issues 25 to 29 of *The MagPi*.

FREE

fuze.co.uk

Last word

The FUZE is a holistic product, where the whole is greater than the sum of the individual parts. It is superb quality, an excellent learning platform, and significantly enhances the Raspberry Pi experience.

★★★★★

Maker Says

❝ It allows you to build 3D structures and shapes

Velleman

VELLEMAN 3D PRINTING PEN

Gareth Halfacree asks if this can be an affordable alternative to a 3D printer

3D printing is an undeniably hot topic in the maker community, and for good reason: a 3D printer lets you create physical objects quickly and easily, from replacement parts through to entirely novel objects. Sadly, there's a drawback: much like early 2D printers, 3D printers are currently expensive and bulky, and while both issues are being addressed with the launch of ever-cheaper and more compact 3D printers, the entry point is still in the hundreds of pounds.

That's where Velleman's 3D Printing Pen comes in. While it's not the first to hit the market, it's the first to come from a big name like Velleman rather than a crowdfunded startup. Not surprisingly, it follows the thinking of its predecessors, taking the technology of a 3D printer and making it more affordable.

The pen does this by doing away with the bulk of what makes a 3D printer. There's no printing bed, no stepper motors driving X, Y, and Z axis, nor any on-board intelligence or means to interface the device with a computer. Instead, the owner provides all these: your brain is the intelligence, and your muscles the motors.

The pen itself, then, is nothing more than the extrusion head of a 3D printer, modified to allow it to be handheld. Bulky yet surprisingly light, the hand-feel is immediately familiar for anyone who has used similar soldering pens, but with a plastic overtone that can't help but make the unit feel cheap.

Controls are located on the side of the pen. A button allows the plastic filament to be fed through the pen, while a reverse button is used to unload unused filament when you've finished; on the other side is a sliding control that adjusts the speed at which the filament is pushed through the pen. The top hides a small adjuster for the temperature of the extruder, allowing adjustment to accommodate different qualities of filament, while the rear contains a hole for the filament to enter and a DC jack for the bundled 12V power supply.

Getting started with the pen is easy, with none of the setup required of a fully fledged 3D printer. The pen is connected to its power supply and set to preheat;

cpc.farnell.com

£59 / $90

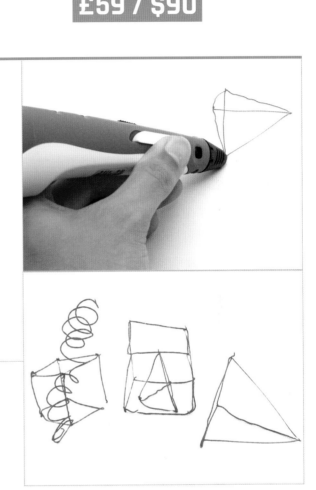

Above Even drawing the simplest of shapes is an exercise in frustration; vertical struts are particularly tricky to create

once heated, indicated by an LED, the filament is inserted into the rear and the feed button depressed until it appears from the nozzle at the front.

It's here where things start to feel a little clumsy. The box shows someone using the pen to 'draw' a three-dimensional representation of the Eiffel Tower; in practice, drawing something as simple as a wireframe cube is an exercise in frustration. Without the heated bed of a 3D printer, the filament often curls or warps as you're working; once you leave the support of a 2D surface to create the vertical struts, the filament proves too soft for too long, although it's possible to get somewhat better results by blowing across the filament as you're drawing, to cool and harden it faster.

The instructions supplied with the pen, along with three coils of PLA filament, warn that the device is for educational use only; that certainly seems to be the case in practice. Any attempts to recreate the Parisian landmark shown on the box will end in frustration, and using the pen for practical purposes seems unlikely.

Treating the pen more like a true 3D printer and constantly moving backwards and forwards to create a solid surface almost works, but the inaccuracy of a human operator means that results are unattractive. Worse, the speed control is near-unusable: a few millimetres into the slider's movement, the speed goes from 'glacial' to 'usable,' but one millimetre past that – and easily knocked into during use, thanks to the slider's position and lack of a

locking system – the filament pours out too quickly to be of any use.

The thin nature of the filament extruded by the pen is another issue: when a 3D printer spends six hours carefully placing thin lines of plastic down it's no real problem, but after a few minutes – nowhere near long enough to create anything exciting – your arm will soon tire.

Last word

Treated like the toy it is, the Velleman 3D Printing Pen is an interesting device, but it's not something that can take the place of even the cheapest of true 3D printers.

★★★★★

pi-supply.com
£61 / $75

Maker Says

❝ So small and simple, you can use this display with any computer that has HDMI output

Adafruit

ADAFRUIT HDMI BACKPACK

Les Pounder looks at a portable 5-inch touchscreen that has a clear picture, on-board hardware, and comes ready to go

P ortable screens for your Raspberry Pi are becoming more commonplace, but there has yet to be a neat and cost-effective portable display. Adafruit has stepped into the breach and built the HDMI Backpack. The screen comes in 5″ (12.7cm) and 7″ (17.8cm) sizes, both with an 800×480 resolution, which is ample for Raspberry Pi projects.

Common connections

Connection is made via an HDMI interface which connects to the built-in TFP401 HDMI/DVI decoder. Power is supplied via an on-board micro-USB, and this – along with the HDMI – results in a very neat board. We tested the 5″ touchscreen version which comes with an AR1100 touch controller, again built into the board. The AR1100 simulates a mouse and enables control of the mouse via the touch interface. One issue that

we encountered was calibrating the AR1100. The calibration software is currently Windows only and is provided by the chip manufacturer, not Adafruit. With the touchscreen configured, we followed the guidance on Adafruit's website on how to edit our config.txt file to ensure the correct screen resolution.

Powered by micro-USB

We then powered up the screen from an external power supply – you can power the unit from the Raspberry Pi itself and there are instructions on how it's done.

At full power, the screen takes only 500mA for the display and the backlight; the latter can be controlled via PWM (pulse-width modulation), which can see the current draw reduced to 370mA. We found that when powering the unit from a Pi, it became glitchy once we unplugged the mouse

and keyboard, the most likely cause being the AR1100 reacting to the event.

The screen is bright and easy to read, providing enough space to work, even for applications such as Scratch and Sonic Pi. The screen does not come with a speaker, though, thus requiring the use of an external speaker attached to the 3.5mm headphone jack.

This is a great screen that merges portability with great design and is another great Adafruit product.

Related

HDMIPI

Funded via a successful Kickstarter, this 1280×720 HD screen inside a custom case is a rugged platform that's suitable for children.

£75 / $117

hdmipi.com

Last word

Adafruit has always produced quality components, and this screen is no different. The portability of the board, thanks to its decoder and power, makes the HDMI Backpack great for any type of project.

WITTY PI

Set your Raspberry Pi to routinely switch itself on and off again with this handy power management board

T he Raspberry Pi is intentionally light on features, and one of the things not included is a built-in battery and real-time clock. Witty Pi is a small extension board that adds a clock battery and real-time clock functionality to the Raspberry Pi. More importantly, Witty Pi provides power management functionality, enabling it to start up and shut down a Raspberry Pi.

Setting up the Witty Pi

Setting up the Witty Pi is easy. The expansion board connects to the 40-pin GPIO header on the Raspberry Pi, and a set of copper stand-offs can be used to mount the board securely. The power cable is connected to the Witty Pi (instead of the Raspberry Pi), and pressing the On/Off button on the Witty Pi automatically starts up (or shuts down) the Raspberry Pi.

Having an On/Off button is neat, but more important is the wittyPi.sh script used to automate power functionality. The script is used to set the date, hour, minute and second to start up and shut down (although the second function is absent from shutdown). Entering 15 07:30:00 ensures that the Raspberry Pi starts up on the 15th day of the month, at 7:30 in the morning. You use '??' as a wildcard: ?? 23:30:00 starts the Raspberry Pi at 11:30 every night, and ?? ??:30:00 starts it up at half past every hour.

There are limitations: you can't set Witty Pi to come on twice a day or every Monday, for example.

Testing the Witty Pi

We set up Witty Pi to come on at five minutes past every hour and switch off at 15 minutes past every hour, and it performed admirably. We used a script in /etc/rc.local to run each time we started up

the Raspberry Pi and log the time to a file.

Witty Pi has three jumpers. One is used to determine if the Raspberry Pi auto-starts when you connect the power. The other two can be used to connect specific GPIO pins to control startup and shutdown, offering some interesting electronic integration options. Witty Pi is also beneficial for battery-powered projects: these can run for weeks if you turn the Raspberry Pi on for brief durations rather than keeping it switched on.

RETRO GAMING
GROUP TEST

On Test

▶ RetroPie
**blog.
petrockblock.
com/retropie**

▶ PiPlay
piplay.org

▶ Raspicade
**sourceforge.
net/projects/
raspicade**

Get your rose-tinted glasses at the ready: here are three
of the best emulator packages for the Raspberry Pi…

E mulation is a wonderful thing. Much like
an old police box or a 1982 DeLorean, it can
take us back in time to when we were driving
in a Grand Prix, saving the world from the brink of
destruction or simply creating lines out of falling
blocks while waiting for the bus. We have a rich
heritage of computer gaming, and with the help of the
Raspberry Pi 1 or 2, it's beautifully preserved through
the emulation software we're looking at today.

It's not all rose-tinted glasses, though. Emulation
does have its issues, and chief among them is the
legal grey area surrounding ROMs. A ROM is a
dump of the game code contained in a file, so ROMs
represent your favourite games from yesteryear
when loaded into your chosen emulator.

Of course, that game code is copyrighted software,
created by companies with the specific goal of
making money. So how can you play retro game
ROMs legally? This is the grey area we face.
Obtaining retro-gaming ROMs is your own
responsibility, so we'll leave you to make
your own investigations online.

Legality aside, emulation provides a
virtual museum of computing in your
home, and will most likely be used to
keep the knowledge of these times
alive, long after the hardware
has gone to silicon heaven.
Let's get cracking…

PiPLAY

Best FOR FEATURES

PIPLAY WAS CREATED BY AUTHOR AND RETRO FIEND SHEA SILVERMAN, VIA A SUCCESSFUL KICKSTARTER THAT RAN IN MAY LAST YEAR

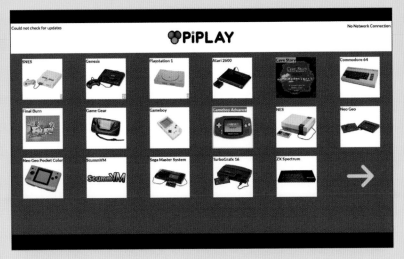

Above PiPlay offers a solid range of emulators in an easy-to-use package

PiPlay is based on the Raspbian operating system and comes with a custom interface that enables easy selection of the many consoles that can be emulated. It comes with a large choice of emulators, including NES, Game Boy, Atari 2600, and Commodore 64, to name a few. In our review, we tested three in particular – SNES, Mega Drive, and PlayStation.

PiPlay is a downloadable image that is copied to a blank SD card of 4GB capacity or greater. To copy the image, you can use the dd utility on a Linux machine, Win32DiskImager for Windows, and PiWriter for Mac OS X.

On first boot, PiPlay presents a quick introduction to the controls and interface which is best read and digested straight away, else it can be a little confusing later on. It comes with a great interface that can be navigated via keyboard or using a joypad. Setting up your ROMs is handled via a built-in ROM uploader, that can be reached using another device's browser and navigating to the IP address of the PiPlay Raspberry Pi. It's a pretty effective system that allows you to quickly upload your ROMs to the correct directory of your Raspberry Pi.

With the ROMs uploaded, the relevant emulators will be activated and loading it will trigger PiPlay to scrape the web for thumbnail images for your collection, creating a slick-looking library.

Configuring your joypad can be done as a default setting or per emulator, enabling you to create your perfect configuration. We used a USB SNES pad, which worked flawlessly. We also tried the Xbox 360

driver with an unofficial Xbox 360 pad, but during the configuration we found some buttons wouldn't map to the Xbox pad, which was a shame.

One of the few issues we encountered otherwise was related to audio output, which forced itself via the HDMI port no matter how often we changed the value in raspi-config. Not a major issue for home users, granted, but those building a cabinet, which normally uses an amplifier to boost sound clarity, might be disappointed.

We first tested the SNES emulator with *Super Mario World* and *Street Fighter 2*; both worked extremely well. Sadly, *Star Fox* wouldn't run, but this isn't terribly unusual. Next we tested Mega Drive emulation, firstly with *Sonic 1*. While that worked well, we had issues with *Sonic 2, 3* and *Streets Of Rage 3*. Lastly, we tried the PlayStation emulator with *Crash Bandicoot* and while it ran fairly well, it was a little sluggish at times. Of course, it doesn't take long to exit PiPlay and use the raspi-config tool to overclock the Pi to 900MHz.

PiPlay is a lovely interface to many different emulators, but requires a few tweaks to make it better.

Final word

PiPlay offers a good collection of emulators that are easily configured to work with many games and controllers. However, there are definite issues when running some games, which are down to PiPlay.

Score ♥♥♥ ✖ ✖

Above Mario jumped for joy, but some games didn't work so well

RETROPIE

RETROPIE IS THE DARLING OF THE EMULATION SCENE, THANKS TO THE MANY TOP-CLASS ARCADE BUILDS THAT ARE POWERED BY ITS SLICK INTERFACE

The RetroPie project is another emulation distribution that is based on Raspbian, and it provides a plethora of emulators. Raspbian may be the operating system, but RetroPie represents the glue that binds the OS to a beautifully simple interface called Emulation Station, a third-party themeable front end for emulation projects.

Copying RetroPie to an SD card is handled in the same manner as PiPlay, by transferring the image to the card using dd or a GUI application. On first boot, it asks the user to insert a controller to configure. We found this a little confusing, as the configuration only refers to the user interface and not the emulators contained therein.

To configure the controller for the emulators, you have to drop into the terminal and hack together a config script that covers all of the emulators, which is far from ideal for those new to emulation.

Since RetroPie emulates the same consoles as PiPlay, we tested the same SNES, Mega Drive, and PlayStation emulators. First, the SNES with *Super Mario World* and then *Street Fighter 2* – both worked very well and were fluid to play. RetroPie was the only emulator to successfully load and play *Star Fox*. A quirk that we found with the SNES emulator was that it did not like ROMs saved as ZIP archives; rather, it preferred games to be unzipped before play.

For the Mega Drive we tested with *Sonic 1* and we were surprised to find that *Sonic 2, 3* and *Streets Of Rage* all worked out of the box, putting RetroPie well ahead of PiPlay in the compatibility stakes.

Lastly, we tested the PlayStation emulator with *Crash Bandicoot* and encountered a slight stuttering

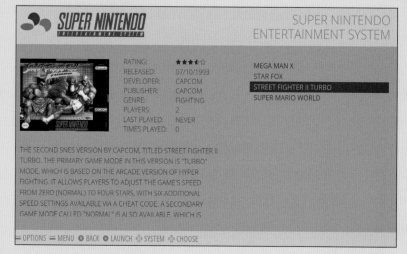

during play, but nothing that a bit of overclocking couldn't solve.

RetroPie boasts a particularly slick user experience and comes with a ROM scraper tool, which prettifies your library of ROMs by downloading thumbnails and information from the web. You manage your ROMs via the Raspbian desktop, and RetroPie includes a great script that detects when a USB stick is inserted into the Pi. When detected, RetroPie creates a directory structure for ROM files that mirrors what is installed on the Raspberry Pi, so all you need to do is then put that USB stick into your desktop PC and copy the ROMs onto it (making sure to put them in the right folder). Now, when you put that memory stick back in your Raspberry Pi, RetroPie automatically puts them in the right directory, which is both rather clever and exceptionally useful.

Ultimately, RetroPie is a highly refined product, but one that's not aimed at the newcomer. If you're an enthusiast who wants to make their own cabinet or home entertainment solution, it's easily the best choice. It's a powerful, beautiful piece of software.

Above RetroPie scrapes the net to get box art and details for games in your collection

Final word

A seriously powerful and configurable experience that offers the best overall experience for those who know their stuff, or don't mind taking the time to learn.

Above All the Mega Drive games we tested performed well

Score

RASPICADE

FINALLY, WE LOOK AT RASPICADE, WHICH IS DESIGNED TO PLAY WELL WITH THE SPECIFIC NEEDS OF ARCADE CABINETS AND INTERFACE WITH ARCADE-QUALITY JOYSTICK AND BUTTONS

Right Raspicade rather confusingly comes with two Mega Drive emulators by default

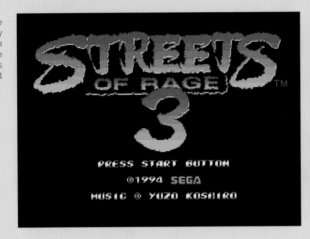

Installation of Raspicade is equally as easy as the other two emulation offerings on test, and it took a grand total of ten minutes to get running from a standing start.

Raspicade is a little different to the others on test, inasmuch as it comes with a configuration script that runs every time the Raspberry Pi boots. Among other things, the script configures the audio output, enabling you to choose between the 3.5mm audio jack and the HDMI port, something lacking from the other solutions. The script also handles your IP address and, in another interesting twist, allows you to choose between three user interfaces: a simple Raspicade bespoke interface, Emulation Station 1 (which is an older interface but very light on resources) and Emulation Station 2, which comes as standard on

Below Raspicade and RetroPie share the same interface

RetroPie. Given the latter fact, we reviewed using Emulation Station 2 to ensure a fair test.

First of all, we configured the joypad to work with Emulation Station, which seemed to go well, but found that there was no way to create a default configuration, so we needed to repeat the process for each emulator we tested. Elsewhere, we found two instances of 'Sega Genesis' in the interface; since the software used both PicoDrive and dgen Mega Drive emulators, we decided to test the latter, which is supported in all three options on test today.

As before, we tested all three *Sonic* games and *Streets Of Rage 3*. All played fluidly, with no issues to speak of. Next, the SNES emulator handled *Super Mario World* and *Street Fighter 2* with ease, but *Star Fox* refused to play along.

While we weren't terribly surprised at that, we were disappointed that Raspicade doesn't offer a PlayStation emulator, so we fired up the NES emulator and tried a built-in game called *Solar Wars*, which – unsurprisingly – worked really well.

Final word

Overall, Raspicade is a good retro-gaming distro, and it provides a low barrier for entry for those wanting to dip their toes into emulation for the first time.

Extra Lives

The Raspberry Pi is helping to revive some age-old gaming classics. **David Crookes** investigates…

It may not feel like it today, but the computing world hasn't always been dominated by the PC and the Mac. Years before they became ubiquitous, scores of home machines left an indelible mark on computing, from the ZX Spectrum and BBC Micro in the UK, to the US-made Commodore 64. The Amstrad CPC did well in France, and that's before you get to the worldwide popularity of the Atari ST and Commodore Amiga.

Companies big and small entered the home computer market in droves, most of them allowing users to 'get under the hood', just like the Raspberry Pi today. That made it possible for people to get their hands dirty with code and see what they could make their computers do. One of the great by-products of this was a flourishing games industry.

Programmers spent time in their bedrooms hunched over their keyboards as they contributed to the thousands upon thousands of titles that were released. Many of them subsequently made the switch to the flourishing home console market, which saw Nintendo and Sega go head-to-head with lots of wonderful games machines. But compatibility problems mean that playing those games today without having the original hardware is impossible. Impossible without using an emulator, that is.

And that's where the Raspberry Pi comes in. Emulators allow modern-day computers to behave like their predecessors, and you will be pleased to know that the Pi has a great many of them. It is possible for your Pi to pretend it is a Speccy or a C64. It can even mimic older consoles and arcade machines. With the right software and access to some gaming ROMs online, you can turn your tiny machine into a fully fledged retro games console. It's time to have some fun…

Beneath a Steel Sky

Why give BASS away?

The game's director, Charles Cecil, discusses his decision to make *Beneath a Steel Sky* a freebie.

"*BASS* was originally published for DOS, way back in 1993, so when Windows 98 stopped supporting DOS a few years later, it looked set for oblivion. We were approached by a group calling themselves ScummVM, looking to resurrect point-and-click adventures by converting the source code to run cross-platform. We duly provided them with all the assets.

"One of the leads, Joost Peters, later came to work for Revolution and is now our technical director. We felt since we were unable to sell the game, that we should give it away for free. I wish I could claim this was a stroke of marketing genius, but actually it was more about doing what we felt was fair. It has ensured the game is very widely played, particularly on Linux-based computers."

Stats

Developer: Revolution Software
Released: 1994
Formats: DOS, Amiga, Amiga CD32
Emulator: ScummVM

Even though *Beneath a Steel Sky* is celebrating its 21st anniversary, this cyberpunk point-and-click adventure will certainly enthral you today. Inspired by the *Mad Max* and *Blade Runner* films, it tells the story of Robert Foster, who is taken under the wing of indigenous Australians following a plane crash, only to later, see his adopted family slaughtered by the army. Foster is flown to Union City, but he suffers a second crash which allows him to escape and search for answers with his robot pal, Joey. The game is a stunning tale of hope amid oppression and it will keep you engrossed for hours.

Players are expected to solve a series of intricate puzzles, each one developed to drive the narrative forward. As you look for clues and search for items that can be used to create often mind-bending solutions, you are introduced to a host of characters. By engaging in interactive conversation with them, the dialogue enriches the story and helps to unravel the mystery. But just as you think you may know what is going on, the game throws a major curveball and it will have you begging for more.

Much of the game is laden with humour, but there is also lots of drama, with Robert's backstory brought to the fore through the little quips between him and Joey. The game was made using Revolution Software's Virtual Theatre game engine, a 'rival' of sorts to LucasArts' SCUMM engine. It helped lend the game a realistic edge and allowed the non-player characters to wander around rather than remaining fixed in one spot.

Revolution released the DOS-based version of *Beneath a Steel Sky* as freeware a few years ago, so it means you can legally play it on your Raspberry Pi for free. There is no doubt that you should.

Keep clicking

The ScummVM emulator allows you to play a host of point-and-click adventure games. It was originally based on the SCUMM engine created by LucasArts' Ron Gilbert and Aric Wilmunder. Learn more at **scummvm.org**. Here is the pick of the bunch:

The Secret of Monkey Island

Introducing hapless Guybrush Threepwood to the gaming world, this swashbuckling 1990 release was chock full of great humour, mind-bending puzzles, and sword fights that were a battle of sharp, insulting wit. It was no surprise that *Monkey Island* spun into an award-winning four-game series that is still loved today.

Broken Sword

Released a fair few years before Dan Brown's *The Da Vinci Code*, this game throws players deep into the legend of the Knights Templar. Starring American hero George Stobbart and French journalist Nico Collard, it takes players on a fantastic journey across France, Ireland, Syria, Spain, and Scotland.

King's Quest

King's Quest was a popular graphic adventure designed by Robert Williams, the co-founder of Sierra On-Line, using the Adventure Game Interpreter engine. The series followed the saga of the Kingdom of Daventry's royal family. Watch out for some memorable guest appearances from the likes of Dracula and Little Red Riding Hood.

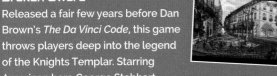

GAMES GAMES GAMES

In order to play games on your Pi, you need to get hold of the gaming ROMs. It's worth checking out Emuparadise, but read the legal boxout on page 188 first.

8-bit Gaming

Spectrum

It may have had just 16kB of memory to start with, and it may have run its games off slow-loading tapes, but the ZX Spectrum sold five million units. Its popularity ensured it was blessed with a wealth of brilliant games.

Matthew Smith

Matthew Smith is revered today as one of the undisputed genius programmers of the ZX Spectrum. If you are emulating the Spectrum, you must play these two games...

Manic Miner

Manic Miner was one of the first platform titles, its colourful graphics and fiendishly difficult gameplay catching the imagination. It had in-game music, being the first Spectrum game to do so, and animated toilets too! Try it to see how easy games really have become.

Jet Set Willy

As the sequel to *Manic Miner*, this game reintroduced hero Willy, who by this point was a rich man tasked with cleaning up his mansion following a riotous party. More of an adventure than the first game, with a fresh structure, *Jet Set Willy* is every bit as addictive.

Commodore 64

The Commodore 64 was the American rival to the British ZX Spectrum and it caused many a playground row to erupt. The C64 boasted more colours, but it also had amazing sound thanks to its SID chip. If digital music is your thing, then emulating C64 games will give you great pleasure.

The classics

Lemmings

Made by DMA Design, which would go on to produce *Grand Theft Auto*, *Lemmings* became one of the best puzzle games ever made when it was released in 1991. Guide the tiny humanoid creatures to safety by putting a good number of them to good use: building bridges and digging tunnels, and by equipping some with umbrellas so they can float gently to the ground. Listen out for the cries of "oh no!" as lemmings explode in a shower of pixels.

Rainbow Islands

Rainbow Islands was not only cute and addictive, but very popular too. Players need to make their way up the screen to avoid rising sea levels. This is achieved by laying down rainbows, allowing bad guys to be squished and giving you leverage to higher platforms. The game has four

rounds of gameplay per island, after which you move on to another. Each time, you are treated to the (eventually annoying) strains of *Somewhere Over the Rainbow*.

Barbarian: The Ultimate Warrior

Featuring decapitated heads and lots of blood and gore, *Barbarian* is a brutal beat-'em-up that keeps players nimbly moving their fingers in order to perform one of the 16 available moves. There is a follow-up to this game which you may also want to try, but before you do, give this one a go in two-player mode. Going head-to-head with a pal makes the game truly sing, providing a lot of fun in the process.

Impossible Mission

As if to underline the excellence of the Commodore 64's sound capabilities, *Impossible Mission* starts off with the line, "Another Visitor. Stay a while. Stay Forever", delivered in a creepy voice that nevertheless thrilled gamers at the time. Exploring the underground lair of Professor Elvin Atombender and seeking clues in order to turn off a bomb, players were also amazed at the fluid animation. *Impossible Mission* was groundbreaking at the time and it remains a lot of fun today.

LEGAL WORRIES

Using emulators to play games has long been a legal grey area. For some games publishers, the answer is clear: don't do it. For instance, Codemasters asked the website World of Spectrum to remove its retro games, while Nintendo states its position clearly at nintendo.com/corp/legal.jsp ("The introduction of emulators created to play illegally copied Nintendo software represents the greatest threat to date to the intellectual property rights of video game developers," it says). In general, the advice has been to use emulators to play games that you already own (so you can emulate a Spectrum game if you still have the cassette copy). In addition, you should certainly not pirate games or seek to profit from them in any way.

OTHER CLASSICS

Alter Ego	Emlyn Hughes Int. Soccer	Myth	Spy vs Spy
Archon	Enforcer	Nebulus	Starquake
Arkanoid: Revenge of D'oh	Grand Prix Circuit	Neuromancer	Steel Thunder
Atomino	Head Over Heels	Paradroid	Stix
Blue Max	IK+	Park Patrol	Stunt Car Racer
Boulder Dash	Jumpman	Pirates!	The Bard's Tale
Bubble Bobble	Laser Squad	Pitstop II	The Sentinel
Buggy Boy	Last Ninja 2	Platoon	The Way of the Exploding Fist
California Games	Law of the West	Pool of Radiance	Turrican
Creatures	Leaderboard	Prince of Persia	Ultima V
Cybernoid	Little Computer People	Project Firestart	Uridium
Dragon Wars	Lode Runner	Rick Dangerous	Winter Games
Elite	Maniac Mansion	Silent Service	Wizball
	Mayhem in Monster Land	Skate or Die!	Yie Ar King Fu
	MicroProse Soccer	Space Taxi	Zak McKracken and
	Midnight Resistance	Spherical	the Alien Mindbenders

Dizzy
The Ultimate Cartoon Adventure

Stats

Developer: **The Oliver Twins**

Released: **1987**

Formats: **Amstrad, ZX Spectrum, Commodore 64**

Genre: **Arcade-adventure**

Once upon a time, there was a little egg-shaped character who lived in a fantasy world with his family and battled against an evil wizard. His name was Dizzy, and he went on to star in a multitude of adventures and a fair few spin-offs. Created by the Oliver Twins, Philip and Andrew, he became synonymous with British gaming in the 1980s and early 1990s, with best-selling games being made available on the Spectrum, Commodore 64, Amstrad CPC, Amiga, Atari ST, and NES.

The original game was made on the Spectrum and ported to the CPC, before the C64 version was made. "We only had 32kB of RAM to store the whole game," says Philip Oliver, "plus the processor was very slow, meaning plotting graphics to the screen was extremely limited." The game involves collecting items to solve subsequent puzzles (using a grease gun to get a cart moving in a mine, for instance). If you play later games in the series, you will be introduced to Dizzy's Yolkfolk and engage in some chit-chat. There are some funny quirks involved, too: try kicking the Dozy's deckchair a few times in *Fantasy World Dizzy* to see what we mean.

Why I love the Pi

"The Pi is a hobby computer designed to inspire people to code. We've always felt 2D games should be the first thing to attempt to write, and not scrolling, either, as that adds a lot of complexity. People shouldn't try 3D until they've really got the hang of 2D games.

Since retro games often means simple, fun, 2D, and there quite a few that don't require scrolling or many elements to make them fun: they make ideal material for Raspberry Pi."

Philip Oliver

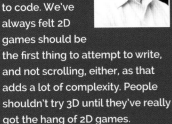

Nintendo

Harking back to the 8-bit days of Nintendo, notably the NES and the Game Boy, is arguably to take a trip down into the origins of the modern-day gaming scene. Nintendo's machines were blessed with amazingly well-designed games.

Super Mario Bros

Often referred to as the greatest game of all time, *Super Mario Bros* is a side-scrolling 2D platformer which came bundled with the NES console. Set over a large playing area, the game has impeccable level design, lots of secrets to uncover, plus lovely graphics and music. It also popularised power-ups, such as Fire Flower, which allowed Mario to grow tall and hurl fireballs.

Tetris

The Game Boy may have been a rather primitive handheld machine – it had a green screen and no backlight, and it paled in comparison to the Atari Lynx – but it had a killer app: *Tetris*. Designed by Russian programmer Alexey Pajitnov, this took the world by storm, with gamers transfixed by the falling blocks and the urge to tidy them away in neat rows.

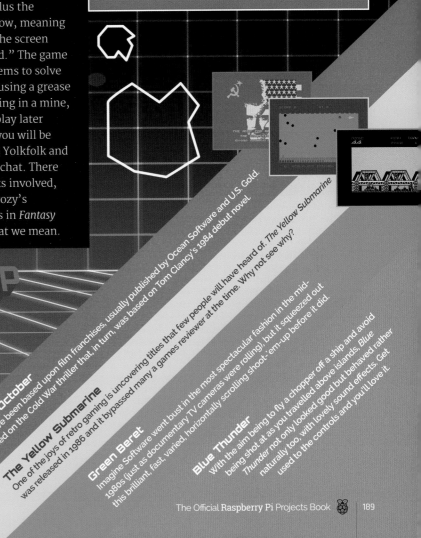

Hunt for the Red October
Many retro games have been based upon film franchises, usually published by Ocean Software and U.S. Gold. This game was based on the Cold War thriller that, in turn, was based on Tom Clancy's 1984 debut novel.

The Yellow Submarine
One of the joys of retro gaming is uncovering titles that few people will have heard of. *The Yellow Submarine* was released in 1986 and it bypassed many a games reviewer at the time. Why not see why?

Green Beret
Imagine Software went bust in the most spectacular fashion in the mid-1980s (just as documentary TV cameras were rolling) but it squeezed out this brilliant, fast, varied, horizontally scrolling shoot-'em-up before it did.

Blue Thunder
With the aim being to fly a chopper off a ship and avoid being shot at as you travelled above islands, *Blue Thunder* not only looked good but behaved rather naturally too, with lovely sound effects. Get used to the controls and you'll love it.

INTERVIEW
Bare-metal Doom

First-year students at Imperial College London have produced a bare-metal partial clone of *Doom* for the first-generation Raspberry Pi in 9,800 lines (see hackaday.com/tag/bare-metal). Csongor Kiss tells us more about it...

MagPi: Where did the idea come from?
Csongor Kiss: As part of our first-year project, we were challenged to make whatever we could, limited by the constraint that it had to work on a Raspberry Pi, and be coded in bare-metal assembly. It turned out to be not so large a constraint.

MagPi: What did the Pi bring to the table?
Csongor Kiss: The Pi is more powerful than the machines running games like *Doom* on release, which let us use a higher screen resolution and better-quality textures than those of the original.

MagPi: What was the process of making the conversion?
Csongor Kiss: The only thing sourced from the original game were the textures. Everything else was built from scratch. We used the *Doom* wiki for inspiration for things like level design and gameplay, but coded it from the ground up, just as you would for any other project.

PORTING A COIN-OP

Many arcade games were ported to home computers and consoles. Things didn't always go according to plan, however, as Ste Pickford, who worked on *Ghosts 'n Goblins*, recalls.

"I was given a pile of photographs taken from the screen of the arcade machine by the publisher, Elite, and asked to 'do the graphics' from that. I had no sense of the layout of the levels or anything. So I went to Stockport arcade with a sketchbook and stood next to its *Ghosts 'n Goblins* machine, watching people playing, and sketching the level from what I was seeing. People kept dying and starting over, but I had a decent sketch of the first level and needed someone to get to level two, but eventually the arcade owner spotted me and accused me of 'ripping off his machines'. I was barred.

"Programmer Nigel Alderton arranged to drive me to Elite's offices in Walsall to play their machine instead. It had been set to free play with infinite continues, but it took us hours and hours to get to the end. We finished around 5am and drove home to Stockport. But I was only 15 at the time, and it hadn't occurred to me to phone home. My parents were frantic and on the verge of reporting me as a missing person. Still, I had the level layouts, so everything was fine."

Quake III Arena

Stats
Developer: id Software
Released: 1999
Formats: Windows, Linux, OS X, Dreamcast, PS2
Genre: First-person shooter

If you love *Doom*, you'll adore *Quake III Arena*. It's a frantic, no-nonsense first-person arcade shooter which runs well on the Pi, pitting players against 30 artificial intelligence bots in a game that eschews a plot in favour of all-out fun. The design is deliberately minimalist, yet it looks amazing and it plays at a fast speed, giving gamers a good choice of weapons – check out the rocket launchers, shotguns, and the melting plasma gun – while thinking about ease of movement around the playing area. Accelerator Pads and Bounce Pads take the place of lifts and ladders, enabling a greater level of fluidity in the action.

One of the game's designers, Graeme Devine says he is thrilled the Pi has the power to open up *Quake III* to a new audience. "I have a Pi sitting right here on my desk," he tells us. "It dizzies me that something so small can do so much, and the fact that people can look through the *Quake III* source just opens up so much possibility all over the world. It feels like the games industry can explode again."

ARCADE
Best of the arcade
Standing for 'Multiple Arcade Machine Emulator', MAME is a way of playing a host of coin-op arcade games, many of which were seen as cutting-edge in their day...

Street Fighter II: The World Warrior
When *Street Fighter II* was released into the arcades in 1991, it sparked a huge boom in fighting games. Not only did it truly establish some well-known virtual fighters, including Ryu, Chun-Li, and Guile, this deeply strategic title also showed the importance in giving players special moves unique to each character.

Metal Slug
For those who love run-and-gun platfomers, the *Metal Slug* series is nigh on perfect. The original has stood the test of time, giving players control of an eight-way joystick and letting them loose on six levels of shooting, bombing, and jumping. The game, while basic in premise, helped to establish the Neo Geo MVS arcade platform.

Ghosts 'n Goblins
Capcom's *Ghosts 'n Goblins* series was a very hard and yet rewarding game, thanks to impeccable level design that makes it fun to play, regardless of how many times you are nobbled. Players assumed the role of a knight called Arthur in a zombie-strewn land, and you only needed two hits to lose a life.

Chocolate Doom

Stats

Developer: **Simon 'Fraggle' Howard**
Released: **2005**
Formats: **DOS, Raspberry Pi**
Genre: **First-person shooter**

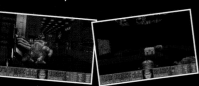

Ported to the Raspberry Pi, *Chocolate Doom* takes the source code of the original game and replicates it faithfully on our favourite computer. The actual source port has been around since 2005, thanks to developer Simon 'Fraggle' Howard, and it exists with all of the original engine's bugs and quirks for the most authentic experience of all. The Pi version supports upscaling to 1920×1080.

Lakka

Create a Pi console with Lakka
Jean-André Santoni has put together a lightweight Linux distribution called Lakka (**lakka.tv**), which lets you turn your Pi into a versatile games console.

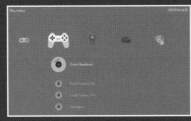

MagPi: Where did the idea for Lakka come from?
Jean-André Santoni: I bought a Raspberry Pi when it [first] came out... and I discovered RetroArch. I loved the fact it was working without big dependencies like X11, and centralising the configuration of all emulators with that libretro API was a bright idea.

MagPi: There is a certain familiarity to the UI. Why did you choose this?
Jean-André Santoni: Ah yes, the PS3 XMB-like interface. I chose this because I wanted an intuitive interface. By looking at just one screenshot of the interface, the user can understand what we are offering: a list of controllers is displayed horizontally – they represent each emulated system – with a list of cartridges vertically, representing the games. Also, this kind of interface is not very difficult to implement, and is extensible.

MagPi: Does the Pi make for the perfect retro machine?
Jean-André Santoni: I like the fact that the bootloader is silent and fast. The resolution of the screen is easily detected. There are no major issues with the GPU driver. I would say that the Pi is a good compromise: its price, its documentation, and its overall quality makes it a serious choice for beginners.

MagPi: What should gamers using a Pi bear in mind when using Lakka?
Jean-André Santoni: Lakka is not yet finished, so people should expect some bugs in the interface. Configuring the Wi-Fi or the Bluetooth controllers will work only by using the command line. We maintain a page on our wiki explaining what is the best hardware to use, though. So far, the best controllers for Lakka are the official Xbox 360 ones.

RetroPie

Get your teeth into the classics
RetroPie supports a huge number of computers and consoles, including the Amiga, Apple II, Atari 2600, Amstrad CPC, C64, Game Boy, Game Gear, MAME, NES, N64, ScummVM, PS1, SNES, and Spectrum. We talk to its creator, Florian Müller...

MagPi: Where did the idea for RetroPie come from?
Florian Müller: I grew up with a whole bunch of 8-bit and 16-bit video game consoles. Home computers such as the Commodore 64, the Amstrad CPC, the Amiga 500, and the first IBM PCs were also parts of my childhood. The idea for RetroPie was born out of nostalgia.

MagPi: How has the project evolved?
Florian Müller: It started with a rudimentary Bash script that automated the installation of some emulators, and set up folders and configuration. This was the birth of the RetroPie-Setup script, which is still the core of RetroPie. One goal from the beginning was to achieve a keyboardless system. A big step towards that was the addition of EmulationStation, a graphical front-end developed by some great enthusiasts of RetroPie. By this time, more and more systems were being added to RetroPie, and supplementary functions such as a USB copy service, game metadata scrapers, splash screens, and configuration possibilities were included. There is a wiki and a forum, too.

MagPi: What is the strength of RetroPie?
Florian Müller: The volunteers who enjoy contributing in various ways. We have source-code maintainers and contributors, people who help each other in the forum and forum moderators, wiki maintainers, and people who post issues or feature proposals. There are people writing blog posts about specific features of RetroPie, and there are video tutorials. RetroPie truly is an open-source project and it evolves by the help of the community.

For more information about RetroPie, and SD card images, visit:
blog.petrockblock.com/retropie

RETROPIE INGREDIENTS

- A Raspberry Pi (preferably version 2 or model B+)
- A case
- A power supply (the official power supply does a great job)
- An SD card (preferably 8GB or larger)
- An HDMI cable
- A USB keyboard (at least for the configuration)
- And, of course, the current RetroPie image

Go to the **bit.ly/1ecWc97** download page and download the correct image for your Pi model. Extract and copy the image to an SD card. If you have an SD card larger than 4GB, expand the root file system: press F4, run `sudo raspi-config` and choose 'Expand root fs'. Restart the Pi. Search for game ROMs and copy them to a USB stick.

RASPBERRY PI
BESTSELLERS

Wiley's top three bestselling Pi books shouldn't be missed...

ADVENTURES IN RASPBERRY PI 2ND EDITION

Author: Carrie Anne Philbin
Publisher: Wiley
Price: £14.99
ISBN: 978-1119046028
tinyurl.com/oov562q

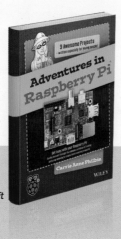

Nine projects – with encouragement, hints and tips – to take 11-15 year-olds through coding, games, *Minecraft* and music on the Pi, as well as GPIO-based projects, with accompanying videos on the website. Full review on page 194.

RASPBERRY PI USER GUIDE – 3RD EDITION

Authors: Eben Upton & Gareth Halfacree
Publisher: Wiley
Price: £14.99
ISBN: 978-1118921661
tinyurl.com/k4dc6zd

Updated for the Model B+, the official guide remains an invaluable introduction to all things Pi, particularly physical computing. Aimed at beginners, the enthusiasm and depth of knowledge give something to every reader.

ADVENTURES IN MINECRAFT

Authors: David Whale & Martin O'Hanlon
Publisher: Wiley
Price: £14.99
ISBN: 978-1118946916
tinyurl.com/oycg9qu

Spurred on by wanting to improve and customise their *Minecraft*, readers will swiftly pick up Python skills and integrate *Minecraft* with building electronic circuits. Recommended by teachers and young people alike.

PYTHON PROJECTS

Author: Laura Cassell & Alan Gauld
Publisher: Wiley
Price: £30.99
ISBN: 978-1118908662
tinyurl.com/kp9w24q

You've completed the Python tutorial – or beginner book, or MOOC – and you're ready to move on. If you learned programming in order to join or begin a particular project, no problem, but if you didn't, then where to go next to learn what you can really do with Python is a problem. Or, rather, it was before Cassell and Gauld produced this excellent compendium of ideas and projects to take you beyond beginner, and get learning by doing.

For Pi users, while physical computing is left to some pointers at the end of the book, there's still a wealth of material. Following a recap of core Python, it's straight into scripts to access the operating system, then managing data. Useful exercises, along with summaries of what's been learned, cement the education experience.

After desktop and web applications comes the tools you need for working on larger projects: testing, debugging, tuning, structuring, and releasing – all essential information. The book closes with a look at areas you may want to try next: SciPy, Pygame, drawing modules and animation, as well as the aforementioned physical computing. Plenty to inspire you to further Python adventures.

Score

BLACK HAT PYTHON

Author: Justin Seitz
Publisher: No Starch
Price: £23.50
ISBN: 978-1593275907
tinyurl.com/pts7hm6

Python is a popular choice in the field of information security, and penetration testing in particular. Seitz, a senior security researcher at Immunity, presents a broad range of security topics, touching on tools traditionally used, then pointing the way to build your own Python equivalents.

Like most good security books, it reveals what an insecure place our computer networks are, but provides you with the tools to do something about it, building Python replacements for many everyday tools like Netcat. This leads to stronger knowledge not just of the network security topics, but

also where you can take Python. Along the way, Seitz respects the intelligence of the reader, but doesn't assume detailed networking knowledge – introducing information if it is necessary for progressing through the book. For example, SSH tunnelling is explained, but the reader is left to look up any extra information she may want on the Address Resolution Protocol (ARP).

The chapter on 'Web Hackery' will be of particular general interest. Anyone with a Joomla, Drupal, WordPress or similar site can feel justifiably alarmed about their security after a few pages of Python brute-forcing scripts, from discovering leftover files and scripts on the server to gaining admin login. A useful eye-opener.

Score

JAVASCRIPT FOR KIDS

Author: Nick Morgan
Publisher: No Starch
Price: £23.50
ISBN: 978-1593274085
tinyurl.com/pz8zyxx

The Pi is a great tool for learning Python, but also anything else about computing. For an even more take-anywhere, instant-results language, try JavaScript. It has a runtime – the web – that's familiar to everyone, and with a bit of HTML and CSS thrown in, children soon gain an understanding of all things web that will spur their creativity on to produce their own sites.

Coding is done straight into Chrome's JavaScript Console, which cuts out install hassles and time wasted on discussing editor choice! While pursuing games and animations, readers will learn objects, arrays, click events, flow control, Boolean operators, and HTML. This culminates in a graphical Snake game, using the canvas element, and suggestions of where to go next. Extra programming challenges, ending each chapter, balance interest and learning.

This is no dumbed-down guide – you can learn everything you need here at the same time as your children – but the material is well judged (Random Insult Generator etc), and well paced to teach JavaScript and programming skills in easy but satisfying steps to younger learners. Add in cute illustrations from Miran Lipovača, of *Learn You a Haskell* fame, and you have a real winner. Recommended.

Score ★★★★★

LAUREN IPSUM

Author: Carlos Bueno
Publisher: No Starch
Price: £11.50
ISBN: 978-1593275747
laurenipsum.org

Wow! The number of great coding books to appear in the last few years, aimed specifically at children, has been a very encouraging part of the movement to get young people coding. But coding – although fun, creative and rewarding – is only a part of computational thinking, which is a set of problem-solving skills including, but not limited to, algorithms, data modelling and logical thinking – invaluable in today's world.

A computer science book with no computers in, written in the grand tradition of Lewis Carroll, it follows the adventures and encounters of Lauren Ipsum, lost in Userland. From Recursion Junction to the Push & Pop Café, meeting characters like Hugh Rustic and the Wandering Salesman, Lauren's journey takes the reader through a history of ideas and logic.

Bueno has an engaging style and the lessons are so integral to the characters (Zeno's tortoise finds infinity in two inches of string) and stories (your kids will want to try the circle-drawing algorithms in Logo or Scratch) that there is no feeling of forced learning. Recommended for anyone of any age who wants to learn, this book would make a great introduction for schools grappling with the new curriculum – were it not too entertaining to be a textbook.

Score ★★★★★

ESSENTIAL READING: PYTHON

Python makes a great first language, but choose a book that matches your learning style...

Learn Python the Hard Way (Third Edition)

Author: Zed Shaw
Publisher: Addison Wesley
Price: £24.99 (free online)
ISBN: 978-0321884916
learnpythonthehardway.org

The 'hard way' is typing it all in until you absorb the syntax and spot mistakes. Works well, but Shaw doesn't cover Python 3.

Program Arcade Games: With Python and Pygame

Author: Dr Paul Vincent Craven
Publisher: CreateSpace
Price: £21.99 (free online)
ISBN: 978-1500825966
programarcadegames.com

Balances games and programming exercises to keep the learner going. Very popular: available in several languages on the website.

Writing Idiomatic Python 3.3

Author: Jeff Knupp
Publisher: CreateSpace
Price: £13.97
ISBN: 978-1482374810
tinyurl.com/bgj8zq9

Get Pythonic from the start. Concise guide to idiomatic code; best after another text, but suits some brave learners.

Dive Into Python 3

Author: Mark Pilgrim
Publisher: APress
Price: £35.49
ISBN: 978-1430224150
diveintopython3.net

Dives straight into code, then the explanations follow. A concise but comprehensive start that will appeal to independent study types.

Learning Python - 5th Edition

Author: Mark Lutz
Publisher: O'Reilly
Price: £43.50
ISBN: 978-1449355739
tinyurl.com/mehbnpo

Comprehensive doorstop (1,600 pages); great for programmers new to Python and object orientation. Covers Python 2.7 and 3.3.

RASPBERRY PI
BESTSELLERS

Packt's 2015 releases for Raspberry Pi users feature three highlights to rival last year's wide-ranging selection...

LEARNING RASPBIAN

Author: William Harrington
Publisher: Packt
Price: £15.99
ISBN: 978-1784392192
tinyurl.com/kk6dac5

Brief but useful 'missing manual' for Raspbian-equipped Pis. Assumes no Linux knowledge and covers getting started, installing and using software, the command line, and even interesting alternatives to Raspbian.

PENETRATION TESTING WITH RASPBERRY PI

Authors: Aamir Lakhani & Joseph Muniz
Publisher: Packt
Price: £18.99
ISBN: 978-1784396435
tinyurl.com/ksjdw33

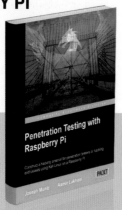

Not a novelty – a serious look at the Pi's possibilities as a pen testing tool that can go where other computers cannot reach. Makes a useful networking security introduction, too.

RASPBERRY PI GAMING 2ND EDITION

Authors: Shea Silverman
Publisher: Packt
Price: £15.99
ISBN: 978-1784399337
tinyurl.com/ncraeez

Gaming and entertainment on the Raspberry Pi: coding your own *Flappy Bird* clone in Scratch, emulators, classic Linux games, and connecting controllers – it's all covered in this highly informative book.

ADVENTURES IN RASPBERRY PI 2ND EDITION

Author: Carrie Anne Philbin
Publisher: Wiley
Price: £14.99
ISBN: 978-1119046028
tinyurl.com/oov562q

Philbin answers the question 'what can I do with my Pi?' – and does so with adventures! Ostensibly aimed at 11- to 15 year-olds, with each chapter (or adventure, as they're labelled) a gentle introduction to an essential Pi topic, it can also be used to help younger learners into coding and learning about hardware, through the last two chapters.

Before hardware – and a GPIO-connected marshmallow (!) – readers start with the command line, the first essential for a generation brought up in GUI-only environments. Then Scratch is introduced in enough detail for those who haven't used it before, turtle graphics, Python, programming *Minecraft* worlds, and Sonic Pi for making music.

Learning resources on the companion website, including videos and achievement badges for each adventure completed, reinforce the lessons. Each written section is very well paced for the intended age group, with tips, new information, and additional challenges appearing to vary the pace along the way. The colourful layout makes for a far more digestible read than many of the books that come our way, perhaps one of the reasons that this book is also popular with readers older than the intended audience! Next steps for each adventure ensure the learning – and the fun – can continue. Recommended.

Score

MAKING SIMPLE ROBOTS

Author: Kathy Ceceri
Publisher: Maker Media
Price: £16.50
ISBN: 978-1457183638
tinyurl.com/pmdle7g

'Anyone can build a robot' is the enticing premise of Ceceri's new book. Building on her previous popular guide to no-tech and low-tech robotics, she pushes the boundaries to what can be achieved using everyday materials and just a smidgen of technology.

What is a robot? The book's definition of a machine which can 'sense, think, act' is a broad umbrella for projects ranging from an inflatable robot (à la *Big Hero 6*) to a swarm of vibrobots from recycled parts. Every project is designed to be manageable for those new to hardware geekery, although some will push the reader away from their comfort zone. Along the way, skills will be gained, knowledge of fascinating areas of robotic research learned, and fun had. Kathy Ceceri is a natural educator: the learning comes lightly from each page read, carried easily by the author's passion for the subject.

Many projects need no computer involvement – a couple of Arduino wearables and some littleBits-based builds are among the exceptions. However there is a Scratch-programmed chatbot project, which Ceceri suggests could be loaded onto a Raspberry Pi and fitted into a robotic body. Other than that, the low-tech angle really helps to keep the focus on simple, achievable projects which combine fun and learning in unusually successful forms.

Score

HOW LINUX WORKS

Author: Brian Ward
Publisher: No Starch
Price: £26.50
ISBN: 978-1593275679
nostarch.com/howlinuxworks2

"You should never have to fight with a computer," says Brian Ward in his preface to this thoroughly revised and updated guide to the inner workings of our favourite kernel and operating system. Part of avoiding a struggle with your computer is understanding, and Linux is open to all with its plain text configuration files, open-source code, and vast online resources.

If the Pi is your first Linux computer, you may look at the title and think this book is more than you need to know. Not so: the fractal layout – starting with basic information, and expanding in finer detail – gives you as much information as you wish to read in each chapter. Just stop when you've learned enough on a topic, then continue later when you're curious.

Ward sets out a more kernel-centred work than the first edition, walking the reader through devices, disk layout, boot order, user space, logging and other housekeeping, processes, and networking. There's something here for every level of user, and while well-written enough to work right through, drawing you onwards, it also earns its place on the shelf as an essential reference – particularly as previous Linux classics have not been updated to keep up with changes in the workings of recent kernels.

Score ★★★★★

CLOJURE WEB DEVELOPMENT ESSENTIALS

Author: Ryan Baldwin
Publisher: Packt
Price: £27.99
ISBN: 978-1784392222
tinyurl.com/lva8c9r

If you've been intrigued by the promises of functional programming (see sidebar), but can't quite see the advantage for that most practical of environments, the web, this could be the introduction for you. Demanding perhaps minimal Clojure experience (those with some exposure to Common Lisp will quickly pick up the thread), Baldwin takes the reader though building a web application in Clojure from scratch, using the Luminus application template and the Ring web application library.

Using these two sensible default choices – which saves a lot of unnecessary discussion on alternatives – means the structural details of the stack and the build dependencies can be packed into the first two chapters. Stick with the book through these; it's worth the effort, even if you're a relative Clojure newbie. Now comes the fun part: really building the app.

From simple routing with Compojure, through the Django-inspired Selmer, pages appear, then forms are handled, and the YeSQL library is introduced. Somewhere along the way – perhaps with bypassing the pain of ORM – readers are likely to find an 'aha' moment, as they discover how much easier things can be in Clojure than their previous framework and language of choice.

Score ★★★★★

RASPBERRY PI
BESTSELLERS

ASSEMBLER PROGRAMMING

ARM is a far better platform for learning assembly language coding than x86 – here are the current top three guides…

RASPBERRY PI ASSEMBLY LANGUAGE

Author: Bruce Smith
Publisher: CreateSpace
Price: £14.99
ISBN: 978-1492135289
tinyurl.com/q6tokqb

A well-paced, example-led introduction to assembly language programming on ARM, from the comfort of Raspbian. The best beginner's book – but read the errata on the website.

BAKING PI: OPERATING SYSTEMS DEVELOPMENT!

Authors: Alex Chadwick
Publisher: University of Cambridge Computer Lab
Price: Free online
ISBN: N/A
tinyurl.com/k4pd38p

Popular online course which "takes you through the basics of operating systems development in assembly code", and starts with controlling the GPIO pins directly. Still mostly works on newer Pis.

ARM SYSTEM DEVELOPER'S GUIDE

Authors: Andrew Sloss, Dominic Symes & Chris Wright
Publisher: Morgan Kaufmann
Price: £57.99
ISBN: 978-1558608740
tinyurl.com/mk588lq

Detailed guide to the ARM instruction set, popular among embedded ARM developers for more than a decade, and still a great introduction to writing efficient C and assembler code for the architecture.

RASPBERRY PI FOR SECRET AGENTS
2ND EDITION

Author: Stefan Sjogelid
Publisher: Packt
Price: £15.99
ISBN: 978-1784397906
tinyurl.com/oknx38x

Many spy film gadgets that were once out of reach can now be built cheaply with a Raspberry Pi. There's no need for a Pi 2 here, but many of the pranks rely on a camera and/or microphone, while some require a WiFi module, GPS, and battery pack. The reason for all these accessories? A multitude of pranks and secret-agent ways of using your Raspberry Pi around the home and beyond.

The first chapter introduces SSH, as it's a lot easier to hide a Pi alone than with a monitor. The Audio Antics chapter brings in ALSA and Sound eXchange (SoX), alias, tmux, scripting, and scheduling – while using the Pi for bugs, calls, and voice distortion. Using the camera, there's motion detection and capture, plus getting the Pi to turn on in the middle of the night to scare the unwary. A Networking chapter includes man-in-the-middle attacks and plenty of useful Linux info. 'Taking Your Pi off-road' encompasses battery packs, GPS, and data encryption.

This book of tricks is a great driver to learn new skills – after all, there are few better motivators embedded in the human psyche than the desire to wind people up, or have a laugh at the expense of those near and dear to you. Good fun and, like so many Pi books, good value too.

IF HEMINGWAY WROTE JAVASCRIPT

Author: Angus Croll
Publisher: No Starch
Price: £13.50
ISBN: 978-1593275853
nostarch.com/hemingway

A valuable counterweight to the excellent but prescriptive Crockford guide to JS [see sidebar on next page]. JavaScript is an expressive language, but it's easy to forget how far you can push the limits until you see a set of examples like this. From Joyce to Woolf, 25 authors are given new voices as putative JS developers on five problems – from Fibonacci to finding prime numbers – separated by poetic interludes.

Each snippet is both entertaining and instructive. While languages like Perl are notorious for 'there's always more than one way to do it' unpredictability, JS has enough regularity to cope with someone moving the boundaries about. As pure entertainment, this is a treat to read, but Croll isn't slow to underline the persuasive calls of different approaches to problem solving.

Complemented by Miran Lipovača's illustrations, these portraits of the artist as a coder throw up countless gems, from memorable variable names to insightful snippets into life and literature. The contrast as we leap from Italo Calvino to J K Rowling is a particular delight, but it's hard to imagine this book without any of the 25 entries – even Dan Brown. The only downside is the way you find yourself, after reading other novels, now wondering about how each and every author would approach problems with JavaScript.

LINUX COMMAND LINE & SHELL SCRIPTING BIBLE

Author: Richard Blum & Christine Bresnahan
Publisher: Wiley
Price: £33.99
ISBN: 978-1118983843
tinyurl.com/p7hcmgb

Command line knowledge isn't just about automating tasks for busy Linux systems administrators – a deeper Linux understanding will enable you to get far more out of Raspbian and your Pi. Although comprehensive and detailed, this guide assumes no prior Linux knowledge and explains much of what's happening internally, making a useful tutorial, as well as reference, for the non-GUI world.

The first section, on the command line, covers similar areas to *The MagPi*'s own command line introductory series (available as an e-book), but in much greater detail. The remaining three sections cover shell scripts in progressively greater, then more practical, detail.

While shell scripting will never match Python, say, for larger programs, here you'll find inspiration for getting Raspbian (and other Linux systems) to create useful utilities, and even to build database-driven code that interacts with your email account and collects web data. So it should prove an inspiration as well as a useful reference.

GNU/Linux doesn't need 750-page books because it's complicated, but because it's powerful. Very powerful. You can live happily with Raspbian without knowing three-quarters of what Blum and Bresnahan examine here, but this is a great collection of Linux knowledge when you do need it.

PROGRAMMING ELIXIR

Author: Dave Thomas
Publisher: Pragmatic
Price: £23.99
ISBN: 978-1937785581
tinyurl.com/o3r7yrl

Elixir runs on the Erlang VM and is a functional programming language that's great for concurrency. It needs a more recent Erlang version than the one in Raspbian, but installing one is easy enough – or SD card images are readily available from someone who's already done the job. That done, you want a quick way to dive in and learn: enter Dave 'Ruby Pickaxe' Thomas's practical introduction.

Aimed at existing coders, the book dives straight into functional programming ("programming should be about transforming data") and the power of Elixir's concurrency – a benefit of the Erlang virtual machine. Elixir's easy syntax, powerful macros, and standard library will get you up and running so quickly, you may not notice that Thomas's well-structured book is carrying you so far through the learning experience.

The real strength of this work is in shifting how you approach coding, teaching functional thinking.

Much shorter than Thomas's famous 'pickaxe' book on Ruby, it's about putting the fun back into programming, in a world of multi-cores and adequate RAM, that begs for functional programming but without the academic trappings. As it says: "It's tomorrow already. Are you ready?"

ESSENTIAL READING: JAVASCRIPT

The web's own language is powerful and eloquent, yet lives in a familiar environment (your browser)...

Eloquent JavaScript Second Edition

Author: Marijn Haverbeke
Publisher: No Starch
Price: £26.50
ISBN: 978-1593275846
nostarch.com/ejs2

One of the best introductions to programming anywhere, updated for current JavaScript, and expanded with projects and more.

JavaScript & jQuery: Interactive Front-end Web Development

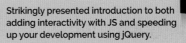

Author: Jon Duckett
Publisher: Wiley
Price: £26.99
ISBN: 978-1118531648
javascriptbook.com

Strikingly presented introduction to both adding interactivity with JS and speeding up your development using jQuery.

Automate with Grunt: The Build Tool for JavaScript

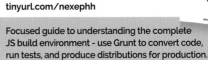

Author: Brian P Hogan
Publisher: Pragmatic
Price: £11.50
ISBN: 978-1941222119
tinyurl.com/nexephh

Focused guide to understanding the complete JS build environment - use Grunt to convert code, run tests, and produce distributions for production.

Data Visualization with JavaScript

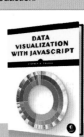

Author: Stephen A Thomas
Publisher: No Starch
Price: £26.50
ISBN: 978-1593276058
nostarch.com/datavisualization

Communicate! Tree maps, heat maps, network graphs, word clouds, and even pie charts – interactively and in your browser.

JavaScript: The Good Parts

Author: Douglas Crockford
Publisher: O'Reilly
Price: £19.99
ISBN: 978-0596517748
tinyurl.com/3zpqdh5

Small but dense, and very rewarding, but not the first JavaScript book you should read. You'll be rethinking your entire approach to coding in JS.

RASPBERRY PI BESTSELLERS

SCRATCH PROGRAMMING

The visual programming language helping learners to progress, from Code Club to college...

SCRATCH PROGRAMMING IN EASY STEPS

Author: Sean McManus
Publisher: In Easy Steps
Price: £10.99
ISBN: 978-1840786125
bit.ly/1H6lEoz

A well-thought-out book for the young and new to coding, which can be confidently given to those without programming parents to support them, and will get the parents programming, too!

SUPER SCRATCH PROGRAMMING ADVENTURE!

Authors: The LEAD Project
Publisher: No Starch
Price: £16.50
ISBN: 978-1593275310
nostarch.com/scratch

The next step after Code Club or the Easy Steps book – children continue to learn by doing as they follow a comic-book story and create games in the classic arcade style.

CODE CLUB

Authors: Code Club
Publisher: Morgan Kaufmann
Price: Free online
ISBN: N/A
codeclub.org.uk/projects

{ code club }

Term 1 and 2 of Code Club, as successfully taught by hundreds of volunteers to thousands of 10- and 11-year-olds across the UK and beyond. CC-licensed, hosted on GitHub, and now translated into several languages.

RASPBERRY PI BLUEPRINTS

Author: Dan Nixon
Publisher: Packt
Price: £29.99
ISBN: 978-1784392901
bit.ly/1KOJLLI

Ten hardware projects to build up your knowledge of hardware, software, and the Pi. The first project, a 'pirate' radio transmitter, needs only a small piece of wire as an antenna – the Pi does the rest. Other projects gradually add more components but retain the wow factor; these culminate in the 'bottle xylophone' which converts MIDI files into sound with the help of 15 glass bottles, played by 15 Pi-controlled servos.

While some projects, like 'home theatre' and arcade cabinet, may be found in a number of places, they are well executed and accompanied by more exotic projects like the bottle xylophone. Certain projects need traditional construction skills, such as the magic mirror, which combines a regular mirror with a web display. Although involved, the instructions for the web-controlled robotic arm are clear, and following the steps takes you through a streaming server and network control of the Pi.

With its combination of software, electronics, and construction hardware, Nixon's book balances useful learning in all of the areas that make the Raspberry Pi such a powerful and flexible basis for projects. The Weather Station project even involves reverse engineering and understanding the workings of off-the-shelf Maplin sensors to get them working with the Pi. Imaginative, educational, and fun.

Score

MAKER PRO

Author: Edited by John Baichtal
Publisher: Maker Media
Price: £13.50
ISBN: 978-1457186189
oreil.ly/1PmhOSc

It starts with curiosity, the purchase of a Pi... and maybe some components to connect to the GPIO pins. Soon, a hobby grows into a passion, and the latest project looks like it could be a business in its own right. What next? *Make:* has collected interviews and essays from 17 makers who've followed diverse paths from passion to profession.

Here we find the artist Susan Solarz, who found the resources and community of her local makerspace gave her what she needed to create the Origami Rocker; the genesis of MakerBot Industries; the excitement of democratising science through DIYbio; the Nintendo guitar; and other projects, familiar and unfamiliar. Not every maker has left their day job behind, and the diversity of routes to professional makerdom exposes a less diverse commonality of background and education, but also shows that the tools are within reach of every reader.

The final, short chapter, Sophi Kravitz's 'Quit Your Day Job – a tale of moving from full-time through part-time work to get time for projects, then striking out on her own – cannily doesn't oversell the dream. A dream it may remain for many, but makerspaces and open source hardware are helping to drive real changes in manufacturing, and small boards like the Pi give the opportunity to join this new world.

Score

BUILD AN HTML5 GAME

Author: Karl Bunyan
Publisher: No Starch
Price: £19.99
ISBN: 978-1593275754
nostarch.com/html5game

There are some great beginner books for learning coding (see the Scratch Bestsellers sidebar), but we're often asked how to take the next step. Bunyan's excellent new book on web programming sits between beginner guides to JavaScript and the many specialist, advanced titles available for experienced web programmers.

Assuming you have the basics of JavaScript, CSS, and HTML, the author walks readers through the creation of a classic Bubble Shooter game to play in the browser. Along the way, development techniques are demonstrated – chapter 1 includes using the browser's own debugging tools, and the JavaScript libraries Modernizr and jQuery are used.

It's not all shortcuts; the game logic chapter works the learner hard to understand the mechanics of implementing a game, and you'll learn a lot of CSS as you program the animations. After each chapter you'll have another stage of the game complete, feeling some sense of achievement, and ready to learn more. CSS transitions are introduced to speed things up, and HTML5 is used to add missing features like scoring and sound effects. By this point you'll be all ready to develop your own game idea, and maybe produce the next answer to *Angry Birds*.

FUNCTIONAL PYTHON PROGRAMMING

Author: Steven Lott
Publisher: Packt
Price: £30.99
ISBN: 978 1784396992
bit.ly/1JMnhee

If you've wanted to try functional programming, but the thought of learning the strange syntax attached to most FP languages has added to your inertia, here's something for you. Python is a multi-paradigm language, coping well with procedural programming for scripts and many Raspberry Pi hardware projects, and object oriented for programs used at the enterprise scale; it can also be used in a functional style. Yes, Python lacks unlimited recursion, lazy evaluation of all expressions, and an optimising compiler, but functions are first class objects in Python and the language does have all of the things you already love about it.

Lott shows you how to add to these, using Python to implement functional techniques and design patterns.

If you really want to throw yourself into functional programming, this is not the only book you should read on the subject. But if you want to improve your Python, you'll find in this book the tools to write functions that will help you work far more efficiently with Big Data, for example. Every chapter has something to offer, and you'll finish this book a better programmer.

ESSENTIAL READING: BUILDING A WEBSITE

Skills needed for building websites and apps cover diverse technologies for many ability levels...

The Essentials of Interaction Design, 4th Edition
Author: Alan Cooper et al
Publisher: Wiley
Price: £33.99
ISBN: 978-1118766576
bit.ly/1L64hYV

Understand interaction design and you won't be doomed to join the ranks of frustrating, unusable websites.

Creating Flat Design Websites
Author: António Pratas
Publisher: Packt
Price: £26.99
ISBN: 978-1783980048
bit.ly/1bTORug

Concise and pragmatic guide to the dos and don'ts of implementing the look *de nos jours*.

MySQL Cookbook, 3rd Edition
Solutions for Database Developers and Administrators
Author: Paul DuBois
Publisher: O'Reilly
Price: £53.50
ISBN: 978-1449374020
oreil.ly/1QOzUJC

Love it or loathe it, you'll find MySQL everywhere, so try O'Reilly's comprehensive tutorial and reference.

SVG Essentials, 2nd Edition
Producing Scalable Vector Graphics with XML
Author: J David Eisenberg, Amelia Bellamy-Royds
Publisher: O'Reilly
Price: £26.50
ISBN: 978-1449374358
oreil.ly/1HkpsrH

Updated for modern browsers, learn the XML-based 2D vector image format built for transformation.

WordPress: The Missing Manual, 2nd Edition
Author: Matthew MacDonald
Publisher: O'Reilly
Price: £19.99
ISBN: 978-1449341909
oreil.ly/1dh6jdJ

Sometimes you just need to get a site up quickly. WordPress does the hard work, and MacDonald fills in the blanks.

RASPBERRY PI BESTSELLERS
ELECTRONICS

Go beyond following instructions for attaching components to your GPIO pins, and learn the nitty-gritty of electronic components...

PRACTICAL ELECTRONICS: COMPONENTS & TECHNIQUES

Author: John M Hughes
Publisher: O'Reilly
Price: £26.50
ISBN: 978-1449373078
oreil.ly/1lCmbEM

Practically oriented book for those who want to get making electronic projects. Comprehensive, but aimed squarely within the reach of the beginner.

PRACTICAL ELECTRONICS HANDBOOK

Authors: Ian Sinclair
Publisher: Newnes
Price: Free download
ISBN: N/A
bit.ly/1QJ3BKf

The 1980 first edition, freely available to download from the Internet Archive, is a great intro to electronics – but the latest edition (with John Dunton) covers newer components and circuits, and is a strong recommendation.

ELECTRONIC CIRCUITS: 4TH EDITION

Authors: Mike Tooley
Publisher: Routledge
Price: £26.99
ISBN: 978-1138828926
key2electronics.com

Welcome update to Tooley's well-regarded further education text: very good on the theories of circuits, with a companion website that helps you design them. Now with a section on Raspberry Pi.

MAKE: THE MAKER'S MANUAL

Author: Paolo Aliverti & Andrea Maietta
Publisher: Maker Media
Price: £16.50
ISBN: 978-1457185922
themakersmanual.com

"A revolution is happening: the manufacture of objects is shifting from big companies... to individuals, producing a previously unseen variety in things we make." That revolution may be at an early stage, but with the easy availability of low-cost boards like the Raspberry Pi, and manufacturing kit like 3D printers (often available as a shared resource at fab labs and makerspaces), all you need to get involved is an idea and a little knowledge.

The Maker's Manual doesn't just set out to provide that knowledge – which it does both with a concise history of the maker movement, and a roundup of practical tools from laser cutters to GitHub – but also how to nurture and grow an idea. The second section of the book looks at the mental skills involved in creativity and how they can be developed; the practical side of managing a project and running a business; and the soft skills of collaboration.

Chapters on basic electronics, Arduino and the Pi provide useful, concise introductions, while a look at the Processing language gets straight down to the artistic possibilities released by its random function. With even the short Internet of Things chapter containing a practical Pi example, there's little fluff and a lot of value packed into this manual's 200 pages.

Score

RASPBERRY PI PROJECTS FOR KIDS

Author: Daniel Bates
Publisher: Packt
Price: £16.99
ISBN: 978-1785281525
bit.ly/1MFA5EI

"The Raspberry Pi exposes programming software to make it as easy as possible to get started," says Daniel Bates in his preface. After a chapter on getting set up with the Pi, the book launches into trying out programming through six mini projects, starting with the excellent Scratch visual programming language: first to do some animation, with programming concepts – and the power and freedom of programming – introduced as a natural part of learning the animation procedure; then an *Angry Birds* clone, which includes physics (gravity and bouncing), scoring, and a chance to add in your own extensions. Python is next, with a random insults generator – always a popular bit of fun – which introduces list handling and functions. Then a connection to the physical world: first through an excellent DIY game controller for a speed test game, then with Google Maps and Tkinter to look at your neighbourhood. Lastly, there's an introduction to music making with software, using Sonic Pi.

All in all, this software-focused introduction gives a quicker starting path than many of the more maker-oriented Pi books, which themselves would make an ideal follow-on. After working through Bates's readable and friendly guide, any child will know a surprisingly large amount of core programming skills, as well as gain a thirst for more. Recommended.

Score

THE GNU MAKE BOOK

Author: John Graham-Cumming
Publisher: No Starch
Price: £23.50
ISBN: 978-1593276492
nostarch.com/gnumake

Not the O'Reilly imprint, the *other* Make! Yes, GNU Make is something most of us only come across when we download a program in source form, and have to untar then run the './configure && make && make install' incantation to compile and install the software. GNU Make is the build automation tool heroically doing the hard work in the background.

Readers may know of John Graham-Cumming from his successful petition to the UK government asking for an apology for its persecution of Alan Turing. Here is a success on a smaller stage – but no less vital, as many people have started out using Make, and writing makefiles, for their own projects, then run up against some hurdle. This is not a beginner's book, but for anyone already using Make in their projects, it's a really well-written guide to getting more from it.

The author gained his Make knowledge writing a complete clone of the software in C++ – not a unique project, as some readers may know the Python Snakemake, designed for complicated workflows in bioinformatics – and he has a comprehensive knowledge of GNU Make. This is most usefully reflected in the excellent chapter on 'Pitfalls and Problems' – essential reading for anyone whose project, and consequently makefile, has grown large enough to run into difficulties.

Score ★★★★★

AUTOMATE THE BORING STUFF WITH PYTHON

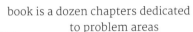

Author: Al Sweigart
Publisher: No Starch
Price: £19.99
ISBN: 978-1593275990
automatetheboringstuff.com

If you've ever found yourself repetitively carrying out the same task over and over, wishing you had a little more command-line experience so that you know the correct Bash magic to get it all done in one go from the terminal, this is your chance to leapfrog past that and learn how to use Python to quickly write programs to take on the tedious tasks.

The first section introduces Python and programming basics, such as flow control, functions, lists, and string manipulation, with practice questions and useful projects rounding off each chapter. The main part of the book is a dozen chapters dedicated to problem areas where a little Python code will smooth away your problems: organising files, getting data from websites, working with text from inside PDF and Word documents, batch-editing images, and even automating when and how programs run on your PC.

Sweigart is an able teacher with a number of well-regarded Python books to his name, and it shows through his clear teaching style and well-paced lessons. Not only are these skills which would benefit any regular computer user, but after working through Sweigart's book, non-coders will find themselves competent and practical beginner programmers.

Score ★★★★★

ESSENTIAL READING: RUBY

There are many ways to learn and use Ruby's expressive power: here are five of the best recent tutorials...

Learn Ruby the Hard Way

Author: Zed A Shaw
Publisher: Addison Wesley
Price: £24.99
ISBN: 978-0321884992
learnrubythehardway.org

Great intro for the new programmer: a little 'Pythonic', but strongly practical, preparing you for real-world coding.

The Well-Grounded Rubyist Second Edition

Author: David A Black
Publisher: Manning
Price: £27.99
ISBN: 978-1617291692
manning.com/black3

Introduction and reference with a strongly object-oriented approach to the language; ideal for Pythonistas new to Ruby.

Ruby Wizardry: An Introduction to Programming for Kids

Author: Eric Weinstein
Publisher: No Starch
Price: £19.99
ISBN: 978-1593275662
nostarch.com/rubywizardry

While the story pulls children in, serious programming concepts are painlessly transmitted by Codecademy author Eric Weinstein: wizardry indeed!

Metaprogramming Ruby 2: Program Like the Ruby Pros

Author: Paolo Perrotta
Publisher: Pragmatic
Price: £25.50
ISBN: 978-1941222126
oreil.ly/1eoIhnN

The next step: gain real insight into Ruby through writing code that writes code. Practical and thought-provoking.

Rails Crash Course A No-Nonsense Guide to Rails Development

Author: Anthony Lewis
Publisher: No Starch
Price: £23.50
ISBN: 978-1593275723
nostarch.com/railscrashcourse

We couldn't leave out Rails, and Lewis's new guide is concise, yet lacking nothing you need to get going.